Electronic Circuits, Systems and Standards:
the Best of EDN

Electronic Circuits, Systems and Standards: the Best of EDN

Edited by Ian Hickman

047693266

Newnes
An imprint of Butterworth-Heinemann Ltd
Halley Court, Jordan Hill, Oxford OX2 8EJ

 PART OF REED INTERNATIONAL BOOKS

OXFORD   LONDON   GUILDFORD   BOSTON
MUNICH   NEW DELHI   SINGAPORE   SYDNEY
TOKYO   TORONTO   WELLINGTON

First published 1991

British Library Cataloguing in Publication Data

Electronic circuits, systems and standards
  1. Electronic equipment. circuits. Design
  I. Hickman, Ian II. EDN
  621.38153

ISBN 0 7506 0068 3

Printed and bound in Great Britain by
Butler and Tanner, Frome and London

Contents

> ## Note
>
> This contents page lists articles in the order in which they appear in this book. To locate an article by subject matter, refer to the *Subject index* at the back of the book.

1 XOR gate controls oscillator frequency
April 14 1982, page 196
1

2 Circuit converts voltage ratio to frequency
October 2 1986, page 203
2

3 MIL-STD-1553 bus finds use in diverse military systems
April 11 1985, pages 60-72
3

4 Diodes and capacitors imitate transformer
April 30 1987, page 223
12

5 Phase-modulate signals digitally
March 3 1983, page 140
14

6 Innovative design techniques yield optimum counter oscillator
October 13 1983, pages 209-19
16

7 Op amp, ADC make zero-droop S/H
October 13 1983, page 255
21

8 ISDN terminals simplify data transmissions
January 22 1987, pages 167-74
22

9 IF chip forms audio decibel-level detector
May 1 1986, page 261
27

10 Versatile ramp generator uses 1kbit RAM
October 16 1986, pages 225-6
28

11 ICs simplify design of single-sideband receivers
April 3 1986, pages 119-26
30

12 Three-rail power supply uses four diodes
October 31 1986, page 248
37

13 Sliding FFT computes frequency spectra in real time
September 29 1988, pages 161-70
38

14 Variable-Q bandpass filter fixes gain
April 28 1982, page 153
45

15 Enhanced op amp delivers 100 V p-p
September 1985, pages 309-12
47

16 Voltage references
January 18 1990, pages 121-8
49

17 CMOS circuit always oscillates
February 2 1989, page 196
55

18 CMOS circuit guaranteed to oscillate
May 11 1989, page 208
56

19 Micropower op amp offers simplicity and versatility
January 7 1988, pages 181-8
57

20 Transistor clipper provides flat-top output 65
September 29 1982, pages 154-6

21 Digitize analog functions using simple procedures 67
March 31 1988, pages 153-8

22 Amplitude-locked loop speeds filter test 71
May 11 1989, page 197

23 Power MOSFETS and IGBTs 72
January 5 1989, pages 128-42

24 Amplifier has infinite time constant 79
July 26 1984, page 365

25 Voltage divider switch adds range to DPM 80
February 15 1990, page 187

26 Troubleshooting is more effective with the right philosophy 81
January 5 1989, pages 147-56

27 Op amp provides phase-locked loop 87
May 5 1979, page 131

28 Failure analyses and testing yield reliable products 88
August 8 1985, pages 165-74

29 Replace exclusive ORs with resistors 98
August 5 1979, page 116

30 MOSFETS provide low-loss rectification 99
February 18 1989, pages 237-9

31 Predictive coding improves ADC performance 101
October 5 1979, pages 137-43

32 Op amp reduces transformer droop 109
October 5 1979, pages 153-4

33 Designed-in safety features ease compliance 110
February 2 1989, pages 149-60

34 JFET serves as low-power logic translator 119
July 23 1987, page 311

35 Floating-point math handles iterative and recursive algorithms 120
January 9 1986, pages 115-21

36 Multiple technologies produce fast clock 126
November 9 1989, page 265

37 Power isolators are bidirectional 128
January 8 1989, pages 203-5

38 Make passive filters active with a floating synthetic inductor 130
June 23 1983, pages 277-82

39 Op amp provides linear current source 134
April 5 1979, pages 112-14

40 Design method yields low-noise, wide-range crystal oscillators 135
March 17 1988, pages 141-6

41 Nonlinear load extends PLL frequency range 139
March 14 1987, page 250

42 Squarewave oscillator spans DC to 20 MHz 140
July 9 1987, pages 266-7

43 Design active elliptic filters   142
with a 4-function calculator
March 3 1982, pages 135-8

44 Transistor powers low-   146
dropout regulator
August 4 1988, page 205

45 Simplify FIR-filter design with   147
a cookbook approach
March 3 1983, pages 119-28

46 Single cell lights LED   155
April 27 1989, page 220

47 Circuit deletes power-line   156
cycles
May 14 1987, pages 246-8

48 Understand capacitor soakage   158
to optimize analog systems
October 13 1982, pages 125-9

49 Analog delay line uses digital   163
techniques
June 11 1987, page 203

50 Nonlinear components lower   164
settling time of noise-
reduction filters
February 15 1990, pages 177-80

51 Intermittent converter saves   167
power
September 1 1989, page 151

52 Amp provides 100 V common-   168
mode range
December 10 1987, pages 328-31

53 Improve circuit performance   170
with a 1-op-amp current
pump
January 20 1983, pages 85-90

54 Two-way amplifier uses few   176
parts
February 19 1987, pages 204-8

55 Amplifier handles duplex line   179
April 27 1989, page 221

56 Active feedback improves   180
amplifier phase accuracy
September 17 1987, pages 179-88

57 Decode overlapped EPROM,   188
RAM and IO
May 14 1987, page 241

58 Gain of two simplifies LP-   189
filter design
March 17 1983, pages 224-8

59 Thermal tester verifies   191
transistors
November 24 1988, page 221

60 Looking through the right   192
window improves spectral
analysis
November 15 1984, pages 319-28

61 Divider displays uncanny   199
accuracy
March 16 1989, page 179

62 Test whether a noise source is   201
Gaussian
December 11 1986, pages 272-4

63 Routine gives nonrepeat   203
random numbers
May 3 1984, page 323

64 Current-feedback amplifiers   204
benefit high speed designs
January 5 1989, pages 161-72

65 Step-up converter produces   212
   5 V from 1.5 V
   November 12 1987, page 294

66 Simple logarithms speed   213
   microprocessor math
   operations
   January 24 1985, pages 231-6

Subject index   217

Introduction

EDN first appeared with the issue dated May 8 1956. It early proved itself a very useful source of information and I have been saving articles from it since shortly after its debut. Of course, some of the earlier articles I saved have since been overtaken by events. Thus, for example, a phase/frequency detector, as described on pages 55 to 59 of the issue of September 20 1976 and realized in MSI, has long since been incorporated as a matter of course in any self-respecting synthesizer chip.

Since those early days, *EDN* has established for itself an unassailable position as the most useful and widely read of the controlled circulation electronics magazines. I get regular copies of most of this type of magazine and frequently save articles from them for future reference. These are kept in files, thinner or more bulging according to how useful I find that particular magazine. A measure of the relative usefulness of *EDN* can be seen from the fact that it long ago overflowed its file and now threatens to overflow a second one. These files contain a wealth of useful information and circuit ideas, as I realize each time when I occasionally browse through them. Just a few of them are reproduced in my book *Analog Electronics,* and it was whilst writing it that I realized how useful and interesting a carefully selected collection of articles from *EDN* would be to the practising electronics engineer. The idea was suggested and in due course approved, and this book is the outcome.

My main qualifications for offering this selection are simply that I have been collecting *EDN* articles for so long and also, I guess, that no one else thought of doing it before me. My selection of articles for inclusion reflects my interests as a long-standing analog circuit design engineer and I make no apology for any resultant slant to the mix of articles presented; whoever had done the job, his or her professional background would have been certain to influence the choice. However, this is not to say that digital topics are ignored, far from it. For like any rounded, professional engineer, I have

always taken a keen interest in what goes on on the other side of the stream from my own particular specialization. Indeed, I was once in the dim and distant past a designer of state-of-the-art 10 MHz digital circuitry, when a 2N705 was the latest and best transistor going. Since then, my interests have expanded with the technology so that I like to keep abreast of what can be done in the field of computers, microcontrollers and other digital hardware, software and algorithms. Consequently, I will save an article if I can see that it is important, even if it is not in my immediate area of specialization – someone sometime at work is sure to ask me what I know about the topic. It may not be much but I can usually point them in the right direction. They can often take it on from there, thanks to the helpful and commendable practice of writers for *EDN* of including at the end of an article, a list of references to other important papers on the subject.

Considerable thought was given as to what sort of order the following collection of articles should be arranged in. After all, some of them run to ten or more pages and others barely to one, whilst the range of topics covered is very diverse. In the end, they were carefully arranged in no sort of order at all, so that the browser will find something different on almost every page. I hope you will find the arrangement satisfactory; it is not nearly as chaotic in practice as it sounds. For in addition to a table of contents with the entries arranged in the order in which the articles appear, there is a tabled *Subject index*. So if, for example, you are interested in looking up digital circuits, just refer to the section *circuits*, digital, and you will find all the circuits of this type listed in page order, and similarly for other topics. To assist in finding the item you are after, where it could be taken to fall into two categories, it is listed in both sections; for instance, you will find a natty little AC coupled comparator circuit with an effectively infinite input time-constant listed under both analog and digital circuits. Incidentally, this circuit is one of the many readers' ideas submitted to *EDN*'s long standing *Design Ideas* section. I know this to be very popular with readers; indeed many of my colleagues tell me that when their copy of *EDN* arrives, they always turn to that section first. A large number of these design ideas are included in this volume, in addition to many informative longer articles, either submitted or staff-written. I have tried to include something to interest everyone, so now – please read on.

Ian Hickman

1 NOR gate controls oscillator frequency

Simple FSK generator

There is an elegance about a circuit which achieves its function with great simplicity. This FSK generator certainly falls into that category. Both centre frequency and shift will be subject to component tolerances, but the circuit fills the bill as is for undemanding applications; alternatively, presets can be designed in to allow adjustment to a standard shift such as 170 or 850 Hz.

Richard Rice
Eaton Corp, Milwaukee, WI

You can make a simple, stable frequency-shift-keying (FSK) generator by adding an exclusive-OR gate to a standard CMOS oscillator. In this circuit (**figure**), the data input controls gate IC_{1D}, establishing positive or negative feedback around the oscillator formed by IC_{1A}, IC_{1B} and IC_{1C}.

When the data input goes LOW, IC_{1D} enters its noninverting mode, and R_2 increases capacitor C's charging rate. When the input returns HIGH, IC_{1D} inverts, and R_2 reduces C's charging current, thus lowering the oscillator's frequency.

R_1 and C set the oscillator's frequency range, and R_2 determines the circuit's frequency shift. To ensure frequency stability, make R_3 much greater than R_1 and use a high-quality feedback capacitor. Note that the three gates constituting the oscillator itself need not be exclusive-OR types—you can use any CMOS inverter.

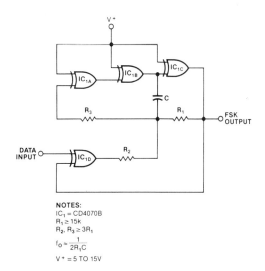

NOTES:
$IC_1 = CD4070B$
$R_1 \geq 15k$
$R_2, R_3 \geq 3R_1$
$f_o \approx \dfrac{1}{2R_1C}$
$V^+ = 5\ \text{TO}\ 15V$

An exclusive-OR gate (IC_{1D}) turns a simple CMOS oscillator into an FSK generator. When the data input goes HIGH, IC_{1D} inverts, and negative feedback through R_2 lowers the circuit's output frequency. A LOW input results in positive feedback and a higher output frequency.

2 Circuit converts voltage ratio to frequency

Find the ratio of two voltages

This circuit provides an output voltage proportional to the ratio of two steady input voltages. The same thing could of course be done with two ADCs and software, but in a system without those facilities, this circuit provides a purely hardware implementation. Watch out for settling time when one of the input voltages changes, though.

Bobircă Florin Daniel
The Electronic Research Institute,
Bucharest, Rumania

The circuit of **Fig 1** accepts two positive-voltage inputs V_N and V_D and provides a TTL-compatible output pulse train whose repetition rate is proportional to the ratio V_N/V_D. Full-scale output frequency is about 100 Hz, and linearity error is below 0.5%.

The output F_O equals KV_N/V_D, where $K=1/(4R_2C_1)$ and provided $R_1=R_3$. Op amp IC_{1A} alternately integrates $V_N/2$ and $-V_N/2$, producing a sawtooth output that ramps between the V_D level and ground. When transistor Q_1 is on, for example, IC_{1A} integrates $-V_N/2$ until its output equals V_D. At that time, the IC_{1B} comparator switches low, causing IC_{1D}'s bistable output to go low, which turns off Q_1. IC_{1A}'s output then ramps in the negative direction. When the output reaches 0V, the IC_{1C} comparator switches, Q_1 turns on, and the cycle repeats. Transistor Q_2 converts the IC_{1D} output to TTL-compatible output logic levels.

Setting V_D to 1.00V yields a linear V/F converter ($F_O=KV_N$), and setting V_N to 1.00V yields a reciprocal V/F converter ($F_O=K/V_D$).

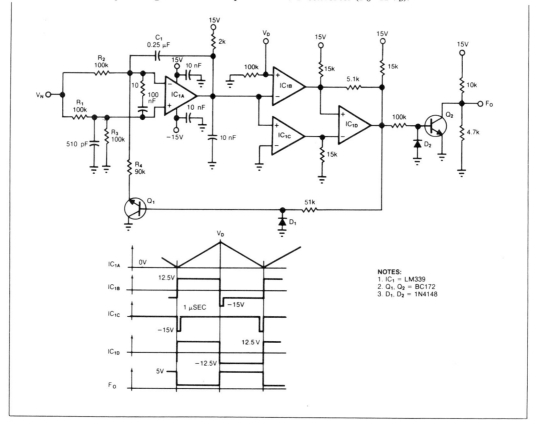

Fig 1—This voltage-ratio/frequency converter produces a TTL-compatible output pulse train that equals KV_N/V_D, where V_N and V_D are the inputs and $K=4R_2C_1$. Linearity error is less than 0.5%.

3 MIL-STD-1553 bus finds use in diverse military systems

> ## Details of an avionics data bus
>
> The MIL-STD-1553 bus has been around for a number of years now, and in the latest generation of military aircraft is likely to be supplanted by a fibre optics bus. However, the 1553 bus is still very widely used and this staff-written article forms a useful introduction. If you are an exclusively analog engineer, you may never need to grapple with it in detail, but it is nice to know basically what it is – knowledge is never wasted. The rounded engineer always likes to know what is on the other side of the fence from his or her own particular specialisation.

Jon Titus, *Associate Editor*

Rather than routing individual cables to interconnect equipment, many military designers use the MIL-STD-1553 bus. The 1553 bus is based on a twisted-pair cable that supports a bus controller and as many as 31 remote devices. The result is a standard and reliable communications system that operates at 1M bps and uses a standard 20-bit serial-transmission protocol. Besides adding reliability to electronic military hardware, the 1553 bus requires no changes when suppliers offer upgraded or advanced system packages. Also, without rewiring an aircraft, technicians can quickly reconfigure electronic "black boxes" for a new mission, perhaps concentrating the avionics on electronic countermeasures rather than on a specific weapon system.

High-speed digital networks and fiber-optic systems may eventually supplant the 12-year-old 1553 bus, but developing the relevant standards for military use takes time. However, the Department of Defense is soliciting bids to install a 1773 fiber-optic bus system in the fourth upgrade of the US Navy's P-3C Orion, an aircraft that detects, classifies, and tracks aircraft, ships, and submarines. Nonetheless, most avionic and military system manufacturers believe that the 1553 bus will be in use for some time. Similarly, most military users indicate that a high-speed data bus may be useful in the future, but the 1M-bps data rate of the 1553 bus is adequate for most current needs. Because the MIL-STD-1553 is well entrenched, a switch to a new bus requires a major commitment by all three military services and their suppliers.

Today, the 1553 bus is found primarily in navigation, flight-control, defensive-system, communication, control, display, and offensive-system avionics hardware. Although many believe that the 1553 bus is an Air Force standard, the Navy and Army use several 1553-bus implementations in such ground-based applications as the Sgt York Division Air-Defense (DIVAD) gun system and seaborne applications such as the navigation system for the Trident II submarine program (see **box**, "Military uses of the 1553 bus").

According to William Hartnett, DIVAD project engineering director at Ford Aerospace, the DIVAD system uses the 1553 bus because it offers a well-established protocol and because of the availability of a well-structured interface. Hartnett also says that the 1M-bps data rate of the 1553 bus is adequate for the DIVAD system's needs.

The 1553 bus standard was formulated in 1973 by a committee of the Society of Automotive Engineers. The committee revised and reissued the standard in 1975 as MIL-STD-1553A, a triservice standard. It was revised again in 1978 when it was also adopted by NATO. The latest revision eliminates ambiguities and leaves fewer interpretations to the designer. Both the original triservice standard and the revision (now called 1553B) specify that bus devices communicate information in the biphase Manchester II format at a rate of 1M bps. The standard also specifies the rise and fall times for the bus signals. Some manufacturers state that their devices are 1553 compatible, while others indicate the specific standard that they comply with—1553A, 1553B, or both (see **box**, "MIL-STD-1553 specifications").

The main bus consists of a shielded, twisted-pair cable with a nominal impedance of 70Ω. Transformers that provide the proper impedance ratios couple 1-MHz biphase signals from electronic systems to the bus. The 1553 standard lets you use short stubs (a foot or less) and long stubs (between 1 and 20 feet) to connect equipment to the main bus (**Fig 1**). Several manufacturers provide both bus terminators and transformer couplers for 1553-based systems.

One supplier of transformers for the 1553 bus is ILC Data Device. This manufacturer's transformers offer a range of turns ratios so that three models meet the impedance-matching requirements of both short and long stubs. For example, the BUS-25679 transformer provides turns ratios of 1.4:1 or 2:1, depending on the windings you select. All three transformers measure 0.63 in. in length and width and have a height of 0.275

MIL-STD-1553 specifications

Although it's more than 12 years old, MIL-STD-1553 (more properly called the Aircraft Internal Time Division Command/Response Multiplex Data Bus) retains its popularity with both the military and the suppliers of military electronic equipment.

The MIL-STD-1553 document specifies the use of twisted-pair wire for asynchronous-serial communications between a bus controller and remote terminals. Transmissions occur at a fixed rate of 1M bps, although it's more exact to say that each bit has a 1-μsec period because there are times when the bus is inactive. Besides transmission formats, the MIL-STD-1553 document specifies voltage levels, bus impedances, waveform rise and fall times, and device-coupling requirements.

Each device on the bus uses a 20-bit word to communicate command, data, and status information (**Fig A**). Each word starts with a 3-bit synchronization sequence that lets the receiver identify the transmission type, and a word always ends with an odd-parity bit. Removing the three synchronization bits and the parity bit from the transmission leaves you 16 bits for information.

The command word uses five bits to identify the remote terminal that will receive the transmission and another five bits to identify a subdevice (if any) controlled by the remote terminal that is to receive the transmission. A set of five word-count and mode-code bits tells the remote terminal how many data words will follow. These five bits also specify a mode code that causes bus devices to perform specific control operations. Although there are 32 possible mode codes, only 15 are allowed

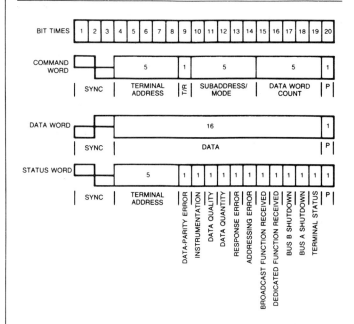

Fig A—The format for the command, data, and status words shows that each word contains 20 bits. The first three bits provide synchronization information, and the last bit contains parity data.

or 0.300 in., depending on the version you choose.

A supplier of prepackaged bus-coupling devices is SCI Systems Inc, which produces 24 such devices. You can specify combinations of connectors, terminating resistors, and outputs for one or two stubs. These couplers offer you a variety of bus connectors, but the choice may depend on the connectors used in your bus. Available connectors include the BJ30, BJ77, BJ377, and BJ150 made by Trompeter Electronics Inc (Chatsworth, CA) and the D-602-55 socket from Raychem Corp (Menlo Park, CA).

To design the circuits that transfer information to and from the bus, you'll have to consider the noise-rejection, signal-threshold, and rise-time requirements of your system. Commercially available transmitter and receiver modules control the proper voltage levels and rise times for transmissions. These modules also filter

input signals and pass on to the receiver only those signals that exceed a preset threshold. Digital bus-controller circuits use TTL-compatible signals to communicate with the bus receiver and transmitter modules.

Although these devices are called transmitters, receivers, and transceivers, they don't encode or decode digital information. The transmitters accept biphase TTL signals and drive the transformer that couples the overall system to the 1553 bus. Receivers perform the reverse operation, converting bus signals into biphase TTL signals for the bus-control circuits. For example, Aeroflex Laboratories' ARX-18553 transceiver module comes in an 18-pin DIP and contains both a receiver and a transmitter circuit. The transmitter accepts biphase TTL signals and produces a 27V p-p differential signal across a 140Ω load. Internally set control voltages let

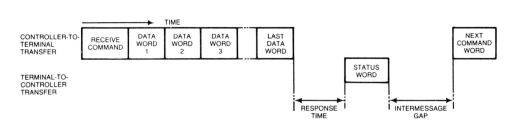

Fig B—A transmission sequence contains a command word followed by data. After receiving the data error free, the receiver responds by sending a status word to the transmitter.

by the 1553 standard. The command word includes a transmit/receive bit that tells the remote terminal to operate in either the receive or transmit mode.

Besides the synchronization and parity bits, the data word has no format. You can thus use the 16 data bits as you wish, but you must use 16 of them.

The status word transfers flag and status information between devices on the 1553 bus. When a bus device receives an error-free transmission, it sends a status word to the transmitting device. If a device receives information that contains an error, such as incorrect parity or an extra bit, no status word is sent. When the transmitter doesn't get the expected status response in a given time, it knows that something is wrong with the receiver. The transmitter can send the

transmission again or can query the receiver for its status information to find out what type of error occurred.

Although the status word seems complex, the 1553 standard requires only the data-parity (or message-error) bit, located at bit position nine. Except for the synchronization, parity, and remote-terminal address bits, the other status bits are optional. **Fig B** shows a transmission sequence.

The 1553 standard specifies 10 types of information-transfer formats. Six of these transfer data and status information between the bus controller and a selected remote terminal or between one remote terminal and another. Four formats apply to broadcasts of information from the bus controller to all of the remote terminals that support the broadcast

format. Receivers don't acknowledge broadcasts because simultaneous responses from all the remote terminals would cause the bus to crash. The bus controller can request responses from individual remote terminals when you need specific status information.

The bus-interface circuits encode bus signals in Manchester II biphase format, which produces a zero-voltage crossing in the middle of each bit position. The only exceptions are the synchronization bits, which have their own format. Because this format isn't a legal Manchester code, the bus devices don't mistake it for data. The Manchester-encoded information is self-clocking and has no dc component, which makes it ideal for asynchronous transformer-coupled bus systems.

the receivers ignore signals that are below a 0.3V p-p threshold. Only those signals that exceed a 1.0V p-p level are converted to TTL levels and sent to the bus-control circuits.

Another Aeroflex module is the ARX-28553, available in a 36-pin DIP and a 36-pin flat package. This device contains two separate transceivers for use in a system that requires two separate but equivalent (dual-redundant) buses. The manufacturer's modules operate from either ±12V or ±15V power supplies and require an impedance-matching transformer for connection to a 1553 bus.

ILC Data Device Corp offers several types of bus transceivers, including the BUS-8554 transceiver, which rejects 1553 bus signals that are below a 750-mV p-p threshold. By connecting a threshold-programming pin to ground through an external resistor you can vary

the threshold from 0V to as much as 2V p-p. The manufacturer also supplies the BUS-8559 transceiver, which has a continuously variable output that is set by a control voltage between 0 and 15V at a control pin. You can vary the transmitter's output level between 0 and 6.5V p-p. By transmitting a series of bus signals at different voltages, you can test the response of a bus receiver.

The COM-1553A transceiver chip provides 15 lines for control and status signals. Eight bidirectional data lines transfer data to and from the chip and its host computer. Instead of using a complete 16-bit word, the COM-1553A chip transfers data one byte at a time. Thus, at the 1M-bps data rate, the chip can receive sequential data bytes that are within 600 nsec of each other. If the transceiver chip's host is a computer system, you may need to use a first-in, first-out (FIFO) buffer or other high-speed memory system between the bus-controller chip and your computer.

Although the 1553 bus provides a standard format, designers have leeway in deciding how to use the bus data.

The COM-1553A chip performs parallel-to-serial and serial-to-parallel conversions, and you have a choice of operating it either as a remote terminal or as a 1553 bus controller. Each bus has only one controller that manages and oversees all of the bus operations. A system that can switch a device from remote-terminal to bus-controller operation can include computer-based remote terminals that can take over the bus controller's functions if the main bus controller fails.

To properly format the information it transfers to and from the 1553 bus, the COM-1553A chip requires an external Manchester encoder/decoder chip. Standard Microsystems recommends the HD-15531 CMOS Manchester encoder/decoder from Harris Semiconductor. The COM-1553A and the HD-15531 together require a 5V power supply. The COM-1553A is also available on a pc board from Grumman Aerospace Corp, which joined with Standard Microsystems to develop the 1553A chip.

Standard Microsystems also produces the COM-1553B chip, an upgraded bus transceiver that is *not* a pin-for-pin replacement for the COM-1553A device. The

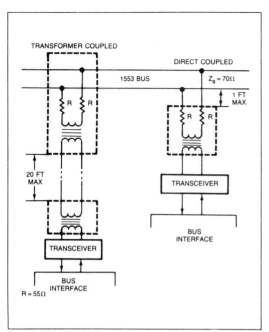

Fig 1—Two types of transformer coupling let you configure a bus device with either a long or a short stub. Long stubs require two transformers, one at the main bus cable and a second at the bus device.

Control chips

Although transceiver modules provide access to the bus, you'll need additional circuits to connect the transceiver to your overall avionic system. These control circuits generate the encoded information for the 1553 bus, and they receive and decode bus information for the system (**Fig 2**). The COM-1553A and COM-1553B chips from Standard Microsystems Corp meet the bus standards and contain the circuits that support the 1553 bus protocol.

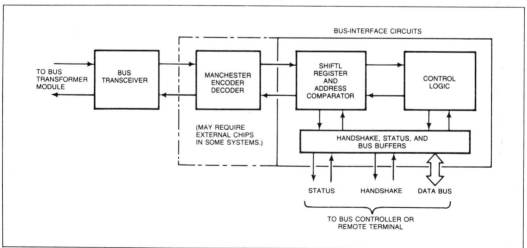

Fig 2—Bus controllers include circuits that decode a transmission and recognize a 5-bit terminal address. The transmitter section serializes the data and adds the synchronization bits and an odd-parity bit. Some devices include a Manchester encoder-decoder circuit.

COM-1553B chip contains the Manchester encoding and decoding circuits, and it uses double-buffered 16-bit data lines to communicate with its host computer (**Fig 3**). Thirteen control lines manage the chip's data-bus handshaking protocol, and they also control the chip's internal operations. In most applications the COM-1553B chip uses direct-memory-access (DMA) techniques to exchange commands, data, and status words with its host computer. The chip operates either as a remote terminal or as a 1553 bus controller, and it recognizes protocol commands and automatically generates the proper responses. This operation relieves the host computer of the overhead processing time it would need to control the data transfers.

New ICs and modules give you access to the bus and free you to concentrate on your system's design.

Many companies have developed their own customized bus controllers as part of their avionic equipment. Besides developing aircraft and military electronic systems, Boeing is exploring several technologies, including CMOS silicon-on-sapphire (CMOS SOS) and gallium arsenide (GaAs), that it could use to produce radiation-hardened controllers for 1553-bus systems as well as military computers. Boeing is sponsoring these efforts with internal funds and now has the capability to produce VLSI devices.

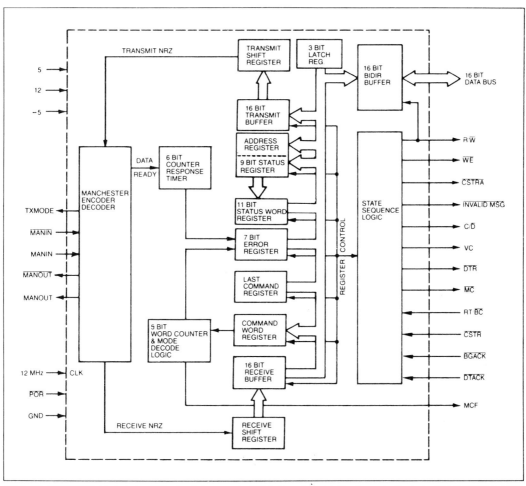

Fig 3—The COM-1553B chip includes all the circuits to support a 1553-bus remote-terminal or bus-controller device. The 16-bit data bus and handshaking signals support DMA operations for high-speed data transfers.

Military uses of the 1553 bus

More than an Air Force standard, the 1553 bus is also used by the Army and Navy. Following is a sampling of the current military uses of the bus.

F-16 fighter

The F-16 fighter was the first aircraft to use and test-fly electronic and avionic equipment that communicates over a 1553 bus. Except for the flight-control system, all of the F-16's avionic systems connect to the 30-ft, dual-redundant (for increased survivability) 1553 bus.

In this dual-redundant bus, any remote terminal can receive a command from either bus at any time. The remote terminal always acts on the latest message it receives, so a transmission on one bus can override a transmission on the other. The basic transmission rate used in the aircraft is 50 Hz, and the bus controller, which is contained in the fire-control computer, automatically polls the remote terminals every 0.64 sec. The inertial-navigation unit takes over the bus controller's operations if the fire-control computer fails.

Singer's Kearfott Division supplies the F-16's SKN-2416 inertial-navigation system (INS),

which consists of a navigation unit, fire-control navigation panel, and battery mount. Except for signals it sends to two display units, the INS communicates with other avionic systems over the 1553 bus.

LAMPS

The Light Airborne Multipurpose System (LAMPS) is a helicopter platform that extends the range of a destroyer's sensors and weapons. In LAMPS, a dual-redundant 1553 bus links two standard AN/AYK-14 computers and a magnetic-tape memory system. One computer controls the avionics equipment, and the other controls the electronic-warfare systems. If the main computer fails, the electronic-warfare computer takes over a limited number of the main computer's operations. A second 1553 bus links the two computers and the avionic equipment.

AH-64 helicopter

Another dual-redundant 1553 bus provides communication between the avionic equipment on the Army's AH-64 Advanced Attack Helicopter. One 1553 bus runs along the right side of the aircraft while the other runs

along the left. The main bus controller and the backup controller are separated for survivability. The bus connects 13 systems that transfer signals from more than 1300 sources. The 13 systems include those for target acquisition and designation, rocket control, gun control, and pilot night vision.

Honeywell manufactures a helmet sight and display unit and an associated controller for the AH-64 helicopter program. Although the helmet does not use the 1553 bus directly, the helmet controller does. Honeywell is also developing a magnetic helmet sight that connects directly to the 1553 bus.

B-52 bomber

The Offensive Avionic System (OAS) is an improved electronic system for the B-52 long-range bomber. A 1553 bus between 250 and 300 ft long links avionic equipment that supports the new air-launched cruise missiles. All of the OAS control and display systems except those that control nuclear-safety operations use the 1553 bus.

B-1 bomber

Eaton's AIL Division (Deer Park, NY) supplies defensive

The F-16 fighter's inertial navigation system uses a standard 1553 bus to transfer information to the aircraft's other systems. This Singer-Kearfott unit provides a backup bus controller that is used when the main fire-control computer fails.

Several manufacturers offer 1553 bus controllers as hybrid circuits and plug-in modules that receive and transmit data. ILC Data Device produces the BUS-65101 module that puts a dumb remote terminal circuit in a 1.6×1.9-in., 68-pin package. Although the manufacturer describes this product as a remote terminal, the module also operates in the bus-controller mode. The module contains a transceiver, a decoder/encoder, control logic, and an internal clock circuit. The module provides six control pins that let you format information in either bytes or words. Whichever format you choose, the data-bus lines have 3-state outputs. The remote-terminal circuit includes a fail-safe timer that signals the host whenever a transmission runs longer than 768 μsec. Long transmissions monopolize the bus and are not allowed by the 1553A/B standard.

If you need an interface that operates only in the remote-terminal mode, Aeroflex offers the ARX-1555 data-terminal bit-processor circuit. In the receive electronic systems that use the 1553 bus to communicate with other avionic equipment in the B-1B bomber. The avionic system uses a network that links all of the main computers. The AN/ALQ-161 defensive avionics system communicates with the computers over a 1553 bus and provides information to the defensive-systems operator, one of the B-1B's four crew members. The AN/ALQ-161 provides a status evaluation and test facility that routes signals around inoperative components.

The B-1B bomber relies on an SKN-2440 high-accuracy inertial-navigation system for such information as position, wind velocity, ground heading, and steering data. A dual-redundant 1553 bus transfers this information to the avionic equipment. Kearfott manufactures this self-contained, 33-lb navigation system.

DIVAD

The Sgt York Division Air-Defense (DIVAD) gun system, manufactured by Ford Aerospace, makes extensive use of the 1553 bus. The DIVAD system includes a data-system controller that uses three Texas Instruments 9989 µPs and about 90k bytes of memory. A West-inghouse computer provides computational capabilities, and a radar computer from the F-16 fighter-aircraft program controls the radar systems. All three computers exchange information over the 1553 bus.

Ford also uses the bus to connect a DIVAD system to a remote data-acquisition and -analysis system that monitors combat activity. Analysis of the bus information lets technicians know how well the system performs. The 1553 bus also passes information and tests the DIVAD's 20 subsystems. The DIVAD system's computers can go into the off-line mode to isolate problems and locate a subsystem that has a faulty circuit.

Other systems

Honeywell Aerospace and Defense produces an automatic flight-control system for such aircraft as the Grumman F-14 and Lockheed SR-71, and for such cargo aircraft as the C-5A and C-5B. The Army's CH-47D helicopter also includes an automatic flight-control system that uses the 1553 bus for communication. Honeywell's AN/APN-194 radar altimeter uses the 1553 bus, and the altimeter is standard equipment on all Navy fixed-wing aircraft.

The Navy's Trident submarine operates with Sperry's Trident II navigation system, which includes a display system manufactured by Sanders' Miligraphic Product Div. The high-resolution graphics display features built-in processing, a keyboard, touch panel, and trackball. The display uses the 1553 bus to communicate with the submarine's navigation system.

The AN/ALQ-136 radar jammer, which ITT Avionics Div manufactures under contract to the US Army, protects attack helicopters and small fixed-wing aircraft from radar detection. ITT and Westinghouse jointly produce the Airborne Self-Protection Jammer, AN/ALQ-165, which is used in the F-16 fighter. The team of Sanders Surveillance Systems Div and ITT manufactures the tactical communications countermeasures system, AN/ALQ-149, which the Navy uses in its EA-6B Prowler aircraft. All three of these electronic-countermeasures systems communicate with other avionic equipment over the 1553 bus.

mode, this module gets serial data from the 1553 bus, detects message errors, decodes command words, and sends parallel data to the host. The receiver circuit also generates control and handshaking signals for the host. In the transmit mode, the unit accepts parallel information from the host and converts it to biphase serial output, which bus-driver circuits require.

Some military applications require you to use doubly redundant buses, which provide a backup path for transmissions in case of component failure, combat damage, or actions that disable one bus path. ILC Data

---

Miniature transformers provide direct bus connections and let you use stubs as long as 20 ft.

Device's BUS-65112 hybrid module is a dual-redundant device that includes two transceivers, two encoder/decoder circuits, and two bit-processor circuits in a 1.9×2.1-in., 78-pin package. This hybrid circuit contains common protocol-sequencer and logic sections that control both communication channels, and it provides handshaking signals for 16-bit DMA transfers that use the host's memory. The 1553 standard specifies 13 mode codes that control dual-redundant remote-terminal units. The BUS-65112 supports all of these codes, and it lets the host computer lock out any combination so the module won't respond to it.

Board controllers

Several manufacturers supply ready-made 1553 bus interfaces on plug-in cards. For systems that require a dual-redundant remote terminal, SCI Systems' MTI-330 board contains all of the redundant circuitry on a 4×5¼-in. card. The circuit uses a 16-bit bidirectional data bus and includes seven signals that control DMA operations. The two bus interfaces each provide eight independent control lines. When the card transmits data 25% of the time, it consumes 7.9W.

Plug-in interface boards let you directly connect general-purpose computers to the 1553 bus. Because the interface boards contain all of the bus-driving and computer-interface circuits, you can put your computer on the 1553 bus without having to design any control circuits. Plug-in boards for Q Bus and Unibus computers, for Data General Nova and Eclipse computers, and for Gould's SEL computers are offered by SCI Systems. The manufacturer also produces the BCU-80B, a 1553 bus interface card for standard IEEE-796 Multibus computers. The BCU-80B contains dual-redundant bus transceivers and operates either as a remote terminal or as a bus controller. The board stores data in a 4k-word, dual-port memory that you map as part of your computer's main memory. A 64-word FIFO buffer saves command and error information.

ILC Data Device, on the other hand, offers the BUS-65500 bus-controller and remote-terminal module, a dual-redundant 1553 bus interface card that is compatible with VME Bus computers. Your software controls the interface circuits with programmed-I/O instructions. The controller contains 4k bytes of 16-bit memory, and it generates four types of interrupts that eliminate the need for I/O device polling routines. When you use the board as a bus controller, the onboard memory stores as many as 62 messages, each 64 words long. When you set up the board to operate as a remote terminal, the circuit responds to messages and saves as many as 119 of them in the onboard memory.

A typical dual-redundant 1553 bus-controller card provides the control chips, transceiver modules, and transformers that couple a system to the bus. SCI Systems Inc manufactures this MTI-330 card.

Recorders

Once your 1553 bus is in place and operational, you'll find that recorders and bus testers are useful in storing information transmitted over the bus and in analyzing the bus itself. Most military computers require storage for information and programs, and several recording systems provide 1553 bus interface circuits that oversee data-transfer and -control operations. Raymond Engineering supplies a basic Model 6450 cartridge tape drive. The drive accepts a 6110 tape-transport cartridge, a precision reel-to-reel cartridge that is hermetically sealed. The Raymond drive comes in three models that the military uses in the LAMPS, B-52D, and EA-6B weapon systems.

Genisco Memory Products Corp also provides a cartridge tape drive that communicates over the 1553 bus. The ECR-40 magnetic tape drive uses a ½-in. tape cartridge that stores as many as 8000 records of formatted information. The 1553 bus connects to the tape drive through a CLR-40 µP-based controller that supports a 48k-word/sec data-transfer rate. The CLR-40 control card offers both direct and transformer coupling to the 1553 bus and lets you operate as many as four tape drives.

Bus testers

Other components that you can add to the 1553 bus are bus testers. Although standard test equipment can locate some bus faults, several manufacturers offer special test instruments for 1553 bus systems. Perhaps the smallest bus-testing devices are the BUS-1555 and -1556 from ILC Data Device. The BUS-1555 module accepts biphase TTL signals from a bus receiver and then tests a bus transmission for parity, sync-bit, Manchester-encoder, and bit-count errors. Output pins provide a signal for each error condition. The module also provides the 16 bits of data received from a transmission and a serial stream of the data in NRZ form. Five control pins furnish signals that indicate the line-active, frame, and load-data conditions as well as the presence of a synchronization pulse and its type.

On the other hand, the BUS-1556 module can generate errors so you can test a 1553 bus device to be sure it either ignores errors or responds to them properly. In addition to being able to produce error-free words, it can produce an error in any one of the 16 bit positions, and in the parity bit. The module also lets you generate a parity error and a transmission with a missing bit or an extra bit. An input pin controls the sync bits so you can delay or advance their logic transition to be sure your interface design responds only to sync bits that have the proper timing. The BUS-1556 and BUS-1555 modules require a 5V power supply, and both come in 2.6×3.1×0.8-in. packages. ILC Data Device also manufactures bus testers for the lab or for portable applications. Its BUS-68003 is a data-bus exerciser that generates errors to test bus devices and also senses errors that occur on the bus during normal use. The front panel displays information, and a small keyboard lets you program the bus exerciser's operating mode.

SCI Systems also provides several bus testers and

simulators. The BST-1123 bus tester uses a DEC LSI-11 computer to simulate as many as 32 remote terminals, each of which can control as many as 32 subdevices, as allowed by the 1553 bus specification. The tester operates as either a bus controller, remote terminal, or bus monitor. The manufacturer also sells a portable bus-activity simulator that stores messages in EPROM modules. You can also load a message from the front panel of the simulator. The front-panel controls let you select from among 19 types of error conditions that the tester puts on the bus.

Some bus systems may be so complex that they require additional diagnostic and data-gathering tools. For such systems, the MPX-53 multiplex bus terminal simulates as many as 31 remote terminals and a bus controller. It also operates as a bus monitor, gathering information about bus operations without taking any part in them. The MPX system gives you control over each remote terminal and its internal operations. This lets you develop and test bus-control routines for each remote terminal. Once your routines operate properly, you can integrate them into the overall control software later. The MPX system lets you inject errors into the bus communications so you can test the response of your interface circuit to these conditions. Software provided with the tester includes driver and handler routines and a Fortran library of control subroutines. The MPX-53 is available from Digital Technology, which offers several other test systems and seminars on using the 1553 bus.

The DIVAD air-defense system uses a 1553 bus for internal operations, and the bus sends information to a remote data-acquisition and -analysis system. DIVAD enhancements may include a 1553 bus link with an integrated air-defense network.

Finally, a line of bus-test instruments from Loral Instrumentation includes four testers that support the development, integration, manufacturing, and deployment stages of a 1553 bus system. For example, the SBA-100A tester simultaneously simulates a bus controller and as many as 32 remote terminals. This test instrument identifies bus failures and analyzes them as they occur, and it lets you inject all error types into the bus's data flow. Acting as both a simulator and a bus monitor, the manufacturer's SBA-200 executes test

sequences automatically and reports results to an optional printer. Loral supplies validation testers to the Naval Avionics Center in Indianapolis, the Air Force at Wright Patterson AFB, and the Army at Ft Monmouth, NJ. All 1553 bus devices go through an extensive procedure that tests their operations under realistic conditions.

The SBA 100A from Loral Instrumentation lets you simulate bus errors. It also identifies bus failures as they occur and logs them for analysis. The tester simulates as many as 32 remote terminals, a bus controller, and a bus monitor in real time.

References

1. *MIL-STD-1553 Designer's Guide*, ILC Data Device Corp, Bohemia, NY.
2. *MIL-STD-1553 Multiplex Applications Handbook*, SCI Systems Inc, Huntsville, AL.
3. Pinkowitz, D, "MIL-STD-1553B: The Military Standard for Avionics Integration," *Electronic Products*, March 28, 1984, pg 58.
4. Crossgrove, A, "Development and Applications of MIL-STD-1553," *SAE Technical Paper Series*, No 801142, Society of Automotive Engineers, Warrendale, PA.

4   Diodes and capacitors imitate transformers

DC transformer

Here is an intriguing circuit which provides a low voltage high current output from a high voltage low (mean) current source. The nominal transformation ratio n in the instance shown is 4:1 step down, but unlike some other voltage-changing schemes using capacitors, n can be any whole number; it is not limited to powers of 2. This advantage apart, the circuit is of limited practical use as the efficiency is not too high due to all the diode drops. But one day someone will invent the perfect rectifier, and then . . . .

Rudy Stefenel
Luma Telecom, Santa Clara, CA

The diode-capacitor network of **Fig 1** accepts low current at a high voltage and delivers higher current at a lower voltage, behaving like a step-down transformer. You drive the circuit with a square-wave input signal as shown.

When the input is at its peak voltage, V_P, current through D_{10}, D_7, D_4, and D_1 charges series capacitors C_4, C_3, C_2, and C_1. The voltage on each capacitor reaches approximately $\frac{1}{4}(V_P - 4V_F)$, where V_F is the forward-voltage drop across one diode. However, the total output voltage doesn't equal the sum of the voltages on the four capacitors; it's less than that by two diode drops. Consequently, the circuit is inefficient for low-amplitude drive signals (too much voltage is lost across

the diodes).

For 15V and 60V p-p inputs, the circuit's corresponding outputs are approximately −1.65V and −12.9V, depending on the load. An input of 28V p-p produces about −5V. Notice that the square-wave generator must sink more current than it sources: It charges the capacitors in series, but discharges them in parallel.

When the input terminal switches to 0V, it connects the capacitors in parallel by pulling the positive side of each capacitor near 0V. The capacitor voltages then produce current flow that creates a negative charge across the load capacitor (C_L). The voltages on C_3, C_2, and C_1 each charge C_L through two diodes in series, but the charging path through C_4 has only one diode, D_{11}. This configuration results in a higher surge current through D_{11} and C_4 and a slightly higher negative output voltage, unless you add a diode in series with D_{11}.

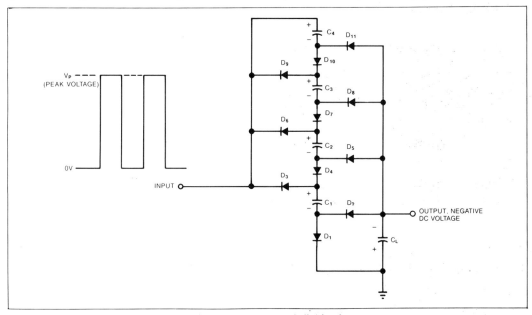

Fig 1—This diode-capacitor network converts an input square wave to a negative dc voltage.

You can change the output voltage by adding or subtracting sections; C_1, D_1, D_3, and D_2 constitute one section, for example. Make the series capacitors equal in value and the total value of these capacitors equal to the load capacitor:

$$C_L = \frac{I}{2V_R f} \, ,$$

where I is the load current, V_R is the maximum allowed ɔ-p ripple voltage, and f is the input frequency.

5 Phase-modulate signals digitally

Digital phase modulator

A neat little circuit this, providing up to ±180 degrees phase modulation in 22.5 degree steps. If you are going to subsequently multiply, or frequency shift, the output to arrive at the final transmit frequency, then the optional sine shaper can be omitted – leaving a phase modulator which could scarcely be simpler!

Noel Boutin
University of Sherbrooke, Quebec, Canada

With two low-cost ICs, you can modulate a square-wave carrier's phase in direct proportion to the value of a 4-bit data input.

In the required circuit (**figure**, part (**a**)), a clock signal running at 16 times the desired carrier frequency drives the 4-binary counter IC_1. The counter's outputs are binary numbers representing 16 equidistant, cyclically generated carrier phase angles.

IC_2, a 4-bit full adder, implements the phase modulation by summing the modulating data with

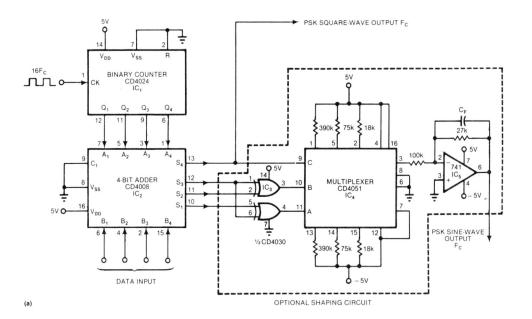

(a)

Phase-modulate a carrier with this simple circuit (**a**). To obtain a sinusoidal output, add the optional shaping circuit: Choose C_F for optimum response at the desired frequency. Part (**b**) shows the phase shifts for the 16 combinations of a 4-bit data input; (**c**) gives the adder input connections for 2-, 4-, 8- and 16-phase resolution.

DATA				
B_4	B_3	B_2	B_1	PHASE
0	0	0	0	0°
0	0	0	1	22.5°
0	0	1	0	45°
0	0	1	1	67.5°
0	1	0	0	90°
0	1	0	1	112.5°
0	1	1	0	135°
0	1	1	1	157.5°
1	0	0	0	180°
1	0	0	1	202.5°
1	0	1	0	225°
1	0	1	1	247.5°
1	1	0	0	270°
1	1	0	1	292.5°
1	1	1	0	315°
1	1	1	1	337.5°

(b)

REQUIRED PHASE LEVELS	B_1	B_2	B_3	B_4
2φ	0	0	0	DATA
4φ	0	0	DATA	DATA
8φ	0	DATA	DATA	DATA
16φ	DATA	DATA	DATA	DATA

(c)

each of the carrier phase angles. The instantaneous binary representation of phase angle at the adder's output is offset from the original by a quantity proportional to the input's value **(b).** Each new data input results in a proportional shift in the cyclically generated phases. The adder's MSB output is the required phase-modulated square-wave carrier at frequency F_C.

If you need a sine wave rather than a square wave, you can add the shaping circuit **(reference).** The table **(c)** shows the required data-input connections to the adder for two, four, eight and 16 phases.

Note that the circuit is not restricted to 16 phase levels. Using an n-bit counter and an n-bit full adder, you can generate a 2^n-level phase-shift-keyed (PSK) signal. Remember, however, that the clock signal driving the binary counter must run at 2^n times the required phase-modulated carrier's frequency. For higher speeds, use high-speed logic (ECL, for example).

Reference

McGuire, *Electronics*, October 2, 1975, pg 104.

6 Innovative design techniques yield optimum counter oscillator

Need a noisy oscillator?

How to ruin the coherence of a frequency standard! RF engineers are used to designing or procuring frequency standards, for example a 10 MHz reference for a synthesizer, where the requirement is not only for long-term frequency accuracy but also short-term stability and low sideband noise. This article describes an application where long-term frequency accuracy is just as important, but short-term stability is deliberately degraded in the interests of measurement accuracy. In addition, it also describes a novel application of that good old standby, the 1496 double balanced modulator.

Johnnie Hancock, *Hewlett-Packard Corp*

Starting with a 10-MHz oscillator and a handful of readily available commercial ICs, you can use the techniques described in this article to configure a 100-MHz counter oscillator that incorporates the random phase modulation needed to break coherence in time-interval-averaging systems (see **box**, "Scope counters need special oscillators").

The quest for incoherence

To eliminate any possibility of harmonic relationships between the oscillator's frequency and that of the input signal, you must randomly modulate the 10-MHz oscil-lator's phase before multiplying its frequency by ten. The phase-modulator section (**Fig 1a**) comprises a 10-MHz tank, a varactor diode and a digital noise source applied to an RC timing circuit.

The noise source used in the 1965A counter is an 8-pin IC widely used in electronic organs. The part—National Semiconductor's Model MM5837—is an MOS/MSI pseudo-random sequence generator designed to produce a broadband white-noise signal for audio applications. A built-in oscillator provides an output that switches between ground and the -12V rail.

L_1, C_2, C_3 and D_1 constitute a tank circuit that's tuned close to 10 MHz. D_1 is an MV836 varactor diode whose capacitance is a function of the reverse-bias voltage; it

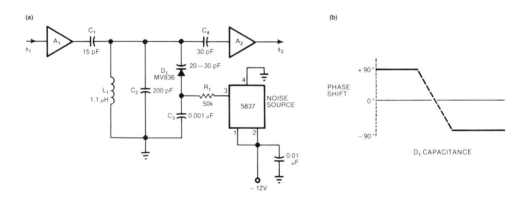

Fig 1—Using an electronic-organ IC, *the circuit in* **(a)** *yields random phase modulation of the 10-MHz reference-oscillator signal. The digital white noise from the IC varies D_1's capacitance to detune the LC tank circuit.* **(b)** *shows the phase variation as a function of the varactor's capacitance.*

varies from approximately 20 to 30 pF. C_3 and D_1 form a series capacitance that's in parallel with the L_1/C_2 parallel combination. C_2's 200-pF value in parallel with the diode's 20 to 30 pF results in a 220- to 230-pF tank capacitance, depending on the diode's reverse bias.

With the tank tuned close to 10 MHz, any change in tuning (arising from D_1's variations) results in a phase shift of ϕ_2 relative to ϕ_1. The change in phase is a function of the non-ideal properties of the tank's components and the amplifier circuitry's input and output impedances. **Fig 1b** shows the phase shift as a function of D_1's capacitance variations.

R_1, connected to the digital noise source's output, forms an RC time constant with C_3. Because the noise source's pulse widths are always less than one time constant, the potential at D_1's anode is a virtually random ramping of the reverse-bias voltage. In **Fig 2a**, trace **B** shows the digital noise applied to the RC

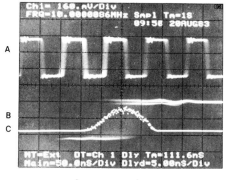

TRACE	VERTICAL	HORIZONTAL
A	160 mV/DIV	50 NSEC/DIV
B	160 mV/DIV	5 NSEC/DIV
C	160 mV/DIV	5 NSEC/DIV

Fig 3—The bell-shaped Gaussian distribution of the 10-MHz reference signal's phase is evident in trace **C**'s digitized waveform.

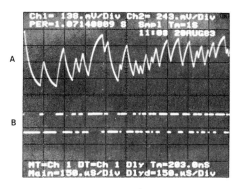

TRACE	VERTICAL	HORIZONTAL
A	138 mV/DIV	150 μSEC/DIV
B	243 mV/DIV	150 μSEC/DIV

(a)

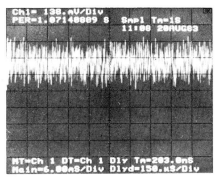

VERTICAL	HORIZONTAL
138 mV/DIV	6 mSEC/DIV

(b)

Fig 2—Random ramping of the varactor's anode voltage is evident in (a)'s upper trace. The ramping is caused by the digital noise seen in the lower trace. (b) shows the anode voltage with a slower time scale.

integrator; trace **A**, the virtually random ramping of D_1's anode voltage. **Fig 2b** shows the same ramping signal on a different time scale.

The instantaneous voltage has an approximately Gaussian distribution, because the voltage applied to R_1 is a broadband white-noise signal that itself has a Gaussian pulse-width distribution. The change in D_1's capacitance has a nearly one-to-one relationship with the change in its reverse-bias voltage, resulting in an approximately Gaussian ϕ_2/ϕ_1 phase distribution. **Fig 3** trace **A** shows the phase-modulated, 10-MHz reference signal—trace **B**'s waveform is an expansion of a leading edge; trace **C**'s digitized waveform shows the relative phase distribution at the leading edge's 50% point.

Although the 10× frequency multiplier multiplies the relative phase shift, the absolute time shift remains constant. For example, if the ϕ_2/ϕ_1 shift changes randomly by 10° p-p, the output shifts by 100° p-p—however, the 10-MHz, 10° and 100-MHz, 100° shifts result in a 2.78-nsec time shift.

How much total phase modulation is needed? This is a critical design parameter, but the answer is not intuitively obvious. The final 100-MHz output needs to have an even distribution of phase shift relative to the unmodulated 10-MHz (ϕ_1) reference. With an even phase distribution, a rising edge of the 100-MHz clock occurs on the average only once in every 10-nsec window. The exact time occurrence of each edge of the oscillator's waveform, however, is totally random.

This situation apparently creates a problem. With a Gaussianly modulated 10-MHz reference clock, the 100-MHz clock also exhibits Gaussian phase-shift distribution rather than the desired even distribution. If the amount of modulation exceeds one full period (>10 nsec, or >360°), the distribution is effectively even for any 10-nsec window. When the output's phase shift exceeds 360° p-p, the clock occurrences overlap into preceding and succeeding windows, resulting in overlapping distributions.

Why use Gaussian modulation?

Summing these overlapping distributions results in an almost even distribution. **Figs 4a** and **4b** show photos of unmodulated and Gaussian-modulated 10- and 100-MHz signals. But, because this technique only allows you to approach an even distribution, why use Gaussian modulation at all? It would seem the ideal solution is to modulate evenly, and you could do this fairly easily.

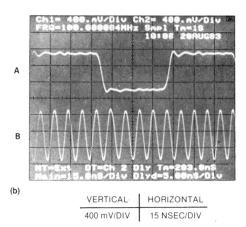

(b)

VERTICAL	HORIZONTAL
400 mV/DIV	15 NSEC/DIV

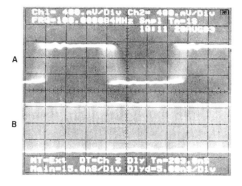

(a)

Fig 4—Modulated and unmodulated 10- and 100-MHz signals are seen in **(a)** and **(b)**, respectively. The modulation shows up, naturally, as jitter in the scope traces.

First, remove the digital noise source and R_1 from the phase-modulator circuit and apply a triangular waveform to D_1's anode. Apply negative offset to the source and tune the frequency for a nonharmonic of 10 MHz in the audio band. Monitor ϕ_2 relative to ϕ_1 and adjust the triangular waveform's peak-to-peak amplitude until exactly 36° phase shift results. With triangular-waveform reverse bias applied to D_1's anode, the anode's instantaneous voltage is always evenly distributed, resulting in a correspondingly even ϕ_2/ϕ_1 phase-shift distribution, as shown in **Fig 5**.

This technique is not without problems, however— you must obtain exactly 36° phase shift; no more, no less. If you obtain only 35° p-p shift, for example, the output will shift by 350° p-p. This scenario produces "voids" in the 100-MHz signal (**Fig 6a**). If, on the other hand, you overmodulate by 1°, the output displays 370° p-p shift. This situation results in the shift's overlapping into preceding and succeeding windows, destroying the evenness of the distribution (**Fig 6b**).

Undermodulation and overmodulation conditions create undesirable bias, which occurs when clock edges are no longer totally random; the counter is biased to trigger in some areas of any 10-nsec window, in preference to other areas in the same window. The result is biased (ie, wrong) answers. For the two described undesirable conditions, each 10-nsec window has two distinct levels of even distribution, as shown in **Figs 6a** and **6b**.

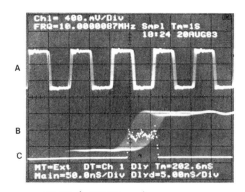

TRACE	VERTICAL	HORIZONTAL
A	400 mV/DIV	50 NSEC/DIV
B	400 mV/DIV	5 NSEC/DIV
C	400 mV/DIV	5 NSEC/DIV

Fig 5—A triangular waveform applied to the varactor's anode results in trace **C**'s even distribution of phase shifts. This method, however, is difficult to control.

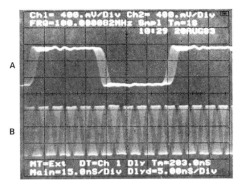

(a)

Fig 6—Undermodulation and overmodulation create problems in the even-distribution method, evident in these photos. Undermodulation creates voids in the 100-MHz signal **(a)**; overmodulation, an uneven distribution **(b)**.

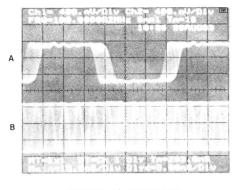

VERTICAL	HORIZONTAL
400 mV/DIV	15 NSEC/DIV

(b)

The exact amount of peak-to-peak phase shift depends on component values in the phase modulator's tank circuit. Because it's not practical to control tightly the components' variances, the best technique for attaining almost-even phase modulation is to overmodulate the 10-MHz signal (in Gaussian fashion) in the range of 50° to 80°. This action results in 500° to 800° p-p modulation of the 100-MHz output. With this Gaussian technique, the exact amount of peak-to-peak modulation is not critical.

Multiplier steps up the reference

The frequency multiplier steps up the reference oscillator's frequency from 10 to 100 MHz, resulting in a 10-nsec reference-clock interval. As **Fig 7a** shows, the multiplier circuit comprises three blocks: a current-impulse generator, a 100-MHz tank and a comparator/amplifier. **Fig 7b** gives a detailed schematic of the multiplier chain.

The 20-MHz current-impulse generator uses a modulator/demodulator IC to create current spikes for each transition of the 10-MHz input signal. The IC used is the industry-standard 1496, produced by Motorola, National Semiconductor, Signetics and Silicon General. **Fig 8a** shows the IC's internal configuration and associated input/output circuitry. In this application, the unit is always operated in a saturated mode, resulting in digital current switching.

The 1496 has two differential-input pairs. The 10-MHz oscillator connects to the upper inputs (pins 8 and 10), driving a quad differential pair ($Q_{1,2,3,4}$). The same signal, slightly attenuated and shifted toward the negative, connects to the lower inputs (pins 1 and 4), driving a differential current switch ($Q_{5,6}$). In steady-state conditions, all current supplied by the constant-current source (-2.6 mA) is dumped from pin 12 to ground. When the input at pins 10 and 4 is high relative to that at pins 8 and 1, the current is channeled through Q_5 and Q_2.

When the input's polarity reverses, all current is channeled through Q_6 and Q_4. The only time the load receives any excitation is during the input's high-to-low or low-to-high transition. At one point during each transition, all transistors are equally biased in their active range, resulting in the dumping of approximately half the current (-1.3 mA) from pin 6 to the load. **Fig 8b** shows a functional timing diagram of the relative transistor base voltages and output current.

With the output of 20-MHz current pulses, it's relatively easy to pick off the fifth harmonic (100 MHz) with a highly tuned, high-Q tank circuit. **Fig 9** shows the tank's output—an exponentially decaying sinusoid ex-

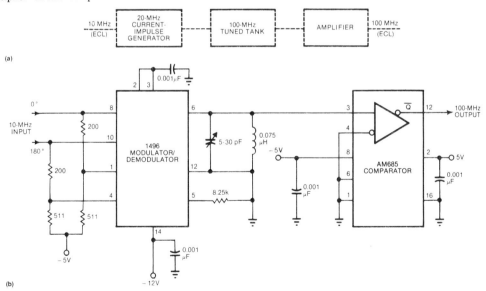

Fig 7—Multiplying the 10-MHz reference signal by ten is easy, with widely available modulator/demodulator and comparator ICs. Current impulses from the first IC cause 100-MHz ringing in the tank circuit; the comparator evens up the waveform.

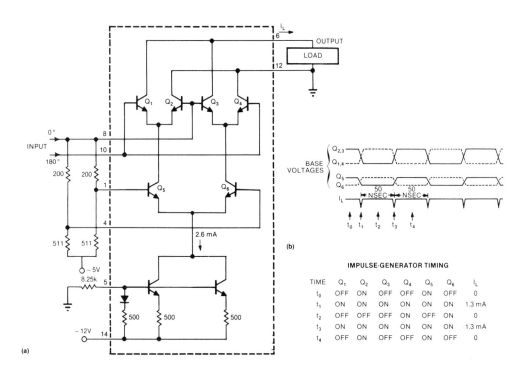

IMPULSE-GENERATOR TIMING

TIME	Q_1	Q_2	Q_3	Q_4	Q_5	Q_6	I_L
t_0	OFF	ON	OFF	OFF	ON	OFF	0
t_1	ON	ON	ON	ON	ON	ON	1.3 mA
t_2	OFF	OFF	OFF	ON	OFF	ON	0
t_3	ON	ON	ON	ON	ON	ON	1.3 mA
t_4	OFF	ON	OFF	OFF	ON	OFF	0

Fig 8—The modulator/demodulator IC *emits a current pulse for each transition of the 10-MHz signal's waveform, resulting in a 20-MHz chain of pulses.*

cited once every 50 nsec. Finally, the AM685 high-speed comparator (made by Advanced Micro Devices) yields the amplified 100-MHz output.

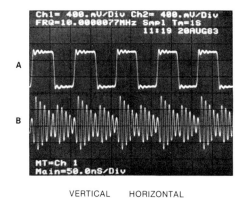

VERTICAL	HORIZONTAL
400 mV/DIV	50 NSEC/DIV

Fig 9—Excited once every 50 nsec by a jolt of current, *the tank circuit creates a series of exponentially decaying 100-MHz waveforms. The comparator then does its limiting and amplifying job to produce a uniform 100-MHz output.*

7 Op amp, ADC make zero-droop S/H

Sample/hold system with indefinite hold capability

In conventional S/H circuits, a trade-off between acquisition time in sample mode and droop rate in hold has to be made. By combining an ADC of the SAR (successive approximation register) variety with a switchable op-amp, this limitation can be avoided.

Jerry Steele
Burr-Brown Research Corp, Tucson, AZ

Using a switchable-input op amp, a 12-bit A/D converter and two 1-shot multivibrators, you can configure a sample/hold amplifier (**figure**) that holds a desired analog sample indefinitely with no droop. Other circuits, shown in some manufacturers' ADC80 data sheets, accomplish this function by using relays in conjunction with the A/D converter. The switchable-input op amp does the same job faster and more reliably.

The high sample command switches the OPA201's input to op amp 1 and triggers a convert command to the A/D converter. The multivibrator delays the sample pulse 100 μsec before presenting a 1-μsec-wide convert command to the A/D converter. This delay allows adequate time for large-signal settling in the OPA201; the A/D converter needs an additional 25 μsec to convert. You can reduce the analog-to-digital conversion time by using a faster A/D converter; ADC84 and ADC85 types, for example, need only 10 μsec. As an added bonus, you can use the A/D converter's digital output (representing the analog output) elsewhere in your system.

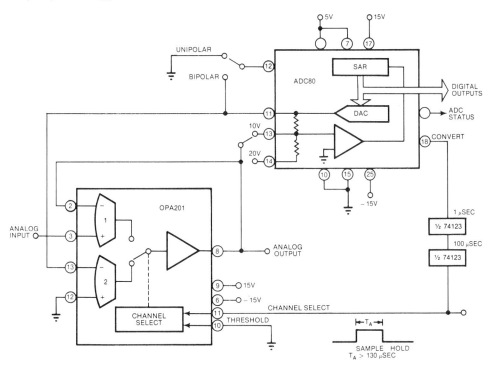

Providing zero-droop hold capability, this circuit uses three ICs to eliminate relays previously used in a similar configuration. Use the spdt switches to choose full-scale range and unipolar/bipolar mode.

8 ISDN terminals simplify data transmissions

An introduction to the integrated services digital network

For years now, all new trunk telephone links have been implemented with digital transmission equipment, and, as it reaches the end of its useful life, FDM (frequency division multiplex) transmission equipment will be replaced by digital kit. The domestic subscribers' local loop is a different matter, but even that must become digital eventually. This article provides some more general background information about the ISDN and then goes on to describe one particular manufacturer's implementation in a chip set.

Tony O'Toole, *Advanced Micro Devices*

Converting digital data to an analog signal is an inefficient and expensive proposition. The conversion often garbles the data, and because it limits transfer speed, it always increases telephone charges. The increased use of computer-based systems has compounded the problem by increasing the amount of data being transferred over long distances.

The solution to this problem is the Integrated Services Digital Network (ISDN), a technique for using phone lines to transmit digital data instead of the analog data they transmit now. The ISDN will also digitize voice signals, so that the same lines will carry voice, facsimile, data, and telex-type transmissions. Furthermore, because this technique doesn't require you to convert your data transmission to analog signals to send it over the phone lines, your transmission will be faster. You can configure an ISDN terminal by using a recently introduced chip set that contains most of the functional blocks required for implementing the ISDN protocols.

Before designing an ISDN terminal, however, you must understand the electrical, data-interchange, and call-rate control protocols recommended by the CCITT (International Consultative Committee for Telegraphy and Telephony) for ISDN devices. These protocols will allow independently designed ISDN devices to communicate with one another.

The basic access interface is the connection point on the ISDN for user terminals. **Fig 1** shows a functional model of the elements forming this interface. The S interface supports terminal connections in either a point-to-point (for maximum range) or a point-to-multipoint environment. ISDN terminal equipment (TE1) connects to the S interface to form the user's access point. Non-ISDN terminal equipment (TE2) connects to an R interface first, and then to the S interface through a terminal adapter (TA). The R interface can accommodate any communication protocol (RS-232C, X.21, etc), but the TA must convert these protocols so that they're compatible with the S interface. The network termination (NT2) converts the point-to-multipoint S interface to a point-to-point T interface.

The 2-wire U interface can extend the range of the basic access interface in a point-to-point configuration. Unfortunately, no international standard exists for implementing a U interface, so the companies that produce ISDN products each have different versions of it. The exchange termination (ET) forms the interface between the local exchange and the basic access interface. Its function depends on the architecture of individual exchanges.

In an ISDN network, the basic access information rate for terminal equipment in each transmit and receive direction is 144k bps. Each user-designated B data channel (B1 and B2) requires 64k bps, and the D channel uses the remaining 16k bps to carry signaling information for B-channel call control. You can also use the D channel for a packet-switched data connection, or for maintenance purposes.

The S interface provides a 4-wire connection between the TE and the NT2. Data transfers every 250 μsec in 48-bit frames (**Fig 2**). The data rate in both directions is 192k bps: 144k bps for the B and D channels and 48k bps for framing control, dc balancing, and the D-channel access protocol.

The CCITT recommendations for terminal-to-network signaling communication are based on layered protocol levels specified by the International Standards Organization (ISO). The use of a layered protocol divides the communication operation into separate functions. Each protocol layer in a terminal performs its intended function by interacting with its peer in the network via a virtual connection (**Fig 3**). Sets of primitives that allow adjacent layers in the protocol to communicate with each other maintain the virtual connections. Keeping these primitives simple ensures that boundaries between layers are well defined, and these established boundaries allow the layers to function independently.

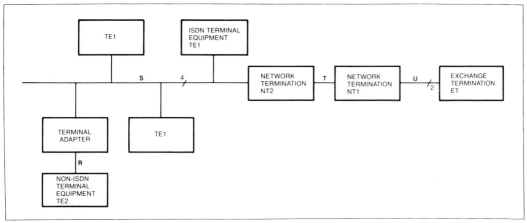

Fig 1—*The connection point on the ISDN* for user terminals is the basic access interface.

Special considerations in terminal design

The intelligence requirement for a basic call is the major difference between a conventional phone and an ISDN terminal. The conventional phone merely translates a given key operation into a line signal. The ISDN terminal must interpret inputs, basing its interpretation on the current progress state of a given call. For example, the terminal may have to generate a message and invoke the level 2 procedure to ensure correct transfer to the exchange. To do so, it must first handle incoming messages at level 2, use their level 3 content to provide feedback to the user, and change the current call status.

Traditional phones are line-powered devices, so they can work when local power is lost and the exchange is operating on a backup supply. It's relatively simple for the conventional phone to function on backup power, because the phone's circuitry is not very complex and its power drain is minimal. The power drain of an ISDN terminal is much higher; an ISDN terminal requires additional circuitry to digitize the voice channel and handle the signaling protocol.

Most ISDN terminals incorporate a display that provides the extensive call information (the calling number, call state, etc) that an ISDN user needs. ISDN terminals must also provide the user with the ring signal and with call-progress tones that are not necessarily available from the network. Furthermore, no ringing voltage can be present on the digital interface; the terminal must provide an alert tone via a loudspeaker.

Your terminal should also allow you to alter the volume, pitch, and pattern of the tones to indicate different incoming-call conditions—internal/external call, emergency call, etc. Call-progress tones, which are normally provided by the network, may not necessarily be available either to the local exchange or to an ISDN terminal; to carry a call-progress tone, both these systems would need to have a B channel allocated. If the local exchange and terminal can carry a call-progress tone, the local exchange may specify the actual frequency and cadence of the tones, so the terminal

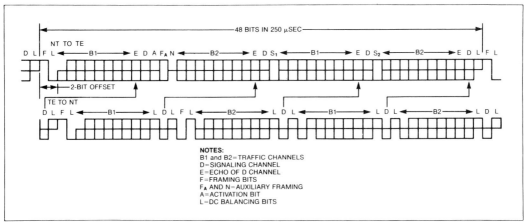

NOTES:
B1 and B2 = TRAFFIC CHANNELS
D = SIGNALING CHANNEL
E = ECHO OF D CHANNEL
F = FRAMING BITS
F$_A$ AND N = AUXILIARY FRAMING
A = ACTIVATION BIT
L = DC BALANCING BITS

Fig 2—*The S interface provides a 4-wire connection* between the TE and the NT2. Data transfers every 250 μsec in 48-bit frames.

must have software control over the tone generation.

When an ISDN network makes a call to a conventional network, the ISDN terminal may have to provide DTMF tones. Existing analog services such as home banking rely on the user to provide DTMF tones during the data-transfer phase of a call, so any ISDN terminal you build now will have to provide these DTMF tones to maintain compatibility with the conventional equipment. Providing these tones will ensure that existing user services are maintained while the communications networks make the transition to a complete digital system.

The two 64k-bit B channels on the S interface are not dedicated to a particular function—you can use them

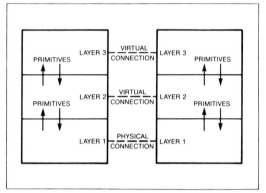

Fig 3—To perform its intended function, a layer in the terminal interacts with its peer in the network via a virtual connection. Sets of primitives maintain the virtual connections.

for voice or data. Therefore, the terminal must be able to route each B channel to either its voice or its data endpoint.

ICs simplify terminal design

Fig 4 illustrates an ISDN terminal design based on the Am79C30 digital subscriber controller (DSC) and the Am7936 subscriber power controller (SPC). An 80C51 microcontroller, configured in the expanded mode to accommodate an external EPROM/ROM for continued program-memory expansion, controls the terminal. The external RAM stores data, and the liquid-crystal display, keypad, and telephone handset form the user interface. The Am79C30 connects the handset to the S interface. The 80C51 accesses the Am79C30, keypad, and display as external memory; port 1 of the 80C51 provides display reset and keypad scanning functions. The Am79C30 is transformer coupled (in both the transmit and receive directions) to the S interface, so it provides access for all information transfer.

The Am79C30 is mapped into eight bytes of the 80C51's external memory space. The 80C51 accesses the Am79C30's most frequently used registers directly and uses the Am79C30's register-pointer mechanism to access the less frequently used registers. The MCLK output of the Am79C30, derived from a crystal oscillator circuit, supplies the system clock to the 80C51. In normal operation, a single interrupt connection be-

tween the Am79C30 and the 80C51 is activated by a change of state in the D channel, in hookswitch operation, or in the S-channel protocol.

The LCD displays call-progress and user-to-user information. The 80C51 accesses the display as two bytes of external memory—one for command inputs, such as cursor control, and one as an ASCII data input. The keypad consists of a simple switch matrix that's read via an octal buffer and scanned via a series of I/O pins on the 80C51. As each I/O line is successively strobed, the 80C51 reads the buffer to determine whether any key is depressed.

The Am7936 SPC—a switched-mode power converter compatible with the S-interface requirements—supplies power to the terminal circuits. Here, the SPC is configured as a step-down converter that supplies a regulated 5V output from an input of 15 to 65V. A diode bridge ensures that the terminal will operate during emergency power conditions, under which the power-feed polarity is reversed to deactivate nonessential equipment. Connecting the serial clock from the Am79C30 to the Sync pin of the SPC synchronizes the converter. This scheme minimizes noise caused by power-supply ripple on the analog voice channel.

The 80C51 scans the keypad, displays information, and controls channel B in the Am79C30. It also has routines for performing the level 2 and level 3 protocols on the D channel. The 80C51's timers provide a real-time clock for scheduling the above tasks and a cadence control for tone generation.

On power up, the reset output from the Am7936 initializes the terminal. The terminal must now negotiate several logical states before it can generate calls. Under the control of the 80C51, the Line Interface Unit (LIU) in the Am79C30 connects the terminal to the interface. If no signal is present on the network side, the LIU signals an activation request by transmitting the INFO1 signal. Once the terminal detects an activation frame (INFO2), it enters the activated state and the D channel is available for data transfer.

Next, the terminal acquires or validates the Terminal Endpoint Identifier (TEI). TEIs can be hardwired into the terminal or allocated by the network. Each of the negotiation messages that the D channel transfers includes a Management Entity Identifier (MEI) header. The terminal can request a TEI value by sending an Identity Request. This request contains a message type and a 16-bit random number. The network uses the random numbers, which are generated by a random-number-generator register (RNG) in the DSC, to evaluate simultaneous requests from multiple terminals. The network responds to the terminals by transmitting an Identity Assigned message. This message contains the original random number and the allocated TEI, which will be used for all future transactions.

After this sequence, the network can issue an Identify Check Request. This message contains no random number. However, the terminal must reply by transmitting a new random number, the identity of the the TEI it is currently using, and an Identify Check Response message. This procedure allows the network to resolve situations in which two terminals are re-

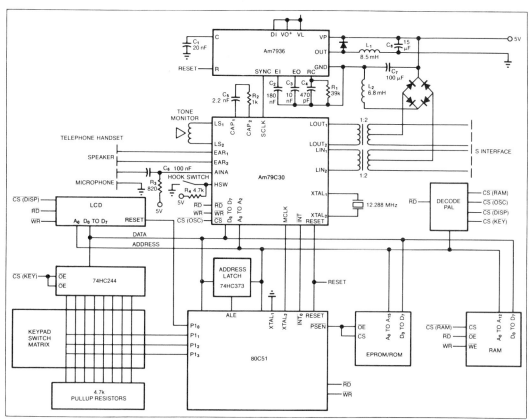

Fig 4—To simplify the implementation of an ISDN terminal, *you can combine the 79C30 digital subscriber controller with the Am7936 subscriber power controller. An 80C51 controls the terminal.*

sponding to the same TEI value. The Service Access Point Indicator (SAPI) forms the other half of the level 2 address field. The SAPI defines the makeup of the required information transfer.

Before the network can transfer signaling information, it must establish the level 2 mode of operation. To achieve data security, level 2 appends a sequence number (either modulo 8 or modulo 128) to each information field it transmits. To select modulo 128 operation, the terminal sends a Set Asynchronous Balance Mode Extended (SABME) signal to the connecting level 2 interface. If the interface can support modulo 128 operation, it returns an Unnumbered Acknowledgment (UA) frame to the terminal. To select modulo 8 operation, the terminal sends a Set Asynchronous Balance Mode (SABM) signal and receives a UA frame. Regardless of the operating mode, the level 2 variables are initialized, and secure data transfer can proceed.

To understand how the terminal implements the protocol to establish communication links, consider the progress of a simple voice call. You initiate a call by taking the terminal off hook. The Am79C30 detects this action and interrupts the 80C51, which interprets the off-hook as a request for service and generates a local dial tone. The 80C51 generates this tone by setting the required frequency register (FTG) and amplitude regis-

ter (ATG) in the Am79C30's Main Audio Processor (MAP) and routing the output back to the phone handset. The dial tone is only local at this point because a B traffic channel may not be available, and the subsequent operation may be a facility that doesn't require a traffic channel.

You now use the keypad to enter the destination number. The display echoes this operation. The tone generator in the MAP provides positive feedback for the caller by sending MF tones to the handset. The call-processing routines now format a level 3 Setup message in memory. This message contains a new-call reference value, the destination number, and the bearer capability. All future messages relating to this call will contain the call reference value, thus distinguishing this call from any others. The bearer-capability information in the Setup message determines the type of data that the B channel must transfer.

The level 3 Setup message now passes to the level 2 (LAPD) processing routines as a DL-DATA primitive. To ensure reliable transmission to the next layer entity, the layer processor appends appropriate information to the message. This information includes the next N(S) value (to establish message-train sequence), the current value of N(R) (to update transfer handshake in the opposite direction), and the message type and address.

The message now passes to level 1 for actual transmission. The memory stores the data in case an error occurs and it becomes necessary to retransmit a level 2 message.

You now program the length of the required transmit message into the transmit count register (TCR) of the data-link controller (DLC) in the Am79C30. The first byte transfers to the transmit data register (TDR), enabling transmission. Once the D channel has been idle for the appropriate number of bits, transmission starts, and the DLC generates an opening flag. Transmission then continues; the Am79C30 generates interrupts to the 80C51 as new bytes are required. When the required number of bytes has been transmitted, the DLC appends a cyclic redundancy check (CRC) and a closing flag to the outgoing message.

If the DLC does not receive the appropriate number of bytes, it generates a transmit-underrun error and does not append a CRC to the frame. If a conflict should occur on the D channel, the E channel echoes the data that has been accepted. The LIU in the Am79C30 monitors the E channel. If it detects an error, it aborts transmission and generates an interrupt for the 80C51. When the D channel is free, the transmit process must begin again from the start of the message. Because the E channel's abort mechanism produces an immediate response, one terminal's data will always transfer correctly when a conflict occurs.

Once the exchange signals that it has received a suitable level 2 response, the terminal's memory can discard the transmitted message. If the exchange doesn't signal a response, the terminal retransmits the message after a level 2 timeout. When a message from the D channel arrives at the DLC, the DLC detects any flags present and checks the SAPI and TEI addresses to determine whether they apply to this terminal. Once there's an address match, the Am79C30 generates an interrupt for the 80C51, indicating the start of a new message. The 80C51 then assembles the message in terminal RAM. If the message should be longer than the one programmed into the maximum-receive-length register (MCR), the DSC generates an error interrupt.

On the other hand, a correct transmission and the presence of a validated CRC generates an end-of-frame interrupt, making message available for the level 2 processing routines. The level 2 processor extracts the LAPD variables so that it can respond to any retransmission, acknowledgment, or peer-busy information. If an information field is present, the processor checks the forward sequence number, N(S). If N(S) is valid, the level 2 processor passes the information field to the level 3 processor as a DL-DATA primitive.

If the local exchange accepts the call, it sends the terminal a level 3 Setup Acknowledge (SETUP ACK) message, which designates the B channel to be used for the call. The multiplexer in the Am79C30 can now make the appropriate connection, on the Line Interface Unit (LIU), between the MAP and the selected B channel.

The local exchange also forwards a SETUP message to the destination terminal. If the destination terminal is deactivated, the network must first activate it by sending INFO2 frames, which are level 2 parameters that must be negotiated. The level 2 parameters at each terminal don't have to be identical. Nor does the SETUP message received by the destination terminal have to match the originating message—parameters such as the selected B channel are unique to the local interface. If the originating terminal receives no response to the initial SETUP message, it will make another attempt to initiate the call.

If the destination terminal is free, it responds to the SETUP message with a Call Proceeding (CALL PRO) message. The called terminal then generates local ringing to its loudspeaker, and displays an incoming-call message that includes the number of the originating terminal. The calling terminal generates distant ringing to its handset. The local Am79C30's tone generators produce both of these ring tones.

A handset-off-hook condition at the called terminal stops the generation of the local tone and sends a Connect (CONN) message. When the originating terminal receives the CONN message, remote ring-tone generation stops; the call is now in the connect phase.

A handset-on-hook condition at either terminal ends the call. The on-hook condition generates a Disconnect (DISC) message, which in turn deletes the connection across the network. The terminals and local exchanges complete the sequence with a Release (REL) and Release Complete (REL COM) message, which terminate the entire call procedure in the terminals and local exchanges. At this point, any off-hook condition at a terminal initiates a new call, and the system enters the dial-tone state.

A look at an ISDN chip set

The Am79C30 Digital Subscriber Controller is a CMOS device that contains most of the functional blocks required by an ISDN terminal. The Line Interface Unit (LIU) connects directly to the S-interface transmit and receive transformers and handles the level 1 protocol for framing, activation/deactivation, and D-channel access.

The Main Audio Processor (MAP) connects to two sets of audio transducers. It uses digital signal processing to perform all the normal codec filter functions, and it provides transmit and receive gain and response adjustments, as well as side-tone control. The MAP also contains two tone generators that users can configure three different ways to produce call-progress tones, a ringing tone, and multifrequency (MF) tones.

The Data Link Controller (DLC) processes the D channel as far as an intermediate stage of the LAPD protocol, performing flag insertion and deletion, zero insertion and deletion, CRC generation and checking, address recognition, and message-length checking. The 8-bit Microprocessor Interface (MPI), which allows external control of all the internal blocks, maintains control. The Multiplexer (MUX) enables the B channels for internal routing between the MAP, LIU, MPI, and the serial port. The port, which has a 192k-bit capacity, can accommodate as many as three external 64k-bit channels.

The Am7936 is a bipolar switched-mode power controller aimed specifically at ISDN applications. It functions in either galvanically isolated or nonisolated configurations to provide a programmable or fixed 5V output from an input of 15 to 65V. The low-power-detection circuit allows users to select a variable minimum operating voltage. The circuit also drives an on-chip reset circuit that's suitable for terminal initialization at power up. The low-power-detection circuit also indicates the emergency power state (reverse voltage on the S interface). To accommodate the presence of analog circuitry in the terminal, a sync input allows you to synchronize the Am7936 to the analog processing circuit, thereby reducing the effects of supply interference on signal-to-noise performance.

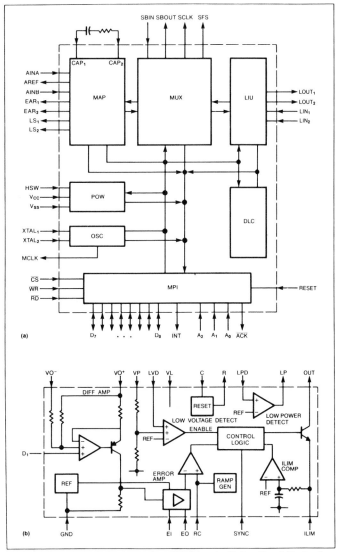

A CMOS device containing most of an ISDN terminal's functional blocks, the Am79C30 (a) handles the level 1 protocol. The Am7936 (b) is a bipolar switched-mode power controller aimed specifically at ISDN applications.

Basic ISDN operation

To understand ISDN message-transfer techniques, consider a simple call from one terminal to another in the same exchange. A terminal initiates a call when the user takes the terminal off hook and keys in digits via a keypad. To initiate a call, level 3 in the terminal always generates a Setup message. The terminal selects a call-reference value and uses this value in all subsequent messages relating to this call between the originating terminal and the exchange.

The Setup message must contain the bearer capability—information that details the type of data to be transmitted on the traffic channel. For this sample call, a normal off-hook condition indicates a voice connection coded in A or μ law. For a data call, the Setup message would indicate the format and data rate. The keyed digits form the destination-address field. If any digits are unknown at the start of the sequence, the terminal supplies them in subsequent Information messages.

When the exchange receives the Setup message, it replies with a Setup Acknowledge, designating the traffic channel (B1 or B2) to be used for the call. The exchange then routes the call and designates a call reference value for all message transfers to and from the destination terminal. Next, the exchange sends a Setup message to the destination terminal. This message contains the originating bearer capabilities, the traffic-channel information, and the destination and origination addresses. The destination address is not redundant information, because a terminal may have several addresses in a network, or the exchange may have rerouted the call.

The destination terminal checks the validity of the bearer capability and replies with an Alerting message if the bearer capability is valid. The destination terminal then alerts its user to the incoming call by generating a ring signal. When the destination terminal goes off hook, it sends a Connect message through the exchange to the originating terminal. The call is now in the voice-transfer state.

Either user can terminate the call by putting the terminal on hook. This action generates a Disconnect message, which breaks down the call in the exchange and then gets passed to the other terminal. Note that a normal termination, such as this, is not the only cause of a Disconnect. A Disconnect could also be the result of network congestion, incompatible bearer capabilities, or other problems.

After the Disconnect, the Release and Release Complete sequence completes the call-teardown procedure between each terminal and the exchange. The exchange then releases the call reference values associated with the call on both data links.

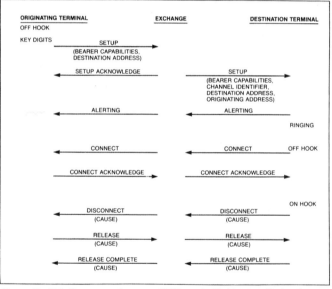

For a call within the same exchange, an ISDN terminal initiates a call when the user takes it off hook and keys in digits via a keypad.

9   IF chip forms audio decibel-level detector

AF levelmeter from RF chip

Here is another example of ingenuity in pressing devices into service in ways other than the original application. There are other ways of getting a log level response at AF, but if accuracy requirements are not too stringent, this one is quite neat.

Robert J Zavrel
Signetics Inc, Sunnyvale, CA

The NE604 is a low-power IF chip that includes a logarithmic signal-strength output. **Fig 1**'s circuit draws less than 5 mA from a 6V supply and offers a signal sensitivity of 10.5 µV. Although the chip is intended for cellular-radio and other RF applications, the log output provides an 80-dB range of response and ±1.5-dB accuracy in the 100-Hz to 10-kHz audio range (**Fig 2**).

You capacitively couple the audio signal to pin 16. The log circuit generates approximately 10 µA per 20 dB of input signal at pin 5; you convert this current to voltage by connecting 100 kΩ (R_2) from pin 5 to ground. You can then measure this voltage directly with a voltmeter, or buffer and filter the voltage as shown using op amps IC_{2A} and IC_{2B}. A standard 0 to 5V meter with a linear decibel scale serves to display 80 dB of signal level. To measure higher audio levels, add a resistive attenuator at the chip's audio input.

R_1 and C_1 form a lowpass filter. Specifying 2 kΩ for R_1 provides maximum linearity; you should adjust C_1 to change the filter's cutoff frequency. A higher value for C_1 lowers the circuit's output to about 0.6V when no audio signal is present (**Fig 2**). Lowering C_1 increases the frequency response, but raises the circuit's output

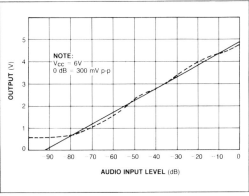

Fig 2—The dotted line indicates the response of Fig 1's circuit for the 100-Hz to 10-kHz audio range; the solid line indicates an ideal response. Full scale (0 dB) equals 300 mV p-p.

when no audio signal is present. The filter R_3/C_3 provides a tradeoff between meter damping and ripple attenuation. If both a quick response and low ripple are required, you must substitute a more complex, active lowpass filter.

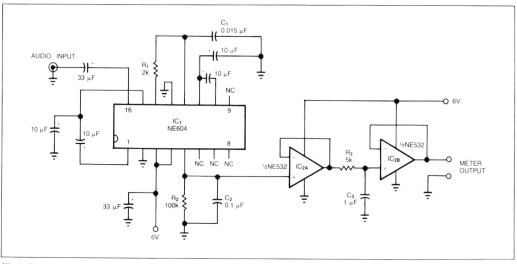

Fig 1—You can measure audio signal levels to ±1.5-dB accuracy using a dual op amp and an FM IF chip (normally used for cellular-radio and other RF applications). Sensitivity is 10.5 µV; power consumption is 30 mW.

10 Versatile ramp generator uses 1kbit RAM

A novel use for a RAM

I am always interested in ways to use a thing for something other than its originally intended purpose – just a novel use, that is; not misuse, like the electronic engineer's propensity to use a pair of pliers as a spanner. Here is a circuit that produces a slow ramp waveform of exceptional linearity. (A misprint in the text should read 'or a one to zero for descending ramps'.)

J Martinez and F Sandoval
ETS Ing Telecomunicacion, Madrid, Spain

The ramp generator in **Fig 1** is an alternative to more-expensive approaches that are based on a D/A converter with 12- to 14-bit resolution. The circuit lets you set the ramp's start and stop levels, select up or down (positive or negative slope), adjust the amplitude and repetition rate, and stop at any level on the ramp. IC_4 is a 1k-bit RAM that provides 1024 steps for any ramp regardless of amplitude and duration; for higher resolution, you need a larger memory.

Op amp IC_9 and associated components filter the memory's serial output. By writing ones (or zeros) to the memory at regular intervals, you can steadily increase (or decrease) the average voltage level $n \cdot V_{CC}/1024$ at D_{OUT}, where n is the number of ones in the memory at that moment.

The nominal 200-kHz square wave at IC_{7B}'s output clocks the memory and counter IC_4. The counter generates addresses that scan through each of the memory's 1024 locations about 200 times/sec; the falling edge at

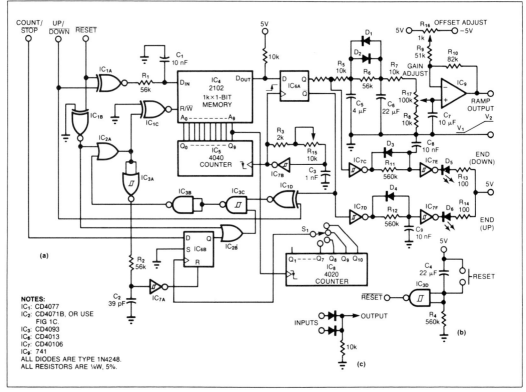

Fig 1—This ramp generator is based on duty-cycle modulation and filtering of the serial output from a $1k \times 1$-bit RAM (**a**). The Reset circuit (**b**) generates a 12-sec low that helps the ramp circuit set up the conditions for a particular ramp signal. You can substitute the 2-input OR-gate circuit (**c**) for the CD4071B.

NOTES:
IC_1: CD4077
IC_2: CD4071B, OR USE FIG 1C.
IC_3: CD4093
IC_6: CD4013
IC_7: CD40106
IC_9: 741
ALL DIODES ARE TYPE 1N4248.
ALL RESISTORS ARE ¼W, 5%.

counter output Q_9 that occurs on the completion of each scan clocks counter IC_8. The setting of switch S_1 provides coarse selection of the ramp duration (potentiometer R_{15} provides the fine adjustment).

Each positive transition on the wiper of S_1 initiates a memory-write operation by clocking flip-flop IC_{6B}. The write operation changes a zero to one for ascending ramps, or a zero to one for descending ramps. LEDs D_6 and D_5 signal the completion of ascending and descending ramps, respectively.

R_2 and C_2 delay the reset of flip-flop IC_{6B} long enough to write into one memory location following each positive transition at the flip-flop's clock input. Also, gates IC_{1D} and IC_{3C} delay the write operation by an increasing amount as the ramp grows, thus allowing time for the readout of those ones (or zeros) written since the ramp began.

When you use the ramp generator in a temperature controller, it can sweep between the temperatures represented by voltages V_1 and V_2, where $V_1 < V_2$. First, set Up/$\overline{\text{Down}}$ to 1 (for ascending ramp), and set Count/$\overline{\text{Stop}}$ to 0. Press Reset (**Fig 1b**), which initiates a 12-sec low on $\overline{\text{Reset}}$. The memory fills with zeros, so flip-flop IC_{6A}'s Q output is low and the filter output (the op amp's noninverting input) is 0V. Use the offset-adjust potentiometer (± 8V range) to set the op amp's output to V_1. Next, set Up/$\overline{\text{Down}}$ to 0 and press Reset again—the memory fills with ones. The filter output (wiper of R_{17}) is V_{CC}. Set the op amp's output to V_2 using the gain-adjust potentiometer. Then, set Up/$\overline{\text{Down}}$ to 1 and press Reset to fill the memory with zeros again; the generator is ready to run when you set Count/$\overline{\text{Stop}}$ to 1.

Ramp-linearity error is very low, and output ripple is less than 0.03%. Power dissipation is less than 250 mW. Because changes in the supply voltage will affect linearity by altering the frequency at IC_{7B}, you should provide good supply regulation or arrange a clock frequency that isn't affected by the power supply.

11 ICs simplify design of single-sideband receivers

Alternatives to the filter method of SB generation and detection

Although some years old now, this article contains some useful ideas in addition to a basic review of methods of SSB generation and detection. The article describes the Weaver method amongst others. The beauty of that particular scheme is that incomplete suppression of the unwanted sideband causes no out of band interference, as it overlays the wanted sideband.

Robert J Zavrel, *Signetics Corp*

Single-sideband (SSB) transmission offers many advantages over FM and full-carrier double-sideband modulation schemes—more efficient spectrum use, better signal-to-noise ratios at low signal levels, and better transmitter efficiency. Unfortunately, SSB systems have historically required the use of expensive multipole filters. Today, however, some new RF and digital ICs allow you to circumvent the need for these filters. You can use these ICs to good advantage in developing a cost-effective SSB receiver.

Good SSB-receiver design requires that you know a little about the three basic methods of single-sideband generation. All three methods use a balanced modulator to produce a double-sideband, suppressed-carrier signal. The undesired sideband is then removed by high-Q multipole filters (the filter method), by phase and amplitude nulling (the phasing method), or by the Weaver method. The reciprocal of the generator functions is used to develop sideband detectors.

Generators accept audio inputs and produce the SSB signal; detectors receive the SSB signal and reproduce the audio signal. The sideband signal is typically in the radio-frequency (RF) range, so you can amplify it and apply it to an antenna or use it as a subcarrier. It's worth noting that all three methods of removing a sideband are complementary; an SSB signal produced by the Weaver method can be reproduced by the phasing method, etc.

In a generation and detection technique using the traditional filter method, the generator (**Fig 1a**) produces a double-sideband signal, and the balanced modulator nulls the carrier. A high-Q crystal-type bandpass filter then removes the undesired sideband. The transmit mixer then converts the SSB signal to the desired output frequency.

The detection scheme (**Fig 1b**) simply reverses the operation. A receive mixer converts the input frequency to the intermediate frequency (IF). The filter has a narrow response and passes only the required SSB bandwidth. The product detector demodulates the signal.

This SSB signal-generation method has one major drawback. The filter is tuned to one fixed frequency. As a result, you'll need to incorporate a number of transmit and receive mixers to satisfy applications involving multifrequency operation.

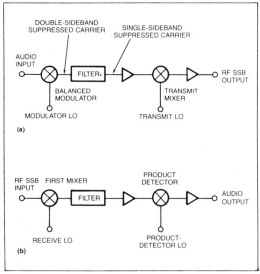

*Fig 1—In the traditional filter method, the generator (**a**) produces a double-sideband signal, and the balanced modulator nulls the carrier. The detector (**b**) simply reverses the generation procedure to develop the audio output.*

Phasing method not suited to voice band

Fig 2 shows block diagrams of generator and detector circuits for implementing the phasing method. In the detector (**Fig 2a**), the input signal feeds in phase to two RF mixers. A local oscillator (LO) supplies a second signal to the mixers in quadrature. Summing the differentiated output of one of the mixers with the output of the second mixer produces an audio output.

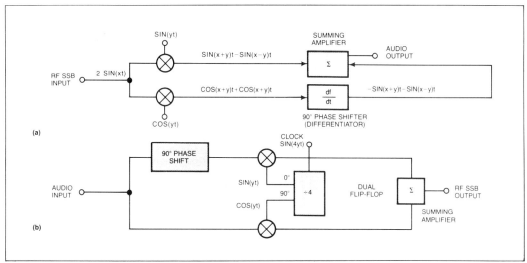

Fig 2—The input signal feeds in phase to two RF mixers in the phasing-method detector (a). A local oscillator (LO) supplies a second signal to the mixers in quadrature. In the generator (b), a divide-by-4 flip-flop provides the sin(yt) and cos(yt) signals for the mixer.

In most cases, the mixers will have an output in the audio passband (300 to 3000 Hz). Running the passband through the differentiator circuit imposes a 90° phase shift over more than three octaves. As a result, it's quite difficult to use the phasing method for voice-band SSB applications.

The phasing method employs a generator (**Fig 2b**) that duplicates the circuit elements found in the detector. Note that in the generator, the differentiator (phase shifter) is located between the audio input and the mixer. In the generator circuit, a divide-by-4 flip-

flop provides the sin(yt) and cos(yt) signals for the mixer. As a result, the clock signal's frequency must be four times the RF output frequency.

Versatility in datacomm systems

You can use the phasing method for FSK, PSK, and quadrature-PSK datacomm systems. In an FSK situation, for example, you can alternately key two discrete frequencies to correspond to ones and zeros. By tuning the receiver at the halfway point, you can let these two frequencies represent the upper- and lower-sideband

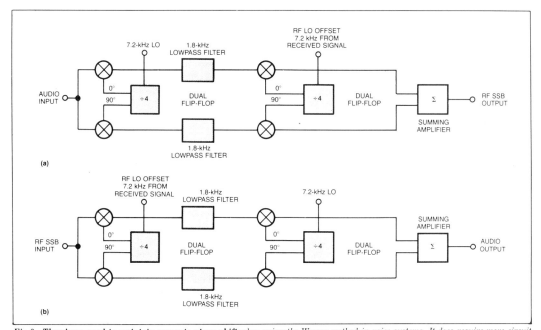

Fig 3—There's no need to maintain accurate phase shift when using the Weaver method in voice systems. It does require more circuit elements than the phasing method—four mixers in both the generator (a) and the detector (b), for example.

signals. When you implement rectification and filtering, you can use the simultaneous upper/lower-sideband detection concept to drive both clock inputs of a flip-flop. This type of FSK receiver can exhibit better sensitivity characteristics than traditional FM receivers. In addition, the scheme uses discrete frequencies, so you will not have to employ a broadband phase shifter; simple discrete RC networks will suffice.

The Weaver method (**Fig 3**) eliminates the difficulty of having to maintain an accurate broadband phase shift in voice communications systems. A derivation of the phasing technique, the Weaver method does require more circuit elements (four mixers as opposed to two, for example) in both the generator (**Fig 3a**) and the detector (**Fig 3b**).

Low-frequency subcarrier vs phase shift

The basic difference between the two schemes is that the Weaver method uses a low-frequency (1.8-kHz) subcarrier in quadrature, rather than a broadband, 90° audio phase shift. The desired sideband folds over the 1.8-kHz subcarrier, and its energy appears between 0 and 1.5 kHz. The undesired energy appears at least 600 Hz away (above 2.1 kHz). As a consequence, you can reject the undesired sideband with a simple lowpass filter.

It's much easier to design a filter with a steep lowpass response than it is to achieve the accurate phase and amplitude balance that the phasing method requires. As a result, the Weaver method will have much better sideband rejection than that obtainable with the phasing method.

Once you've chosen the manner in which you wish to develop the SSB signal, you're ready to add the other circuits that help complete an SSB receiver. You'll need quadrature-dual-mixer circuits for the first stage when using the Weaver method. **Fig 4** illustrates two methods of obtaining quadrature LO signals for dual-mixer applications. Both circuits are inherently broadband circuits; they are far more flexible than designs using passive LC circuits (which fail to maintain a quadrature relationship when the operating frequency changes), and they do not require adjustments. In addition, the circuits shown in **Fig 4** are not limited to SSB applications; you can also apply them in FSK, PSK, and quadrature-PSK digital communications systems.

In **Fig 4a**'s circuit, a divide-by-4 dual flip-flop generates all four quadrature signals. Most of the popular dual flip-flops will work in this circuit; the choice depends on the application. This example employs the HEF4013 CMOS device, which consumes little power and maintains excellent phase integrity at clock rates ranging to several megahertz. As a result, it will work quite well at the ubiquitous 455-kHz intermediate frequency.

For higher clock rates (to 120 MHz), the fast-TTL 74F74 is a good choice for the flip-flop. Tests on this device at 30-MHz operating frequencies show good results—greater than 20-dB SSB rejection. At frequencies in the neighborhood of 5 MHz, use of the 74F74 will result in sideband rejection of nearly 40 dB. The ultimate low-frequency rejection is mainly a function of the audio phase shifter. You can improve performance by employing resistors and capacitors with tighter tolerances in the phase shifter.

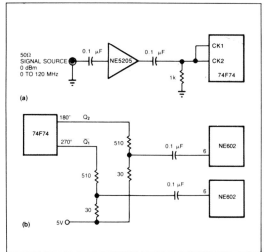

Fig 5—*You can effectively drive the 74F74 and other TTL gates with the circuit shown in* **a**. *The total resistance in the interface circuit* (**b**) *establishes a conservative current drain (approximately 10 mA) from the 74F74, and the divider tap optimizes NE602 operation.*

Match clock and operating frequencies

The circuit shown in **Fig 4b** illustrates a different technique for producing a broadband quadrature phase shift for the LO. In this case, the clock and operating frequencies are identical—an advantage when compared with the flip-flop circuit, because you don't need the high-speed components. Phase accuracy, however, is more difficult to achieve.

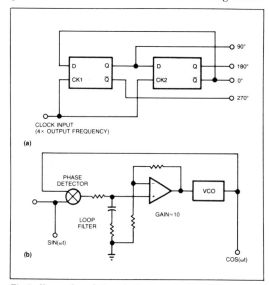

Fig 4—*You need quadrature dual mixers whether you're using the phasing or the Weaver method. The mixer in* **a** *maintains good phase integrity at clock rates ranging to several megahertz. Clock and operating frequencies are equal in the mixer circuit* (**b**), *which marks an advantage over the flip-flop design.*

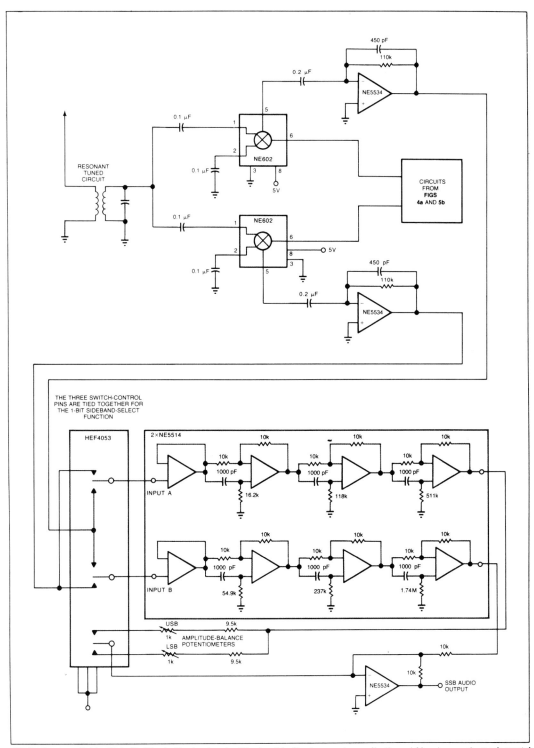

Fig 6—You can reliably obtain 35-dB rejection levels using this circuit in direct-conversion applications. Add an inexpensive 2-pole crystal or ceramic filter and you will realize the required 70-dB sideband rejection levels.

A phase-locked loop (PLL) will maintain a quadrature phase relationship when the loop is closed and the VCO voltage is 0V. The dc amplifier enhances the accuracy of the quadrature output by providing gain for the VCO control circuit. PLL circuits tend to be noisy, however, and noise can be a problem. Sideband noise is troublesome in both SSB and FM systems, but SSB transmission is less sensitive than frequency modulation to phase noise in the LO.

After developing the LO signals, you have to provide some drive circuitry. The circuit shown in **Fig 5a** provides an effective means of driving the 74F74 (or other TTL gates) with an analog LO. Assuming you're using 50Ω input and output impedances, the NE5205 amplifier provides approximately 20 dB of gain from dc to 450 MHz.

External-component requirements are minimal. The 1-kΩ value of the resistor is about optimum for pulling the input voltage down near the logic threshold. A 0-dBm output level will drive the NE5205 and 74F74 to 120 MHz. By cascading two NE5205s, you can increase the sensitivity without sacrificing the wide bandwidth.

Fig 5b shows the interface circuitry between the 74F74 and the NE602 mixers' LO ports. The total resistance establishes a conservative current drain—about 10 mA—from the 74F74 outputs; the voltage-divider tap optimizes the operation of the NE602s. The low signal-source impedance helps maintain phase accuracy. For dc isolation, use a miniature ceramic device for the isolation capacitor.

Amplifying and switching functions

The use of active mixers like the NE602 will provide conversion gain—typically 18 dB. In more traditional applications, which use passive diode-ring mixers, you experience a conversion loss—typically 7 dB. Consequently, the detected audio level will be about 25 dB higher when you use the active-mixer approach. This fact means that you can significantly reduce the noise and gain requirements of the first audio stage and eliminate the microphonic effect. This is a great advantage in direct-conversion receivers.

Traditional direct-conversion-receiver designs use passive audio LC filters at the mixer output and low-noise discrete JFETs or bipolar transistors in the first audio stages. Because of the conversion loss associated with passive mixers, these amplifiers must have a very high audio sensitivity, so they readily respond to mechanical vibration and produce microphonics. The conversion gain available from an active mixer allows you to use a simple NE5534 op-amp stage **(Fig 6)**, set up as an integrator to eliminate ultrasonic and RF instability.

You can use an HEF4053 CMOS-analog switch to provide the sideband-select function. This triple double-pole switch drives the phase network and engages one of two amplitude-balance potentiometers—one for each sideband. The buffer op amp shown with the two sideband-select sections reduces the total harmonic distortion, maintains amplitude integrity, and prevents changes in the resistance values of the filter network due to switch resistance. If the gain distribution within

both legs of the receiver is consistent, you can eliminate the amplitude-balance potentiometers in less demanding applications.

Phase shifting comes next

In the phasing method, the broadband audio phase shifter (differentiator) is a critical stage. The analog all-pass differential phase-shift circuit shown in **Fig 6** is one of several available broadband phase-shift techniques. When you short the inputs together and drive them with a microphone circuit, the outputs will be 90° out of phase over the 300- to 3000-Hz band. This splitting and phase-shift action is required for phasing-generator operation.

For phasing demodulation, the circuit's filters receive their inputs from the two audio detectors. The filter outputs are then summed to null the undesired sideband and reinforce the desired sideband.

The filter circuit employs standard 1% values for the resistors and capacitors. You can improve gain tolerances by using 0.1% laser-trimmed integrated resistors. To maximize audio performance, it's best to use polystyrene, polypropelene, or Mylar capacitors.

Two quad op amps (NE5514s in this case) fit nicely into **Fig 6**'s approach. One section of each quad IC serves as a switch buffer, and the other three form a phasing section. The quad op amps also yield high linearity and high dynamic range. These characteristics are much easier to achieve at audio frequencies than they are at common intermediate frequencies. Audio IF systems have other things going for them as well: They have no IF-tuned circuits, they have no need for shielding, and power requirements are low.

Putting it all together

High-quality SSB radio specifications call for sideband rejection greater than 70 dB. Using the circuit shown in **Fig 6**, you can reliably obtain rejection levels of 35 dB. Add an inexpensive 2-pole crystal or ceramic filter, and you can meet the 70-dB requirement.

Fig 7 shows a complete SSB receiver that uses the phasing-filter technique. The block labelled "direct-conversion phasing SSB receiver" is **Fig 6**'s circuit. The antenna connects (via a bandpass filter) directly to the inputs of the NE602s.

The direct-conversion phasing SSB receiver circuit has a 10-dB signal/noise sensitivity of 0.5 μV and a dynamic range of about 80 dB. Single-tone audio harmonic distortion is less than 0.05%, and 2-tone inter-modulation products are more than 55 dB down at RF input levels only 5 dB below the 1-dB compression point. The sideband rejection is about 38 dB at a 9-MHz operating frequency.

You can also use the same quadrature dual mixer in a Weaver-method receiver. **Fig 8** shows an experimental Weaver receiver circuit. The subcarrier stage here can use HEF4066 CMOS analog switches to minimize power drain.

A 1.8-kHz subcarrier requires a 7.2-kHz clock frequency. In the Weaver-method circuit, a common 3.6864-MHz crystal combines with the HEF4060 oscil-

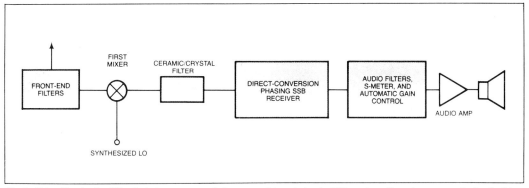

Fig 7—Using the phasing filter technique, you can design a complete, yet simple, SSB receiver. The antenna connects directly (via a bandpass filter) to the inputs of the NE602s' mixer stage.

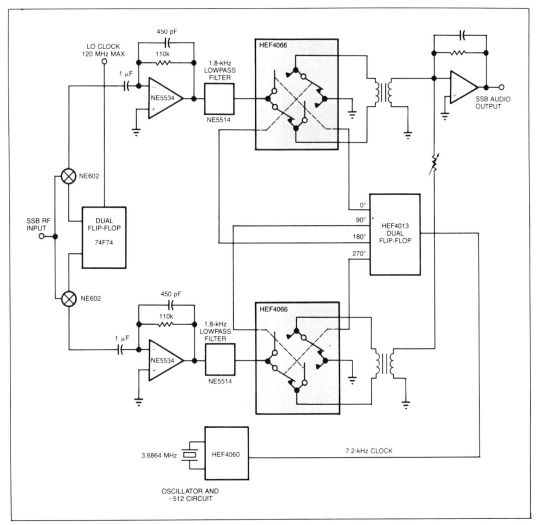

Fig 8—To minimize power drain, you can use HEF4066 CMOS analog switches in the subcarrier stage of this experimental Weaver receiver circuit.

lator and ÷512 circuit to provide the required clock signal. When you use switched-capacitor filters for the lowpass audio circuits, a single clock generator (with appropriate dividers) suffices for all circuit-timing signals.

12 Three-rail power supply uses four diodes

Economy and elegance

Of all the readers' *Design Ideas* which have appeared over the years in *EDN*, this is one of my very favourite ones. A three-rail supply is powered by a two-winding transformer using only four diodes. The −5 V and +12 V regulators, which are usually comparatively lightly loaded, are driven by a half wave circuit and a voltage doubler respectively. The main +5 V regulator on the other hand is supplied by a full wave rectifier circuit – a deliciously economical arrangement.

Luis de Sa
Universidade de Coimbra, Coimbra, Portugal

The circuit shown in **Fig 1** generates three supply voltages using a minimum of components. Diodes D_2 and D_3 perform full-wave rectification, alternately charging capacitor C_2 on both halves of the ac cycle. On the other hand, diode D_1 with capacitor C_1 and diode D_4 with capacitor C_3 each perform half-wave rectification. The full- and half-wave rectification arrangement is satisfactory for modest supply currents drawn from the −5 and +12V regulators (IC_3 and IC_2).

You can use this circuit as an auxiliary supply in a μP-based instrument, for example, and avoid the less attractive alternatives of buying a custom-wound transformer, building a more complex supply, or using a secondary winding (say 18V ac) and wasting power in the 5V regulators.

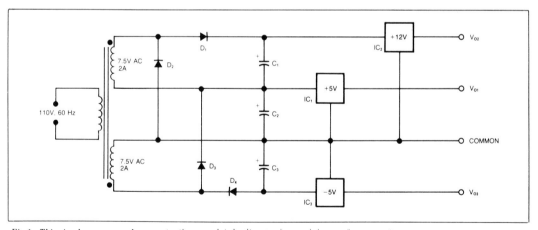

Fig 1—This simple power supply *generates three regulated voltages using a minimum of components.*

13 Sliding FFT computes frequency spectra in real time

Efficient algorithm for repeated FFTs

This is an article which I saved, because it looked to me like a good idea. My digital engineering friends who are into DSP confirmed that this is the case, so I am happy to pass it on to you.

Tom Springer, *Pinson Associates Inc*

Many digital-signal-processing applications, such as certain types of adaptive filters, require you to perform real-time spectral analysis of a nonterminating data sequence (**Ref 1**). The usual approach to such problems calls for computing power of a very high order, as exemplified by the latest VLSI DSP chips, which can calculate fast Fourier transforms (FFTs) at blinding speed, using standard algorithms. However, for a wide range of practical problems, a simple method for calculating frequency spectra—the sliding FFT algorithm—has a number of advantages over the conventional FFT algorithms. For instance, it can calculate spectra at a rate more closely approaching the sampling frequency than conventional algorithms can do.

You can best understand the computational difficulties that real-time spectral analysis entails if you consider the operation of a Fourier analyzer or dynamic signal analyzer. You can use such an instrument—for example, Hewlett-Packard's Model 3562A Dual Channel Dynamic Signal Analyzer (**Ref 2**)—to view and record signals as they appear in the complex frequency domain. However, there is a fundamental difference, which is not always understood, between a Fourier analyzer and a spectrum analyzer.

The spectrum analyzer displays the output of what is effectively a swept filter; it therefore presents an *average* spectral distribution over a sampling interval. Consequently, you can only use the spectrum analyzer for continuous frequency measurements. The Fourier analyzer, on the other hand, updates the spectrum at approximately the sample rate, and therefore presents the *instantaneous* spectral characteristics of the input signal. You can therefore use it to perform transient analysis; unlike the spectrum analyzer, it provides phase as well as magnitude information.

FFT computation time delays the response

Ideally, the Fourier analyzer would compute the discrete Fourier transform as quickly as the signal is sampled. In practice, however, the computational limitations of the processor make it impossible to realize this

ideal, so real instruments specify both an input-signal bandwidth and a real-time bandwidth. The input-signal bandwidth is limited by the sampling rate of the instrument and represents the highest frequency that the instrument can detect without aliasing; this frequency is called the Nyquist frequency. The real-time bandwidth defines the fastest transient event that the instrument can record, and it's directly related to the length of time required to calculate the discrete Fourier transform. Because of this computational delay, the real-time bandwidth is typically narrower than the input-signal bandwidth by approximately an order of magnitude.

Any system that must detect transient phenomena in the frequency domain must meet the same performance requirements that a Fourier analyzer must meet in order to generate quasi-instantaneous frequency spectra. The transformation of discrete data from the time domain to the frequency domain is almost always accomplished by means of the FFT; thus, the ability of a system to track dynamic changes in the spectral content of a signal often depends primarily on the speed with which the system can execute the FFT algorithm.

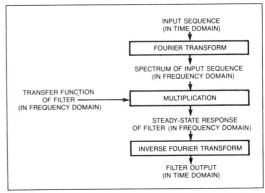

Fig 1—You can describe the steady-state behavior of a linear system in the frequency domain by computing the product of the system transfer function and the complex frequency spectrum of the input signal.

Feedback loops may not tolerate delays

This speed limitation can be an important consideration in digital-filter design. You'd commonly define such filters in terms of frequency-domain parameters and implement them with frequency-domain techniques. Filter design usually begins when you specify a desired frequency response, so frequency-domain methods provide a very direct approach to filter design. Furthermore, it's very simple to describe the steady-state behavior of a linear system in the frequency domain by computing the product of the system transfer function and the complex frequency spectrum of its input (**Fig 1**). Because the FFT efficiently carries out the necessary time/frequency domain transformations, frequency-domain signal processing is computationally attractive for filter applications.

You may find, however, that in some real-time applications such as control systems, using the conventional FFT algorithm renders the filter unsuitable. The reason is that an N-point FFT operates on blocks of N points at a time; thus, it doesn't generate spectra instantaneously for each incoming sample; it generates spectra only at regular intervals. The resulting propagation delay in the computed response of the filter might not be tolerable within a feedback loop. The example below shows the effects of the delay for a 64-point FFT.

Consider a system at steady state that experiences a perturbation (a spike at $t = 64$). **Fig 2a** shows the data sequence. Because the FFT is a block operation, it must accumulate 64 new samples before it reevaluates the spectrum; in other words, at $t = 63$ it transforms $\{x(0),...,x(63)\}$, at $t = 127$ it transforms $\{x(64),...,x(127)\}$, and so on. **Fig 2b** shows a 64-point block of samples beginning at $t = 0$ (which doesn't include the spike), and **Fig 2c** shows the frequency spectrum of the block. **Fig 2d** shows the block of samples beginning one sample period later at $t = 1$ (now containing the spike), and **Fig 2e** shows its corresponding spectrum. Note the spectral components that the spike introduces—the actual spectrum of the signal has changed at $t = 64$, but the system can't detect the change until the next transform. After the spike has occurred, the system must collect 63 more samples before it can revise the spectrum that it calculated at $t = 63$. Thus, computing the FFT introduces a delay into the system's response.

In many applications, you can't afford to ignore the dynamic behavior of signals in the frequency domain; however, the FFT updates the frequency spectrum only at the rate f_s/N (where f_s is the sample rate). In Fourier-analyzer terminology, the "real-time bandwidth" is limited to $1/N$ of the "input-signal bandwidth." This situation would be improved if the system could generate spectra at the sample rate.

Sliding FFT algorithm reduces delays

You might at first think that in order to update the frequency spectrum on a real-time basis, the system would have to recalculate the FFT for each new sample of the input sequence. Intuitively, you'd conclude that

this procedure is wasteful, because only one point in the sequence changes for each recomputation of the FFT. Under certain conditions, however, you can apply a faster method of calculating frequency spectra in real time.

It turns out that you can derive an FFT for a segment of the N-point data sequence, beginning at time $k + 1$, directly from the FFT computed for the prior segment that began at time k; this procedure saves a considerable amount of computation time. As suggested by its name, the sliding FFT "slides" over the data sequence, N points at a time (**Fig 3**). The important constraints are that the input data must be presented in a nonterminating sequence, and that the input-signal bandwidth must be no greater than the real-time bandwidth.

To understand how the algorithm works, let the FFT of the kth sampling interval be $X^k_{(m)}$; that is

$$\text{FFT of } \{x(k),...,x(k + N - 1)\} = X^k_{(m)}.$$

Then,

$$X^{k+1}_{(m)} = e^{j(2\pi m)/N}(X^k_{(m)} + x_{k+N} - x_k).$$

This equation states that the FFT of the $k + 1^{th}$ sampling interval is equal to the phase-shifted sum of the previous FFT and the difference between the newest sample and the oldest—that is, between the sample entering the leading edge of the window and the sample leaving the trailing edge. For the mathematical details of this relationship, see **box,** "Derivation of the sliding FFT."

Thus, if you know the transform of the input sequence at time k, you can derive the next transform (at time $k + 1$) without computing another FFT. You can calculate $X^{k+1}_{(m)}$ from $X^k_{(m)}$, using N complex multiplications and N complex additions. By contrast, recomputing the FFT requires $N/2 \times \log_2(N)$ multiplications and $N \times \log_2(N)$ additions. To see how much computation time you'll save, consider that a 1024-point FFT requires 5120 complex multiplications and 10,240 complex additions if you use a standard "decimation-in-time" algorithm. Computing the sliding FFT requires only 1024 complex multiplications and 1025 complex additions, including $x_{(k+N)} - x_{(k)}$. The amount of time you save will be system dependent, and it will increase with the size of the FFT.

An additional advantage of the sliding FFT is that it doesn't require bit reversal, as most FFT algorithms do. Further, the sliding FFT doesn't require that the data sequence be of a particular length, as fixed-radix FFTs do. Sliding FFTs make it easier to format the input data, therefore.

The sliding FFT is defined *recursively*. That is, at each point in time the algorithm demands that you know the spectrum that existed at the previous point in time. Obviously, an initial value—$X^0_{(m)}$—is necessary to start, or "seed," the process. You can supply this value by computing the transform of the first N points of the sequence with a conventional FFT; thereafter, you can use the more-efficient sliding FFT to

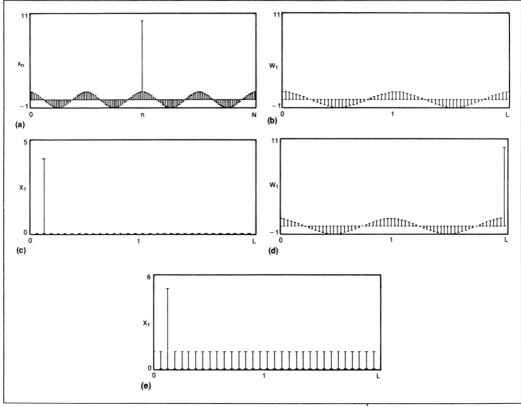

Fig 2—*When a system in steady state experiences a perturbation* (a spike at $t=64$) **(a)**, *the system may experience a delay before it detects the spike. A 64-point FFT, computed for samples 0 through 63* **(b)**, *generates a spectrum containing no harmonics* **(c)**. *If you sample at $t=1$ through $t=64$* **(d)**, *the spike appears in the sample, and if you could perform instantaneous computations, you'd see that at $t=65$ the spectrum looked like* **e**. *In practice, because the system requires 64 sample times to compute an FFT, the changed spectrum is not available until (at least) $t=127$.*

generate all subsequent spectra.

Alternatively, you can arbitrarily define the input sequence so that the first N points are zero (a condition that's equivalent to delaying the input by N), thus forcing $X^0_{(m)}$ to be all zeros. From that point on, you can apply the sliding-FFT algorithm. After the first N iterations, the frequency spectra produced will be

valid. Remember, however, that it takes longer to calculate N sliding FFTs than it does to calculate an N-point FFT by the conventional method. You'll find the results of a quick benchmark comparison between the conventional-FFT and sliding-FFT algorithms in **Tables 1 and 2.**

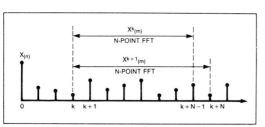

Fig 3—*You can reduce the propagation delay by computing the first spectrum with the ordinary FFT algorithm, but thereafter deriving each new spectrum from the previous one with the aid of a simpler algorithm. In effect, you slide the window over the data, one point at a time.*

TABLE 1—BENCHMARK RESULTS FOR AN IBM PC/XT

FFT LENGTH (POINTS)	CONVENTIONAL	SLIDING
128	9 SEC	1 SEC
256	21 SEC	3 SEC
512	46 SEC	6 SEC
1024	1 MINUTE, 40 SEC	12 SEC
2048	3 MINUTES, 38 SEC	24 SEC
4096	7 MINUTES, 50 SEC	49 SEC
8192	16 MINUTES, 50 SEC	1 MINUTE, 37 SEC

Derivation of the sliding FFT

To derive a sliding FFT, let $X^k_{(m)}$ denote the N-point FFT over the segment of the input sequence $\{x_{(k)},...,x_{(k+N-1)}\}$. From the definition of the FFT you have

$$X^k_{(m)} = \sum_{n=0}^{N-1} X(n+k)\, e^{-j\frac{2\pi mn}{N}}$$

and

$$X^{k+1}_{(m)} = \sum_{n=0}^{N-1} X(n+k+1)\, e^{-j\frac{2\pi mn}{N}}.$$

Substituting $p = n+1$, you can write $X^{k+1}_{(m)}$ as

$$X^{k+1}_{(m)} = \sum_{p=1}^{N} X(p+k)\, e^{-j\frac{2\pi m(p-1)}{N}}.$$

The summation can be expanded,

and the index of summation adjusted, to yield

$$X^{k+1}_{(m)} = \sum_{p=0}^{N-1} X(p+k)\, e^{-j\frac{2\pi m(p-1)}{N}}$$
$$+ X(k+N)\, e^{-j\frac{2\pi m(N-1)}{N}} - X(k)\, e^{j\frac{2\pi m}{N}}.$$

Expanding the exponential factors yields

$$X^{k+1}_{(m)}$$
$$= e^{j\frac{2\pi m}{N}} \cdot \sum_{p=0}^{N-1} X(p+k)\, e^{-j\frac{2\pi mp}{N}}$$
$$+ X(k+N)\, e^{-j\frac{2\pi mN}{N}} \cdot e^{j\frac{2\pi m}{N}}$$
$$- X(k)\, e^{j\frac{2\pi m}{N}}.$$

Finally, noting the periodicity of the exponential term $(e^{j2\pi m} = 1)$, and substituting $X^k_{(m)}$ for the summation, you simplify the expression and arrive at the working form of the sliding FFT:

$$X^{k+1}_{(m)}$$
$$= e^{j\frac{2\pi m}{N}} \left[X^k_{(m)} + X(k+N) - X(k) \right].$$

TABLE 2—BENCHMARK RESULTS FOR AN 8-MHz IBM PC/AT

FFT LENGTH (POINTS)	CONVENTIONAL	SLIDING
128	<1 SEC	<1 SEC
256	<1 SEC	<1 SEC
512	1 SEC	<1 SEC
1024	3 SEC	<1 SEC
2048	6 SEC	<1 SEC
4096	14 SEC	1 SEC
8192	31 SEC	3 SEC

The Turbo-Basic source listing for the benchmark program appears in **Listing 1.** The program measures performance by using Basic's TIME$ system call to time random data sequences of varying length. The program calculates the conventional FFT first and uses the result to seed the sliding FFT, as described above. Obviously, the execution speed of the Basic interpreter running on an IBM PC/XT or PC/AT is far below the speed that any practical DSP application would require; however, this crude example clearly shows the advantage of the sliding FFT. Also note that, as expected, the margin of improvement is greater for longer data sequences.

Although you can use the sliding FFT to enhance real-time spectral analysis, you must observe its inherent constraints. First, the input data must be part of some nonterminating sequence. The benefit of the sliding FFT algorithm is that performing recursive calculation of the spectra of an unending sequence is inherently more efficient than applying the general methods for calculating the discrete Fourier transform to each

N-point window as though it were unrelated to the previous one. However, if $X^{k+1}_{(m)}$ and $X^k_{(m)}$ actually *are* unrelated, the algorithm is of no use.

Second, if the system must sample the data at a faster rate than the rate at which it can compute the sliding FFT (input-signal bandwidth exceeds real-time bandwidth), you can't use the algorithm. The reason is that the recursive calculation of the transform presumes that the samples are consecutive, so the time required for calculation effectively limits the sampling rate. If the input sequence contains frequency components that are higher than the sampling rate, aliasing will occur in the resultant spectra.

Don't assume that the sliding FFT's computational efficiency applies to all circumstances. In fact, only when you need to compute spectra at a rate that's close to the sampling frequency does the sliding FFT become attractive in comparison with the ordinary FFT. The system must repeat the calculations in the sliding algorithm for each sample; after N samples, you have N^2 multiplications. With a conventional FFT, the same N samples could be transformed at a cost of only $N/2(\log_2(N))$ multiplications. The big difference is that you have to wait until the entire block of N samples has been acquired before the ordinary FFT can yield the spectrum.

If that much delay would reduce the system's transient performance to an unacceptable level, you can choose either to compute the FFT more often or to use the sliding FFT. The latter becomes a bargain whenever the rate at which spectra must be recomputed exceeds $f_s/\log_2 \times \sqrt{N}$ (see **box,** "Update rate governs sliding FFT's efficiency"). For example, the sliding FFT would be preferable in a system that had to update a 256-point spectrum at any frequency greater

LISTING 1

```
'----------------------------------------------------------------------
'
'                    SLIDING FFT ROUTINE   4-28-88
'          This routine compares the length of time required to compute
'       an N-PT. FFT using a conventional decimation-in-time algorithm vs.
'       the "Sliding FFT" technique discussed in the accompanying article.
'
'          Since the Sliding FFT is a recursive algorithm the Transform
'       resulting from the first algorithm is used as an input.  In other
'       words, the frequency spectrum at time k is provided and the Sliding
'       FFT is used to calculate the spectrum at the next point in time (see
'       FIG. 1).
'
'          The program prints a record of the calculation time required;
'       this is a rough indication of the speed with which a non-terminating
'       data sequence could be sampled and its frequency spectrum updated.
'
'----------------------------------------------------------------------
DEFINT A-N: CLS
PRINT "Enter the exponent of 2 which determines the length of the FFT"
INPUT M
N=2©M                               'length of FFT=N
DIM XR(N), XI(N)                    'input/output arrays (real & imag.)
DIM ER(N), EI(N)                    'exponential phase shift table
FOR I=1 TO N                        'create random input array
XR(I)=RND
XI(I)=RND
NEXT I
XROLD=XR(1): XIOLD=XI(1)            'save old sample
XRNEW=RND: XINEW=RND                'save new sample
PI=3.14159
'---------  BEGINNING OF CONVENTIONAL FFT --------------------------
TIME$="00:00:00"
NV2=N/2
NM1=N-1
J=1
FOR I=1 TO NM1                      'do bit-reversal of input data
IF I>=J THEN GOTO 520
TR=XR(J)
TI=XI(J)
XR(J)=XR(I)
XI(J)=XI(I)
XR(I)=TR
XI(I)=TI
520  K=NV2
530  IF K>=J THEN GOTO 570
J=J-K
K=K/2
GOTO 530
570  J=J+K
NEXT I
FOR L=1 TO M                        'begin decimation-in-time alg'thm
LE=2©L
LE1=LE/2
UR=1!
UI=0!
WR=COS(PI/LE1)
WI=-SIN(PI/LE1)
FOR J=1 TO LE1
FOR I=J TO N STEP LE
IP=I+LE1
TR=XR(IP)*UR-XI(IP)*UI
TI=XR(IP)*UI+XI(IP)*UR
XR(IP)=XR(I)-TR
XI(IP)=XI(I)-TI
XR(I)=XR(I)+TR
XI(I)=XI(I)+TI
```

LISTING 1 *(Continued)*

```
NEXT I
TR=UR*WR-UI*WI
TI=UR*WI+UI*WR
UR=TR
UI=TI
NEXT J
NEXT L
'--------- END OF CONVENTIONAL FFT -----------------------------------
M1$=MID$(TIME$,4,2): S1$=MID$(TIME$,7,2)
'
'    Since the exponential phase shift table is a constant factor, and
'    not re-computed each time the algorithm is used, it is not included
'    in the performance comparison.
'
FOR I=1 TO N
ER(I)=COS(2*PI*(I-1)/N)            'Real part of phase term
EI(I)=SIN(2*PI*(I-1)/N)            'Imaginary part of phase term
NEXT I
'---------   BEGINNING OF SLIDING FFT ------------------------------
TIME$="00:00:00"
DR=XRNEW-XROLD: DI=XINEW-XIOLD        'diff. term = (newest term)-(oldest)
FOR I=1 TO N
TR=XR(I)+DR: TI=XI(I)+DI    'add above term to terms in previous spectrum
XR(I)=ER(I)*TR-EI(I)*TI    'multiply previous spectrum by phase shift
XI(I)=ER(I)*TI+EI(I)*TR    'term-by-term
NEXT I
'--------- END OF SLIDING FFT ----------------------------------------
M2$=MID$(TIME$,4,2): S2$=MID$(TIME$,7,2)
CLS: PRINT TAB(10);"TIME REQUIRED FOR ";N;"-POINT FFT": PRINT
PRINT TAB(10);"CONVENTIONAL";TAB(40);"SLIDING"
PRINT TAB(10);M1$;" MIN.  ";S1$;" SEC.";TAB(40);M2$;" MIN.   ";S2$;" SEC."
END
```

than 1/4 the sampling rate.

Finally, consider the fact that the sliding FFT is eminently suitable for hardware implementation. The block diagram (**Fig 4**) depicts a basic design for an N-point sliding FFT unit. One of the two FIFO regis-

ters represents the window that slides over the input data, and the other represents the recursively-updated frequency spectrum. The ROM contains the exponential phase-shift terms.

The system clocks the input data sequence (at the

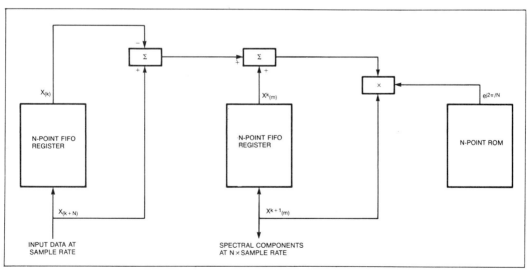

Fig 4—You can implement the sliding FFT algorithm in hardware with the aid of two FIFO registers and a ROM that holds the system transfer function.

sample rate f_s) into the FIFO register at the left. The oldest sample (x_k) is subtracted from the newest sample (x_{k+N}). The previous spectral data is clocked through the second FIFO register at a much higher rate ($N \times f_s$). As the mth point, $X^k_{(m)}$, emerges from the FIFO register's output, it is summed with $x_{k+N} - x_k$ and multiplied by the mth entry in the phase-shift ROM, $e^{j(2\pi m)/N}$, resulting in the mth point in the updated spectrum, $X^{k+1}_{(m)}$.

From the block diagram in **Fig 4**, you can see that the inherent simplicity of the sliding-FFT algorithm lends the algorithm to a very straightforward hardware realization. Further, you can easily include parallel paths for arithmetic operations. Well-designed parallel computation paths will give you very high data rates.

Update rate governs sliding FFT's efficiency

To find out whether the sliding FFT is computationally efficient for your application, you have to find the sampling rate at which the sliding FFT requires fewer complex multiplications than the conventional FFT does. In the conventional algorithm, each computation of an N-point frequency spectrum requires $N/2(\log_2(N))$ multiplications, whereas the sliding FFT requires only N^2 multiplications.

The computational requirements of the conventional FFT will equal those of the sliding FFT when the spectrum-update rate—f_r (number of updates per sampling period)—is such that

$$f_r \cdot \frac{N}{2} \log_2 (N) = N^2,$$

where $0 < f_r \leq N$. Then, for

$$f_r \geq \frac{2N}{\log_2 (N)} = \frac{N}{\log_2 (\sqrt{N})},$$

the sliding FFT will require fewer complex multiplications. Relative to the sample rate $f_s = N$, the sliding FFT is computationally more efficient when:

$$\frac{f_r}{f_s} \geq \frac{1}{\log_2 (\sqrt{N})}.$$

References

1. "VSP Application Examples," *Digital Signal Processors Data Book*, Zoran Corp, Santa Clara, CA, 1987.

2. "Signal Analyzers," *Test and Measurement Catalog*, Hewlett-Packard Corp, Palo Alto, CA, 1988.

14 Variable-Q bandpass filter fixes gain

Vary Q at constant gain

The state variable filter provides low-, band- and high-pass outputs and centre frequency and Q are separately adjustable. However, adjusting the Q alters the centre-frequency gain at the band-pass output, as well as the Q. In this circuit, the band-pass characteristic is produced by summing the low- and high-pass outputs to form a notch (of width adjustable by changing Q) and then summing this with the input, which is in antiphase. At the notch (centre) frequency, the output simply equals the input, whereas at other frequencies the notch output cancels out the original input. Note, however, that the roll-off either side of the pass band does not continue indefinitely, but reaches an attenuation floor set by how exact is the cancellation – in turn set by resistor tolerances, etc.

Yishay Netzer
Honeywell Inc, Lexington, MA

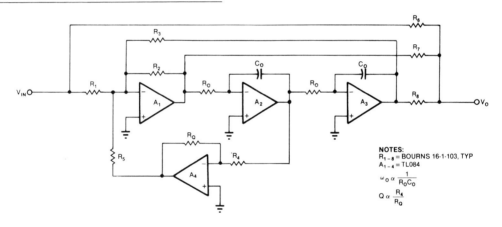

A fixed-gain, variable-Q bandpass filter *results when a state-variable filter's high- and low-pass responses are summed with the input signal. The filter's center frequency changes with R_O and/or C_O, and Q varies with R_Q.*

A major problem with standard variable-Q bandpass filters is that their gain also varies, as shown by

$$G(S) = \frac{\omega_0 S}{S^2 + \frac{\omega_0}{Q} S + \omega_0^2},$$

where ω_0 is the center frequency and Q equals the selectivity at the 3-dB points. This Q-dependent gain becomes especially troublesome in swept (ie, variable selectivity) applications, where you must compensate for such gain changes.

You can, however, realize a constant-gain, varia-

ble-bandwidth transfer function by using

$$F(S) = 1 - \frac{S^2 + \omega_0^2}{S^2 + \frac{\omega_0}{Q} S + \omega_0^2} = \frac{\frac{\omega_0}{Q} S}{S^2 + \frac{\omega_0}{Q} S + \omega_0^2}.$$

Here, the transfer function of the second term of the middle expression duplicates that of an active notch filter with variable Q.

You can achieve an excellent realization of this form by employing the design depicted in the **figure**.

Here, you combine the individual high- and low-pass outputs of a 4-op-amp state-variable filter. The 4-stage version, unlike standard 3-stage filters, has a Q-independent gain. Thus, by superimposing these two filter characteristics, you get a fixed-gain notch filter. This circuit implements a fixed-gain, variable-Q bandpass characteristic by summing the original input signal with the high/low signal emerging from the notch filter.

You can continuously vary the filter's center frequency by synchronously changing resistor R_o, or step-wise change it by switching capacitors C_o. And by varying R_Q, you can modify the filter Q—without changing gain.

As with any active filter, the op amps' gain-bandwidth products must accommodate the filter's $\omega_o Q$ product. When you've satisfied this requirement, your design can supply stable Qs with values of several hundred. But note that because the filter's internal nodes operate at high gains under high-Q conditions, you must ensure that the input signal's level stays low enough to preclude saturating the amplifier.

15 Enhanced op amp delivers 100 V p-p

High output voltage from an op amp

The type of circuit shown below has recently been the subject of a lot of learned discussion, but this article appeared in *EDN* in 1985 and is itself an improvement on the basic scheme, which appeared back in the 1970s. It makes an economical alternative to a special high voltage op amp.

Barry Kline
Technicare Corp, Solon, OH

If you need an amplifier that provides more than $\pm 50V$ output swing along with the high gain and low offset of a high-performance op amp, consider the **Fig 1** circuit. It employs a gain stage (Q_1-Q_4, R_1-R_4) to multiply the op amp's $\pm 10V$ output swing to the desired level. The combined op amp and gain stage may be regarded as a high-voltage amplifier.

The gain stage is based on a design by Jerald Graeme (**Ref 1**), but adds current feedback via R_4 to achieve three performance improvements: reduction of open-loop output impedance (reduced sensitivity to changes in load current); reduction of output current I_A from the op amp; and increased dynamic range due to a reduction in signal voltage across the current-sensing resistors R_{1A} and R_{1B}.

Q_1 and Q_3 act as cascode stages for the op-amp supply currents I_{A1} and I_{A2}. Q_2 and Q_4 sense these currents and provide amplified output currents I_1 and I_2:

$$I_{O1} = I_{A1} \times \frac{R_1}{R_2}$$
$$I_{O2} = I_{A2} \times \frac{R_1}{R_2} \tag{1}$$

Also, because the difference in supply currents is equal to the op-amp output current ($I_A = I_{A1} - I_{A2}$),

$$I_{O1} - I_{O2} = (I_{A1} - I_{A2}) \times \frac{R_1}{R_2} = I_A \times \frac{R_1}{R_2}. \tag{2}$$

Feeding this current imbalance back to the op-amp output terminal provides negative feedback for the booster stage. Recall that:

$$I_{O1} - I_{O2} = I_A \times \frac{R_1}{R_2}. \tag{3}$$

In addition,

$$I_4 = (I_{A1} - I_{A2}) - I_L = \left(I_A \times \frac{R_1}{R_2}\right) - I_L.$$

But, $I_A = I_3 - I_4$.

$$\tag{4}$$

So, $I_4 = (I_3 - I_4) \times \left(\frac{R_1}{R_2}\right) - I_L.$

Or, $I_4 \left(1 + \frac{R_1}{R_2}\right) = \left(I_3 \times \frac{R_1}{R_2}\right) - I_L.$

Substitute V_A for the op amp's output voltage:

$$I_4 = \frac{V_{OUT} - V_A}{R_4}$$
$$I_3 = \frac{V_A}{R_3} \tag{5}$$
$$I_L = \frac{V_{OUT}}{R_L}.$$

Therefore:

$$\frac{V_{OUT} - V_A}{R_4}\left(1 + \frac{R_1}{R_2}\right) = \frac{V_A R_1}{R_3 R_2} - \frac{V_{OUT}}{R_L}. \tag{6}$$

The equation can be solved for voltage gain of the booster stage:

$$\frac{V_{OUT}}{V_A} = \frac{1 + \frac{R_4}{R_3}\left(\frac{R_1}{R_1 + R_2}\right)}{1 + \frac{R_4}{R_3}\left(\frac{R_2}{R_1 + R_2}\right)} \tag{7}$$

$$= 1 + \frac{R_4}{R_3}\left(\frac{R_1}{R_1 + R_2}\right)\left(\frac{R_L}{R_O + R_L}\right).$$

Output impedance (R_O) is:

$$R_O = \frac{R_4 \times R_2}{R_1 + R_2}. \tag{8}$$

To calculate the op amp's output current (I_A):

$$I_A = I_3 - I_4 = \frac{V_A}{R_3} - \frac{V_{OUT} - V_A}{R_4}$$
$$= V_A\left(\frac{1}{R_3} + \frac{1}{R_4} - \frac{V_{OUT}}{V_A R_4}\right). \tag{9}$$

The no-load booster gain is obtained by setting R_L to infinity in **Eq 7**:

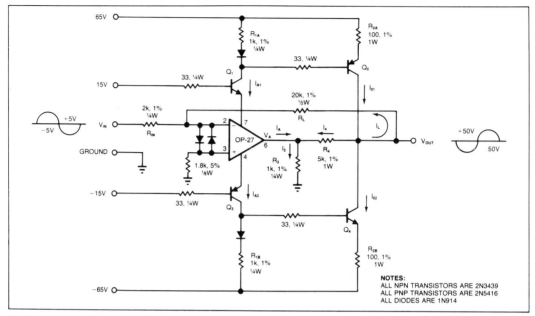

Fig 1—Gain stage with current feedback boosts a conventional op amp's output to more than 100V p-p.

$$\frac{V_{OUT}}{V_A} = 1 + \frac{R_4}{R_3}\left(\frac{R_1}{R_1 + R_2}\right). \tag{10}$$

Substituting the **Eq 10** no-load booster gain into **Eq 9** yields:

$$I_A = \frac{V_A}{R_3}\left(\frac{R_2}{R_1 + R_2}\right) \tag{11}$$

The use of current feedback reduces the output impedance and the required op-amp output current by a factor of $R_2/(R_1+R_2)$. Also, reducing I_A reduces signal current variations in the supply lines.

Be careful not to exceed the power-dissipation capacity of components Q_2, Q_4, R_2, R_4, and R_L. In addition, quiescent current in Q_2 and Q_4 is proportional to the current gain R_1/R_2, so choose this ratio carefully.

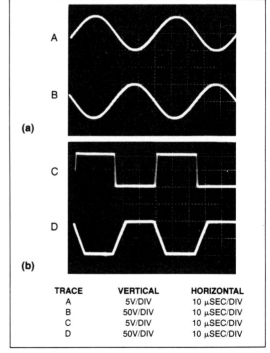

TRACE	VERTICAL	HORIZONTAL
A	5V/DIV	10 μSEC/DIV
B	50V/DIV	10 μSEC/DIV
C	5V/DIV	10 μSEC/DIV
D	50V/DIV	10 μSEC/DIV

Fig 2—The Fig 1 circuit produces 100V p-p sine- and square-wave outputs—**a** and **b**, respectively. Slew response to the square wave is a product of the OP-27 slew rate (2.8V/μsec typ) and gain of the booster stage (approximately 5.5).

Reference

1. Graeme, Jerald G, *Designing with Operational Amplifiers—Applications Alternatives*, McGraw-Hill, 1977, pg 14.

16   Voltage references

Voltage references

This is an example of the handy staff-written reports which *EDN* does so well. The coverage of the basic principles is simplified, but perfectly adequate for the practising electronic design engineer, and this is followed by a review of just a few selected types from the vast range now available from the many manufacturers of these devices. Included is a list of manufacturers of voltage references which, though far from complete, is a very useful starting point.

Dave Pryce,
Associate Editor

Integrated-circuit voltage references are available in a variety of voltage ratings and package styles and with widely differing specifications. All, however, base their performance on the action of either a zener diode or a bandgap cell, each of which has its own peculiar set of characteristics. The most widely used reference is probably the temperature-compensated zener diode, particularly for voltages above 5V. Although bandgap cells are often scaled to provide voltages as high as 10V, the principal advantage of a bandgap reference lies in its ability to provide a stable low voltage such as 1.2, 2.5, or 5V. Before looking at the specifications of some of the available devices, consider how each of the two basic types works.

Although discrete zener diodes are available in voltage ratings as low as 1.8V to as high as 200V, they don't make very good references. The typical 10% tolerance and poor temperature characteristics of these devices preclude their use in applications requiring even a moderate degree of precision and stability. Moreover, zener diodes rated at less than about 6V suffer from high output impedance. For these reasons, discrete zener-diode-based references include temperature compensation and, in the case of IC types, the additional circuitry needed to obtain specific performance objectives.

A zener diode has two distinctly different reverse-bias characteristics: zener breakdown and avalanche breakdown, both of which are evident in the 4- to 6V range. The zener breakdown voltage (**Fig 1**) *decreases* as the temperature increases (negative TC); the avalanche breakdown voltage *increases* as the temperature increases (positive TC). At low current values, the zener effect dominates; at higher values, the avalanche effect dominates. Because these current-dependent effects oppose each other, you can, at least theoretically, cancel them by adjusting the operating point, thus obtaining a TC of zero.

Practical temperature compensation

Another way to provide temperature compensation is by connecting a conventional forward-biased diode in series with a zener diode operating in the avalanche mode. In this case, the negative TC (-2 mV/°C) of the conventional diode cancels the positive TC of the zener diode. Manufacturers use this method in most zener-based references.

If you're primarily concerned with temperature stability and the exact reference voltage is unimportant, a good combination might be a 5.6V zener diode in series with a single forward-biased diode. **Fig 2** illustrates this simple circuit. The 0.7V typically developed across forward-biased diode D_1 adds to the 5.6V of zener diode D_2 to provide a temperature-compensated reference of about 6.3V. Resistor R_1 sets the current level through the diodes. Although you can buy such a diode combination in discrete form (the 6.2V 1N821 series is

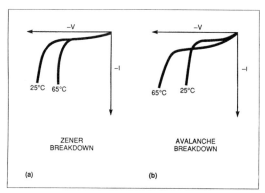

Fig 1—A zener diode has two different breakdown characteristics. *In the zener mode (a), the breakdown voltage decreases with increasing temperature. In the avalanche mode (b), the breakdown voltage increases with increasing temperature.*

similar), most voltage references come in IC form, which offers advantages over discrete versions.

In its most basic form, the circuit for a zener-based IC reference is similar to that of **Fig 3**. The IC can be either a hybrid or monolithic type; the choice depends on the manufacturer's objectives and processing capabilities. In this circuit, R_4 provides the startup current for the diode combination, thus setting the positive input of the op amp at V_Z. R_3 sets the desired bias current for the diode combination. The current through R_3 equals $(V_{OUT} - V_Z)/R_3$ and remains at that value, independent of the supply voltage and amplifier loading.

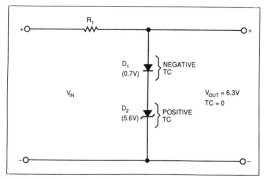

Fig 2—In this simple voltage reference, *the voltage across forward-biased diode D_1 adds to the zener voltage of D_2 to provide an output of 6.3V. The negative TC of D_1 cancels the positive TC of D_2 to provide temperature compensation.*

A zener-based IC reference has several advantages over a simple discrete reference. Manufacturers can scale the output voltage to a value different from that of the zener voltage and, by trimming the ratio of R_1 to R_2, set the output voltage to the desired accuracy. It's also possible to trim R_3 to optimize the bias current of the zener diode, thus decreasing its output temperature coefficient.

Many of today's monolithic zener-based references have ion-implanted buried zeners, which exhibit superior TC characteristics and better stability over time than do surface-based zeners. TC specifications as low as 1 ppm/°C are possible for a buried-zener reference. Compared with a bandgap reference, a zener-based reference also has less output noise because the zener voltage needs less amplification than does a 1.2V bandgap cell. Although frequency dependent, a typical 10V bandgap reference might have two to three times more noise than an equivalent zener-based reference.

Consider the bandgap reference

Bandgap references are available with output-voltage ratings of about 1.2 to 10V. The 1.2, 2.5, and 5V types can operate from lower supply voltages than can zener-based references, a distinct advantage in some applications. Although bandgap cells typically have a lower output impedance than low-voltage zeners, the additional circuitry used in both bandgap and zener-based references usually masks any difference.

Because the bandgap voltage of about 1.2V is often scaled to a higher voltage by an internal amplifier, bandgap references of 5 and 10V tend to have more

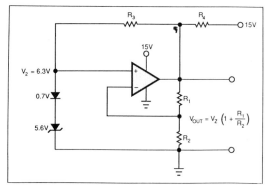

Fig 3—This basic IC reference *uses a temperature-compensated zener diode, an op amp, and voltage divider R_1 and R_2 to scale the zener voltage to a higher output voltage.*

noise than equivalent zener-based references, which need much less amplification. Moreover, the TC of a well-designed bandgap reference, although very good, is not quite as good as that of the best buried-zener references. Typically, the TCs of bandgap references range from about 5 to 50 ppm/°C.

The operation of a bandgap reference is based on the difference between the forward base-emitter voltage (V_{BE}) of two similar transistors operating at the same current but at different current densities. Extrapolated to absolute zero, V_{BE} is equal to 1.205V, the bandgap voltage of silicon. By adding a voltage to V_{BE} that increases proportionally with temperature at the same rate that V_{BE} decreases, a bandgap reference can, theoretically, generate a constant 1.205V at any temperature. Practically, however, designers can only approach that ideal.

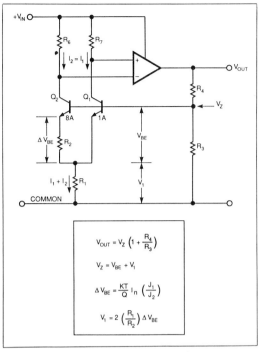

$$V_{OUT} = V_Z \left(1 + \frac{R_4}{R_3}\right)$$

$$V_Z = V_{BE} + V_1$$

$$\Delta V_{BE} = \frac{KT}{Q} \ln \left(\frac{J_1}{J_2}\right)$$

$$V_1 = 2 \left(\frac{R_1}{R_2}\right) \Delta V_{BE}$$

Fig 4—The operation of bandgap reference depends on the difference between the base-emitter voltage of two similar transistors operating at different current densities. In this basic circuit, the emitter area of Q_2 is eight times that of Q_1. And although both transistors operate at the same current, their current densities are vastly different.

Fig 4 illustrates the basic operation of a bandgap circuit. In this circuit, the emitter area of Q_2 is eight times that of Q_1. Calculations show that this ratio provides a near-zero TC by generating an optimum difference in current densities (J_1 and J_2) between Q_1 and Q_2. **Ref 1** and **Ref 2** provide a rigorous analysis of these calculations. V_{BE} is the base-emitter voltage of Q_1, and ΔV_{BE}, which appears across R_2, is scaled by the R_1/R_2 ratio to V_1. This voltage has a TC that cancels that of V_{BE}. The op amp raises the V_Z bandgap voltage, which is the sum of V_1 and V_{BE}, to a higher voltage at the output of the reference. This voltage, V_{OUT}, is determined by $(R_4/R_3) + 1$ and is usually in the range of 2.5 to 10V, although it can be the bandgap voltage itself.

Designers of IC bandgap references often incorporate additional features to make the devices more flexible. For example, some circuits have terminals brought out from an internal voltage divider, which lets you program a variety of fixed, calibrated voltages, such as 2.5, 5, 7.5, and 10V. You can also use these terminals with external resistors to set arbitrary voltages. Although special-purpose hybrid types are available, most bandgap references are fabricated in the less expensive monolithic form.

Look at the specifications

An ideal voltage reference would have no errors at all. Its output voltage would be initially exact and not vary with time, temperature, input voltage, or load conditions. In the real world, an ideal reference is not possible, and manufacturers provide specifications to let the user know what the expected variations are for a number of key parameters. Of prime importance are the specifications for output voltage error, temperature coefficient, line regulation, load regulation, and long-term stability. You should look at these specifications both individually and collectively to obtain a true picture of a reference's expected performance.

The *output voltage error* is the initial, untrimmed accuracy of the reference at 25°C at a specified input voltage. Specified in millivolts or a percentage, the measurement is normally made using a device that is traceable to a voltage standard. Some references provide pin connections for trimming their initial accuracy with an external potentiometer.

The *temperature coefficient* of a reference is its average change in output voltage as a function of temperature compared with its value at 25°C. Specified in ppm/°C or mV/°C, the TC is independent of variations in other operating conditions.

Line regulation is the change in output voltage for a specified change in input voltage. Usually specified in %/V or μV/V of input change, line regulation is a measure of a reference's ability to handle variations in supply voltage.

Load regulation is the change in output voltage for a specified change in load current. Specified in μV/mA, %/mA, or ohms of dc output resistance, load regulation includes any self-heating effects due to increased power dissipation at high values of load current.

Long-term stability is the change in the output voltage of a reference as a function of time. Specified in ppm/1000 hours at a specific temperature, long-term stability is difficult to verify. As a result, manufacturers usually provide only typical specifications based on device data collected during the characterization process.

Although these specifications are the most important, others, such as *dynamic impedance* and *noise*, may also be of concern. In particular, noise is an important consideration when using a reference with a high-resolution A/D or D/A converter. For example, a 12-bit A/D converter has an LSB weight of about 0.0244% of its full-scale range. For a full-scale range of 10V, the value of the LSB weight would be about 2.44 mV. The noise from the reference should be less than 10% of that value, or less than 244 μV. For a 16-bit converter, the requirement gets even tougher—the LSB weight is about 0.0015% and the reference noise should be less than 15 μV. You need to look carefully at the data sheet to make sure that the specifications you're interested in are well defined. Data sheets for some low-cost references don't always provide information on all possible parameters.

The level of sophistication and pricing for voltage references runs the gamut from simple and inexpensive to complex and costly. Devices are available for, literally, almost any conceivable application.

Typical of the lower-cost, general-purpose references is the LM136 series, which is available from companies such as National Semiconductor, SGS-Thomson, and Texas Instruments. Categorized for operation over the military, industrial, and commercial temperature ranges, respectively, the LM136, -236, and -336 are bandgap references with an output voltage of 2.5V and an accuracy of 1 or 2%. These references find application in digital voltmeters, power supplies, and op amp circuitry. They're particularly useful in obtaining a stable reference from a 5V logic supply.

Because the LM136, -236, and -336 operate as shunt regulators, you can use them as either positive or negative references. Characterized for operation at 1 mA, these references have a typical TC of 3.5 mV from −25 to +85°C and 12 mV from −55 to +125°C. A pin connection lets you trim the devices externally for minimum temperature drift. At 25°C, the typical dynamic impedance is 0.2Ω, and long-term stability is ±20 ppm. Available in TO-92, TO-46, and SO-8 packages, commercial and industrial versions range in price from about $0.70 to $1.30 (1000).

Although better known for its power-supply and motion-control circuits, Silicon General also has a modest line of bandgap references. Its SG103 series—equivalent to National Semiconductor's discontinued LM103 series—is available in 13 voltage ratings ranging from 1.8 to 5.6V. Packaged in a low-profile TO-46 metal can, the $12.75 (100) SG103 complies with MIL-STD-883B and is specified for operation over the military temperature range of −55 to +125°C. Primarily used in low-voltage power supplies, the 2-terminal device features a typical TC of −1 mV/°C and a dynamic impedance of 5Ω.

Other manufacturers of bandgap voltage references include Analog Devices, Linear Technology, Maxim Integrated Products, Motorola Semiconductor, Precision Monolithics (PMI), and Teledyne Semiconductor. Many of these companies' references are interchangeable with devices from other manufacturers, and some offer improved performance compared with the original versions. For example, the LT1019 from Linear Technology is a direct and, in many cases, improved replacement for many bandgap references, including the AD580, AD581, REF-01, REF-02, MC1400, MC1401, and LM168.

Available in voltage ratings of 2.5, 4.5, 5, and 10V, the LT1019 is a third-generation device utilizing thin-film technology and wafer-level trimming of both the reference voltage and the output voltage. Typical specifications for the LT1019 include an output voltage error of 0.02%, a TC of 5 ppm/°C, line regulation of 0.5 ppm/V, and load regulation of 0.1 mV/mA. For low-drift applications, you can achieve a TC of less than 2 ppm/°C by operating the LT1019 in a heated mode using its internal resistor and an external amplifier. Available in either an 8-pin metal can or plastic DIP, the LT1019's prices start at $3.90 (100). Applications for this device include A/D and D/A converters, V/F converters, precision regulators, and strain-gauge bridge excitation.

Maxim Integrated Products offers improved replacements for the 10V REF-01 and the 5V REF-02 bandgap references, two standards introduced by PMI. Maxim's 10V MAX674 and 5V MAX675 have a pretrimmed output voltage that is accurate to ±0.15%, compared with ±0.3% for the REF-01 and REF-02. In addition, the load regulation of 0.002%/mA for the MAX674 and MAX675 is somewhat better than that specified for the REF-01 and REF-02. The MAX674 and MAX675 are available in 8-pin metal cans, plastic DIPs, and SO packages; prices start at $4.25 (100).

Designed for large-volume customers who need a precision reference but can't justify a high cost, the REF-03 from Precision Monolithics 2.5V bandgap reference offers good performance at a unit cost of only $1.75 (100). The REF-03 features a typical output voltage tolerance of ±0.2% (±0.6% max) and a typical TC of 10 ppm/°C (50 ppm/°C max). Typical line and load regulation are 0.002%/V and 0.006%/mA, respectively. The REF-03 is available in 8-pin DIPs and 8-pin SO packages.

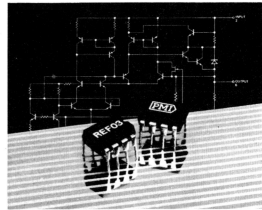

Low-cost references, such as this 2.5V bandgap device from PMI, often come in 8-pin plastic DIPs.

A companion to the REF-03, the REF-43 operates at a lower supply current (450 μA max vs 1.4 mA max) and offers better performance, albeit at the higher starting price of $3.75 (100). The 2.5V REF-43 features a maximum output voltage tolerance of ±0.05% and a maximum TC of 20 ppm/°C. The REF-43 is available in a variety of package styles, including 8-pin TO-99s, 8-pin DIPs, and 20-pin LCCs.

For very low-cost applications, Teledyne Semiconductor offers its 1.25V TSC04 and 2.5V TSC05 bandgap references. Although these devices provide only moderate performance, they can satisfy many applications and—at $0.70 (100) in a TO-92 plastic package ($0.95 in TO-52 metal)—are cost effective. The TSC04 and TSC05, which can operate over a range of 20 μA to 20 mA, have an output tolerance of 2% and a maximum TC of 50 ppm/°C. By not using thin-film resistors in these devices, Teledyne is able to reduce manufacturing complexity—and cost. Teledyne also offers bandgap references rated at 5 and 10V, which offer tighter specifications at higher costs.

An unusual device, the micropower LT1034 from Linear Technology, combines a 1.2 or 2.5V bandgap reference with a 7V zener-based auxiliary reference in a single package. Operating at 100 μA, the bandgap reference features a 1% initial tolerance, a TC of 20 ppm/°C typ, and a dynamic impedance of 0.5Ω typ. Useful for less demanding applications, the 7V reference has a 5% initial tolerance and a typical TC of 40 ppm/°C. The LT1034 comes in 3-pin TO-46 or TO-92 packages; prices start at $2.15 (100).

Zener-based references

Although bandgap references that can operate from 5V supplies are widely available, zener-based references, which are usually used with analog circuits that operate from 12 to 15V supplies, are just as plentiful. In addition, compared with bandgap references, many zener-based references have superior performance characteristics. Major suppliers of zener-based references include Analog Devices, Burr-Brown, Linear Technology, National Semiconductor, and Precision Monolithics.

Typical of the high-performance possible with zener-based references is the 10V REF102 from Burr-Brown. Available in a range of temperature grades and degrees of precision, the REF102's best incarnation features a maximum initial error of only ±2.5 mV, a TC of 2.5 ppm/°C, line regulation of 1 ppm/V, load regulation of 10 ppm/mA, and noise of only 5 μV p-p from 0.1 to 10 Hz. Moreover, the REF102 achieves its performance without the use of a heater, which results in a quiescent current of only 1.4 mA. The REF102's combination of specifications make this device well suited for use with high-resolution A/D and D/A converters or as an accurate comparator threshold reference. Available in industrial and military temperature grades and in three grades of precision, prices for the REF102 range from $2.75 to $14 (100).

Analog Devices offers a wide range of both bandgap and zener-based precision references as part of its line of data conversion products. Unique among its offerings is the AD689, an 8.192V zener-based reference that bridges the gap between 5 and 10V references. Many data-conversion and analog circuits operate from ±12V supplies, which can vary over a 10% range. However, using a 10V reference when the supply drops to ±10.8V is a marginal situation at best. Before the availability of the AD689, designers were forced to choose between a 5V bandgap reference or a less complete zener reference between 5 and about 7V. The 8.192V AD689 lets designers maximize a circuit's signal swing when operating from 12V supplies.

The AD689 uses an ion-implanted zener diode and laser-trimmed thin-film resistors to obtain its high precision. The part features an initial accuracy of ±4 mV and a TC of 5 ppm/°C, and its 8.192V rating provides a convenient 2-mV/LSB scaling for 12-bit converters. Other specifications include a line regulation of ±200 μV/V max, load regulation of 100 μV/mA max, and noise of 2 μV p-p typ from 0.1 to 10 Hz. Long-term stability is typically 15 ppm/1000 hours. For applications requiring higher initial accuracy, the AD689 pro-

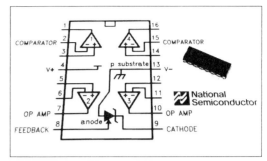

Exemplifying a trend to higher integration, this IC from National Semiconductor contains an adjustable 1.2 to 6.3V reference in addition to dual op amps and dual comparators.

vides connections for fine trimming the output to 8.000V. In addition, force and sense connections allow remote sensing of load and ground variations. Available in 8-pin ceramic DIPs, prices range from $2.95 to $25 (100), depending on accuracy and temperature range.

If your application requires maximum performance and cost is no object, you may want to check out the LTZ1000, a 7.2V zener-based reference from Linear Technology. The LTZ1000, which requires external circuitry to set the operating currents, incorporates a subsurface zener, a heater resistor for temperature stabilization, and a temperature-sensing transistor. Designed for use in standard cells, calibrators, and precision voltmeters, the LTZ1000 features a thermal drift of 0.05 ppm/°C, about 1.2 μV p-p of noise, and long-term stability of 2 μV per month. Packaged in an 8-pin metal can, the LTZ1000 operates over the temperature range of −55 to +125 °C and costs $35.50 (100).

Stand-alone IC references will continue to dominate many applications, but there's a gradual, definite trend toward incorporating voltage references in other circuits—notably A/D and D/A converters. In addition, at least one company has incorporated adjustable references in monolithic building blocks containing op amps and comparators.

For example, over the course of the past year, Maxim Integrated Products has introduced a family of 12-bit A/D converters that include either bandgap or zener references. Analog Devices, among others, offers a wide range of A/D and D/A converters with on-chip references. And National Semiconductor recently introduced several monolithic chips containing single, dual, or quad op amps and a voltage reference.

The main advantage of this higher level of integration is convenience. The designer is freed from the task of matching a specific reference to a particular converter or op amp. In addition, there are advantages in cost and board space. Manufacturers can often include an on-chip reference with little penalty in chip real estate and no change in packaging. For many applications in which a reference is needed, this approach offers a cost-effective alternative.

Manufacturers of voltage references

For more information on voltage references such as those discussed in this article, circle the appropriate numbers on the Information Retrieval Service card or use EDN's Express Request service. When you contact any of the following manufacturers directly, please let them know you saw their products in EDN.

Analog Devices
1 Technology Way
Norwood, MA 02062
(617) 329-4700
Circle No. 650

Burr-Brown Corp
Box 11400
Tucson, AZ 85734
(602) 746-1111
Circle No. 651

Cherry Semiconductor Corp
2000 S County Trail
East Greenwich, RI 02818
(401) 885-3600
Circle No. 652

Linear Technology Corp
1630 McCarthy Blvd
Milpitas, CA 95035
(408) 432-1900
Circle No. 653

Maxim Integrated Products
120 San Gabriel Dr
Sunnyvale, CA 94086
(408) 737-7600
Circle No. 654

Motorola Inc
Linear IC Div
7402 S Price Rd, MD-PR340
Tempe, AZ 85283
(602) 897-3840
Circle No. 655

National Semiconductor Corp
Box 58090
Santa Clara, CA 95052
(408) 721-5000
Circle No. 656

Precision Monolithics Inc
Box 58020
Santa Clara, CA 95052
(408) 727-9222
Circle No. 657

SGS-Thomson Microelectronics
1000 E Bell Rd
Phoenix, AZ 85022
(602) 867-6100
Circle No. 658

Silicon General
11861 Western Ave
Garden Grove, CA 92641
(714) 898-8121
Circle No. 659

Teledyne Semiconductor
1300 Terra Bella Ave
Mountain View, CA 94039
(415) 968-9241
Circle No. 660

Texas Instruments
Box 809066
Dallas, TX 75380
(800) 232-3200, ext 700
Circle No. 661

References

1. *Analog-Digital Conversion Handbook*, edited by Daniel H Sheingold, Analog Devices Inc, Prentice-Hall, Englewood Cliffs, NJ, 1986.

2. Knapp, Ron, "Selection criteria assist in choice of optimum reference," *EDN*, February 18, 1988, pg 183.

17 CMOS circuit always oscillates

Surefire oscillator

I have never known the circuit of Figure 1 (a) fail to oscillate, but then I have never made up the circuit using gates from different packages. If you have to do so, be warned.

W F McClelland
Electronic Resources, Stamford, CT

The common clock oscillator in **Fig 1a** has two small problems: It may not, in fact, oscillate if the transition regions of its two gates differ; and, if it does oscillate, it may sometimes oscillate at a slightly lower frequency than its equation predicts because of the finite gain of the first gate. If the circuit does work, oscillation occurs usually because both gates are in the same package and, therefore, have logic thresholds only a few millivolts apart.

The circuit in **Fig 1b** resolves both problems by adding a resistor and a capacitor. The R_2-C_2 network provides hysteresis, thus delaying the onset of Gate 1's transition until C_1 has enough voltage to move Gate 1 securely through its transition region. When Gate 1 is finally in its transition region, C_2 provides positive feedback, thus rapidly moving Gate 1 out of its transition region.

The equations for the oscillator in **Fig 1b** are

$$R_2 = 10R_1$$
$$R_3 = 10R_2$$
$$C_1 = 100C_2$$
$$f \cong \frac{1}{1.2R_1C_1}$$

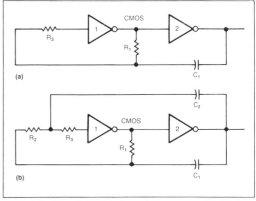

*Fig 1—The conventional CMOS oscillator in **a** sometimes does not oscillate. Or, if it does oscillate, it can oscillate at a lower frequency than you have calculated. The circuit in **b** adds hysteresis to overcome these problems.*

18   CMOS circuit guaranteed to oscillate

Another surefire oscillator

I have always liked the three-gate oscillator since it produces nice sharp waveforms compared with the two-gate version. As in the latter, the AC coupled positive feedback encloses two inverters, but the DC coupled negative feedback encloses three, rather than just one inverter.

Carl Spearow, Senior Engineer
Sundstrand Corp, Rockford, IL

I am writing in response to the Design Idea, "CMOS circuit always oscillates," which appeared in EDN on February 2, 1989, pg 196. The author is correct: The first circuit shown may not oscillate under certain conditions. The second circuit solves the problem, but it is somewhat awkward and uses more parts than are necessary.

The circuit shown in **Fig 1** is guaranteed to oscillate at a frequency of about $2.2/(R_1 \times C)$ if $R_2 \gg R_1$. You can reduce the number of gates further if you replace gates 1 and 2 with a noninverting gate.

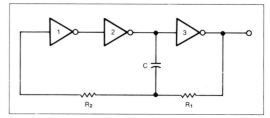

*Fig 1—This circuit will **never** fail to oscillate.*

19 Micropower of amp offers simplicity and versatility

A little nearer the ideal op amp

As every analog engineer knows, the ideal op amp would have zero input offset voltage and tempco of same, zero bias current, rail-to-rail input common mode range, infinite CMRR and PSRR, zero open loop output impedance with rail-to-rail swing and wide bandwidth with high slew rate: they also know that it will not be available in their lifetime, if ever. However, the common mode input range of a few op amps includes the positive rail and of many more (with the popularity of single rail applications) the negative rail. Here is an op amp which includes both and offers a rail-to-rail output swing to boot.

Zahid Rahim, *Signetics Corp*

Linear circuits intended to meet the stringent demands of medical and industrial instrumentation, remote data acquisition, and portable equipment must deliver precision at low voltages. A low-power, battery-operated op amp, for instance, requires precision dc characteristics to process low-level signals from high source impedances, low supply current to conserve power, and wide bandwidth to process audio-frequency signals. Because low-voltage applications produce low signal levels, the op amp should have a wide dynamic range at the input and output. Moreover, both it and its external circuit should function properly at the end-of-life battery voltage.

The NE5230 op amp is suited to such requirements. It operates from a supply voltage of 1.8 to 15V and performs well in systems powered by single 5V sup-

plies. The op amp not only offers precision dc characteristics, its common-mode voltage can swing within 100 mV of either supply rail—a characteristic matched by few other commercially available op amps.

Furthermore, the bias-adjust terminal lets you adjust the op amp's slew rate from 90 to 250V/msec by varying the op amp's internal bias currents. The device also offers decent performance in two other parameters of concern in low-power applications—noise and output-current drive. The NE5230's input voltage noise is 22 $nV/\sqrt{Hz}$ at 1 kHz, and it can source and sink 5 and 11 mA, respectively, when operating from a 1.8V supply at 25°C. Other key specifications are listed in **Table 1.**

These attributes allow you to use the op amp in battery-powered applications such as half-wave and full-wave rectifiers, window detectors with rail-to-rail

TABLE 1—SALIENT SPECS FOR THE NE5230
(V^+=1.8V; V^-=GND)

	BIAS CURRENT*	T_A=25°C	0°C<T_A<70°C
SINGLE/DUAL SUPPLY VOLTAGE	—	1.8 TO 15V OR ± 0.9 TO ± 7.5V	
SUPPLY CURRENT	LOW HIGH	110 μA 600 μA	250 μA MAX 800 μA MAX
OUTPUT SWING	ANY	1.6V	1.4V MIN
V_{OS}	ANY	0.4 mV	4 mV MAX
I_B	LOW HIGH	20 nA 40 nA	150 nA MAX 200 nA MAX
A_{VO}	LOW HIGH	150V/mV 200V/mV	50V/mV MIN 100V/mV MIN
CMRR	ANY	95 dB	80 dB MIN
OUTPUT SOURCE CURRENT OUTPUT SINK CURRENT	HIGH HIGH	5 mA 11 mA	4 mA (TYP) AT LOW BIAS 5 mA (TYP) AT LOW BIAS
SLEW RATE	LOW HIGH	90V/mSEC 250V/mSEC	90V/mSEC 250V/mSEC
BANDWIDTH	LOW HIGH	250 kHz 600 kHz	—

*NOTE: THE NE5230 OPERATES AT LOW BIAS CURRENT IF THE BIAS ADJUST PIN (PIN 5) IS LEFT OPEN. SHORTING THE NE5230's PIN 5 TO V^- PROVIDES MAXIMUM BIAS CURRENT. CONNECTING A VARIABLE RESISTOR BETWEEN PIN 5 AND V^- LETS YOU ADJUST THE AMPLIFIER'S BIAS CURRENT AND HIGH-FREQUENCY CHARACTERISTICS.

input ranges, temperature-limit alarms, sound-activated intrusion detectors, and supply-voltage splitters. An equally important application involves signal-conditioning circuits for bridge transducers—circuits that require no reference voltage or instrumentation amplifier.

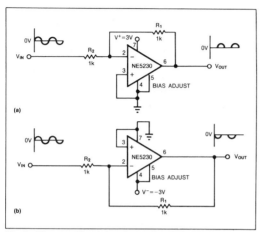

Fig 1—These positive (a) and negative (b) half-wave-rectifier circuits accomplish their job without the use of diodes. The resistors give you the option of gains other than unity.

Rectify signals without diodes

To keep costs low, battery-operated circuits for consumer applications should have a minimum component count. Fewer components also bestow the bonus of higher reliability. These considerations led to the half-wave-rectifier circuits of **Fig 1**. Neither circuit uses diodes. Because the op amp's input common-mode range extends beyond the supply rails, you can simply ground the noninverting terminal and thereby configure the amplifier as an inverter. You should also short the bias-adjust terminal (pin 5) to V⁻ to provide a maximum slew rate.

The amplifier behaves as a unity-gain inverter for negative inputs; positive inputs drive the output into saturation (**Fig 1a**). The NE5230's internal detectors prohibit the hard saturation that would occur in most op amps, however. Recovery from saturation is relatively fast. Operating from a 3V supply, the circuit can rectify signal amplitudes as high as ±2.85V at frequencies well above 10 kHz. If the input signal has a reference level between 0V and V⁺, you can simply reference the amplifier's noninverting input to the same level. If required, resistors R_1 and R_2 can provide a gain other than unity.

To obtain a negative-polarity half-wave-rectified signal using a conventional op amp, you have to provide dual (bipolar) power supplies. The NE5230's rail-to-rail input range and near rail-to-rail output range, however, let you achieve this function using a single supply. Simply connect the supply's positive terminal and the amplifier's V⁺ terminal to ground, and connect the supply's negative terminal to the amplifier's V⁻ terminal (**Fig 1b**).

The amplifier's common-mode range lets you reference the input signal to the positive rail (ground) by tying the noninverting and V⁺ terminals together. (You can't do this with most op amps, and most op amps' output voltage must remain at least one V_{BE} voltage below the positive rail.) In short, you can use the amplifier with a single negative supply to condition the signal output from a variety of ground-referenced sensors. Again, if the input-signal reference is a voltage between 0V and V⁻ instead of ground, you should connect the amplifier's noninverting input to the same potential.

Overdriving most op amps (beyond the supply rail, for instance) saturates the input stage, causing a phase reversal within the amplifier that can reverse the feedback signal's polarity. Circuitry within the NE5230 prevents phase reversal for inputs as large as 2V beyond the supply rail. This feature allows the amplifiers of **Fig 2** to produce half-wave rectification without external components for input signals referenced to 0V.

In **Fig 2a**, the amplifier output follows the input signal above 0V and goes into negative saturation for inputs below 0V. (The output clamps near 0V for negative inputs.) The circuit as shown can rectify signals of ±2V at frequencies above 10 kHz. Inputs below −2V will cause internal phase reversal, however, allowing the output voltage to rise. You can prevent this situation by adding a large resistor in series with the amplifier's input. To obtain a negative-polarity half-wave rectifier, simply reverse **Fig 2a**'s supply-voltage connections (**Fig 2b**). Again, this circuit can rectify 0V-referenced signal amplitudes to ±2V at frequencies above 10 kHz.

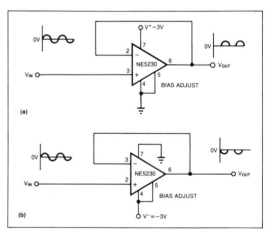

Fig 2—Requiring no external components, these op amp circuits perform positive (a) and negative (b) half-wave rectification for ground-referenced ac signals.

Fig 3's circuit performs full-wave rectification using a single positive power supply. When a negative input voltage causes IC_1 to clamp IC_2's noninverting input to 0V, IC_1 delivers current through D_1 and R_3 to the signal source. IC_2 acts as an inverting amplifier for negative input signals. Positive input signals produce a differential voltage between the IC_1 inputs and create reverse-bias across D_1, placing IC_1's output in negative satura-

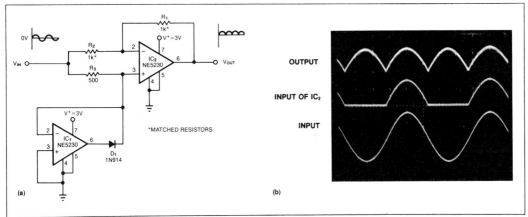

Fig 3—*This absolute-value circuit* (*a*) *achieves full-wave rectification by clamping* IC_2's *noninverting input to 0V when* V_{IN} *is negative, and removing the clamp when* V_{IN} *is positive. Thus,* IC_2 *alternates between an inverter and a follower every half cycle. The photo* (*b*) *shows circuit performance at 400 Hz for a 5.7V p-p input signal. The vertical scale is 2V/div, and the horizontal scale is 0.5 msec/div.*

tion. This condition removes the 0V clamp at IC_2's inverting input by breaking IC_1's feedback loop. Consequently, IC_2 behaves as a follower during positive excursions of the input voltage.

Although D_1 is reverse-biased, clamp diodes at IC_1's inverting input turn on and draw current through R_3. Accordingly, R_3's value should be 500Ω or less to avoid a significant offset due to this parasitic current flow. (R_1 and R_2 can be large-valued resistors.) **Fig 3b** shows the circuit operating with a 5.7V p-p signal at 400 Hz. Similar to the way it rectified the half-wave circuits, the NE5230 performs negative full-wave rectification in **Fig 4** using a single negative power supply. The same precautions apply as for **Fig 3**.

You can also use the NE5230 to monitor a signal and to detect fault conditions in which the signal is shorted to either supply voltage. The window-detector circuit of **Fig 5** must have the same supply voltage as that of the remote signal source. Power-supply currents through R_1 and R_2 create small offsets essential to the circuit's operation.

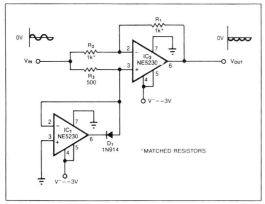

Fig 4—*This circuit* (*obtained by reversing* *the power-supply connections in* **Fig 3**) *performs negative full-wave rectification using a single supply voltage.*

Both op amp outputs remain in positive saturation for V_{IN} values between approximately 0 and 3V, which keeps the LED off. If V_{IN} shorts to V⁺, however, IC_1 saturates negatively (at 0V), turning on the LED.

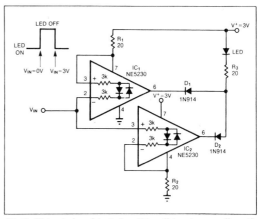

Fig 5—*This window detector's rail-to-rail* *input range allows the circuit to detect faults in which the input signal becomes shorted to either rail.*

Similarly, IC_2 turns on the LED by saturating negatively when V_{IN} shorts to ground. As you can see, the op amp inputs' series resistors and clamp diodes limit the current drawn from the V_{IN} source.

Normally, building a 2-limit temperature alarm requires a temperature sensor and two op amps. The NE5230 itself becomes a temperature sensor, however, if you make use of the PTAT (proportional to absolute temperature) voltage at pin 5. This voltage is independent of the supply voltage and measures 14 mV at 27 °C. What's more, it changes predictably at a rate of 46.667 μV/°C. For instance, at +85 and −15°C, the pin 5 PTAT voltage is 16.7 and 12.04 mV, respectively.

The alarm circuit (**Fig 6**) uses these trip points to activate a buzzer when the ambient temperature moves outside of the −15 to +85°C window. The R_1/R_2-divider voltage sets the upper temperature limit and the R_3/R_4-divider voltage sets the lower one. When the ambient temperature exceeds 85°C, IC_1's inverting-input voltage is more positive than that at the noninverting input, and the resulting saturated output (0V) causes the buzzer to sound. Conversely, IC_2's output sounds the buzzer when the ambient temperature drops below −15°C, again by going into negative saturation.

The resistors that you use in the voltage dividers should have similar temperature coefficients to prevent a shift in threshold voltage as the temperature changes. On the other hand, the op amp's input-offset voltage (V_{OS}) has a greater effect on the circuit's accuracy. Because V_{OS} is a significant percentage of the small PTAT voltage, you must set the temperature limits far apart to reduce error. The typical 400-μV V_{OS} and 5-μV/°C V_{OS} drift can introduce an uncertainty of ±15°C or more. Although **Fig 6** isn't intended for precision applications, you can improve its accuracy by selecting NE5230s with low V_{OS}.

The battery-operated intrusion detector of **Fig 7** illustrates another type of alarm circuit possible with the NE5230 op amp. Using an electret-microphone sensor, the circuit activates a buzzer when the ambient sound exceeds a user-specified threshold. Resistor R_3 biases the microphone and capacitor C_1 blocks the microphone's dc signal component. IC_1 is connected as an inverting amplifier with adjustable gain. The amplifier can't respond to positive inputs because the V^- terminal is grounded, and without sound the amplifier's input and output are near 0V. The output drives an RS (reset-set) flip-flop formed by the cross-coupled CMOS Nor gates. Therefore, in the absence of sound the flip-flop's $\overline{Q}$ output is high, and the buzzer is off. IC_2's negligible standby current and the low quiescent cur-

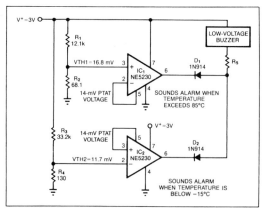

Fig 6—The op amp's bias-adjust pin (pin 5) is the PTAT (proportional to absolute temperature) voltage, which lets you use the amplifier as a temperature sensor. This circuit activates the buzzer when the temperature exceeds a user-specified limit.

rent of the microphone and op amp ensure long battery life.

Sound detector has adjustable threshold

Sound causes the microphone to produce an ac signal

whose reference is ground on the other side of C_1. (The capacitor you choose should have low leakage current.) This signal's negative excursions produce positive excursions at the flip-flop's S input. If the amplifier's gain (set by R_1) is sufficient, the signal at S will cross the gate's switching threshold and latch the $\overline{Q}$ output low, activating the buzzer. The buzzer will remain on until you reset the latch by momentarily pressing S_1. Remember that high closed-loop gain settings will reduce the circuit's sensitivity to high-pitched sound by lowering the amplifier's −3-dB bandwidth. If you need more sensitivity, you can cascade two op amps and split the required gain between them.

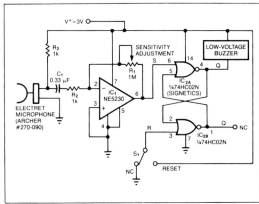

Fig 7—Ambient sound above a user-determined threshold activates this intrusion detector. Once triggered, the alarm will sound until you momentarily press the switch (S_1).

Circuits that process ground-referenced signals often require dual power supplies, but dual-voltage battery supplies can increase a system's size and cost. You can avoid this extra hardware in some cases by converting a single 3V lithium-battery output into a ±1.5V output (**Fig 8a**). The R_1/R_2 divider splits the 3V supply, and the op amp's 40-nA input-bias current offers a minimal load to the divider. The amplifier's output becomes the common terminal for all ground-referenced loads and signals.

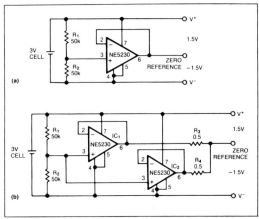

Fig 8—The circuit in a converts a 3V cell into a ±1.5V dual tracking supply. By connecting two amplifiers in parallel (b), you can nearly double the circuit's load-current capability.

The NE5230's low output impedance minimizes any offset voltage created by the connection of loads between the amplifier's output and V^- or V^+. Moreover, the dual voltages track in magnitude as the battery cell discharges—a feature useful in applications that must maintain a precise voltage null despite fluctuations in the supply voltages. The **Fig 8a** circuit sources and sinks 15 and 24 mA, respectively.

To obtain higher load currents, you can connect two NE5230s in parallel (**Fig 8b**). The difference in offset voltages (ΔV_{OS}) appears across R_3 and R_4. The standby current in one op amp increases by $\Delta V_{OS}/(R_3+R_4)$, but current in the other op amp decreases by the same amount, so the sum of the supply current through the two op amps remains constant.

Large load currents divide equally between the two op amps, and you would expect this circuit to provide twice the output current of **Fig 8a**, but the load-current capability is generally less because of mismatch in the op amp's output resistances and mismatch between R_3 and R_4. The **Fig 8b** circuit sources and sinks 24 and 35 mA, respectively, when operating from a 3V supply.

Bridge transducers for precision applications usually require an accurate low-drift voltage reference and a precision instrumentation amplifier (see **box**, "What you should know about bridge circuits"). The **Fig 9** circuit, however, acquires and displays the bridge transducer's output without using a voltage reference or an instrumentation amplifier.

Op amp IC_1 buffers the fixed arm of the bridge and provides a reference potential for all ground-referred loads. Choosing this node as the reference potential converts the bridge's differential output signal to a single-ended signal referred to ground. This reference remains halfway between V^+ and V^- even if the battery discharges. The reference potential is thus a floating ground, often called an active guard.

Converting the bridge's differential signal to a ground-referred signal eliminates the bridge output's common-mode voltage, which also eliminates the need for common-mode rejection, usually obtained by adding an instrumentation amplifier. IC_2 amplifies the bridge's output signal, and R_5 lets you adjust the circuit's full-scale output level.

The IC_2 output V_{OUT} will change as the batteries discharge, but the V_{OUT}/V^+ ratio will remain fixed. This relationship lets you remove the effect of battery discharge by operating the panel meter's A/D converter in the ratiometric mode. Connect the wiper of R_6 to the converter's reference input to ensure that the signal and reference remain in proportion as the supply voltage changes. Finally, note that IC_2 amplifies its own input-offset voltage. You should null this effect by first balancing the bridge, and then adjusting R_6 for an all-zeros output at the panel meter.

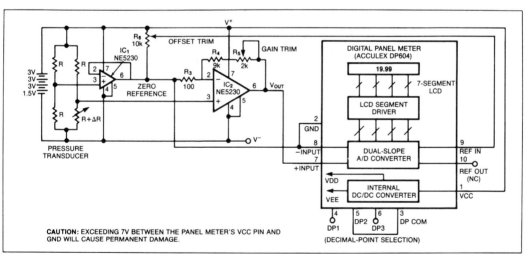

Fig 9—This bridge-transducer interface circuit *conditions the bridge's output signal for ratiometric operation and eliminates the need for a reference voltage and an instrumentation amplifier.*

What you should know about bridge circuits

A bridge circuit, often known as a Wheatstone bridge, consists of a pair of series-connected resistors connected in parallel with a similar pair of resistors (**Fig A**). Bridge circuits are widely found in precision-null applications because the differential voltage $(V_1 - V_2)$ across the bridge is 0V when the bridge is balanced.

What's more, this balanced condition is unaffected by voltage drops across line resistances or shifts in the reference voltage V_R. You can use such a balanced bridge to measure capacitance,

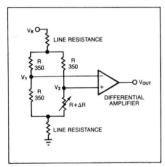

Fig A—In a conventional transducer bridge, *the parameter of interest causes a variation (ΔV) in the bridge's output. The amplifier senses the resulting small differential signal and also rejects the bridge's relatively large common-mode voltage.*

inductance, or its own frequency of excitation (when applied in place of V_R).

A more common application for a bridge circuit is as a bridge transducer for converting physical parameters such as temperature or pressure into electrical signals. Normally, the resistance in one arm of the bridge varies with the measured parameter as resistances in the other three arms remain constant. This type of application usually includes a differential amplifier to amplify the bridge's differential output voltage.

The amplifier's output indicates any change in the measured parameter with respect to a reference level corresponding to the condition of a balanced bridge. You do need a fixed reference voltage; shifts in V_R will change the amplifier's output voltage unless the bridge happens to be balanced. The bridge's output signal usually consists of several millivolts riding on a much larger common-mode signal.

Accordingly, you should choose a bridge amplifier that minimizes inaccuracies through high common-mode rejection

(CMR), low input-offset voltage (V_{OS}), and low V_{OS} drift with temperature. The amplifier should have high open-loop gain to ensure a linear transfer function and low input-bias current to avoid loading the bridge. An instrumentation amplifier meets all these requirements and is designed specifically for conditioning the output of bridge transducers.

Note that even an ideal bridge amplifier will have a nonlinear response because the bridge itself is inherently nonlinear. The following derivation shows why:

$$
\begin{aligned}
V_O &= A_{CL}(V_1 - V_2) \\
&= A_{CL}\left[\frac{V_R}{2} - \frac{V_R(R+\Delta R)}{R+R+\Delta R}\right] \\
&= -\frac{A_{CL}V_R}{4}\left(\frac{\Delta R/R}{1+\Delta R/2R}\right).
\end{aligned}
$$

A_{CL} is the amplifier's closed-loop gain. The bridge's output signal is nonlinear because both the numerator and the denominator contain the transducer-deviation term ΔV. The signal is approximately linear over a small range of amplitudes, however. Such signals are held to low amplitude for that reason.

References

1. Huijsing, Johan H, and Linebarger, Daniel, "Low-voltage operational amplifier with rail-to-rail input and output ranges," *IEEE Journal of Solid-State Circuits*, Vol SC-20, December 1985, pg 1144-1150.

2. Huijsing, Johan H, "Multistage amplifier with capacitive nesting for frequency compensation," US Patent Application Serial No 602.234, filed April 19, 1984.

3. Blauschild, Robert, "Differential amplifier with rail-to-rail capability," US Patent Application Serial No 525.181, filed August 23, 1983.

20   Transistor clipper provides flat-top output

> ## A waveform modifier
>
> Here is an ingenious circuit in search of an application – can you think of any? I have used a version intermediate between Figure 1(b) and Figure 2(b), in experiments with electronic organs. This provided alternative outputs, containing even harmonics, to the primary outputs of sinewave type tone-generators, on a per note basis, in a free phase organ.

Rudy Stefenel
San Jose, CA

If you use the diode clipper shown in **Fig 1a** to clip a sine wave, you won't get a perfect flat-topped waveform because of the diode's forward characteristic. A simple transistor circuit (**Fig 1b**) does a much better job, however, because the transistor's base gets its signals from the circuit input and output.

You can understand the transistor circuit's operation by looking at the effect of each base signal separately. **Fig 2a** shows the circuit with the base signal coming only from the output—a configuration that provides the same result as **Fig 1a**'s diode clipper. **Fig 2b**, on the other hand, shows the circuit with the base signal coming only from the input. With this configuration, the output actually sags, because as the transistor's base gets driven harder as a result of the input pulse's rounded top, the collector saturates harder.

The combination of the two base signals thus provides the flat-top characteristic. For different transistor types, the optimum resistor values might vary.

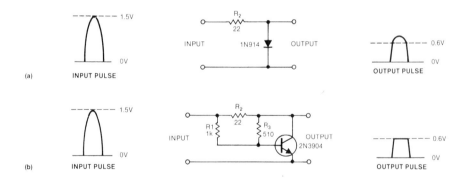

Fig 1—A simple diode clipper (a) *provides a signal with a rounded top when driven by a sine wave. Substituting a transistor whose base accepts two input signals **(b)** results in a flat-top characteristic.*

Add one component—another transistor—to **Fig 1b**'s circuit, and you have a symmetrical clipper, shown in **Fig 3a** along with its diode counterpart. And add another resistor, and you can raise the clipping-voltage level (**Fig 3b**). This latter circuit functions at levels into the tens of volts. However, at higher voltage levels, it's more efficient to use zener diodes.

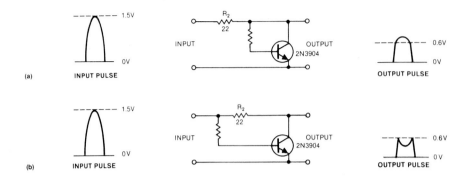

Fig 2—**Without the resistor** *from the input to the transistor base* **(a)**, *Fig 1b's circuit's action is the same as that of* **Fig 1a**'*s diode clipper. And with the resistor from the output to the base removed* **(b)**, *a sag appears in the pulse's center because the transistor is driven harder there.*

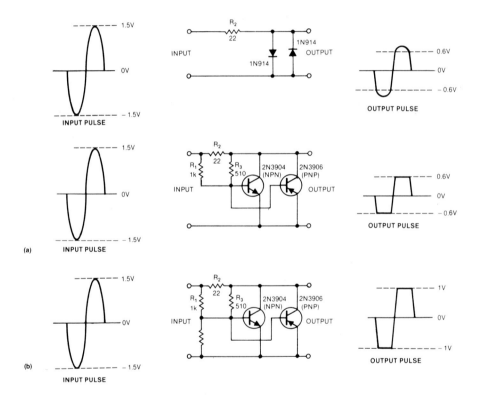

Fig 3—**Symmetrical action** *results when you add a complementary transistor to* **Fig 1b**'*s design* **(a)**. *And adding a resistor* **(b)** *raises the complementary circuit's clipping level.*

21 Digitize analog functions using simple procedures

> ## Time domain signal processing
>
> As basically an analog engineer, I found this article a useful, informative and interesting introduction to an area where I seldom need to tread.

George Ellis, *Industrial Drives*

As µPs become smaller, less expensive, and more powerful, more and more designers are using them to implement signal-processing functions that once were considered exclusively analog in nature. Digital implementations of filters, integrators, compensators, and similar functions yield greater flexibility, lower temperature drift, and much smaller unit-to-unit variation than their analog counterparts, which use op amps. Further, digital versions may also be cheaper, particularly if they are part of a system that already contains many digital components.

Even expert analog designers sometimes find it difficult to change the analog versions' frequency-domain parameters to the time-domain parameters needed by the corresponding digital versions. It's not that difficult, however, if you divide the task into three major stages:

1. Design the function you want in the frequency domain.
2. Convert the parameters from the frequency domain to the sample-data domain.
3. Convert the parameters from the sample-data domain to the time domain.

First design in the frequency domain

Analog designers generally are familiar with the basic principles of frequency-domain design—the use of root-locus and Bode plots, for example. These principles are based on the Laplace operator s, which is sometimes written as "$j\omega$." The normal practice is to write the transfer functions as H(s). To implement an integration expression, you would replace instances of $1/s$ with integrators consisting of op amps and capacitors, and you would use resistors for scaling.

When you want to convert an analog function to the time domain for digital implementation, however, a few restrictions apply. First, you must write the function as a ratio of zeros to poles; and second, the poles and zeros must appear either as real and single elements or as complex conjugate pairs. Because many analog functions inherently impose these restrictions, you'll find that most frequency-domain functions are already in this form.

A familiar example is a single-pole lowpass filter, for which the frequency-domain expression is

$$H(s) = 2\pi f/(s + 2\pi f),$$

where f is the break frequency. If you set the break at 100 Hz, the filter's expression becomes

$$H(s) = 628.3/(s + 628.3).$$

The second stage is to convert the frequency-domain (s-plane) expression to an equivalent sample-data (z-plane) expression. The difference between the two planes is that s-plane functions are based on integrations, and z-plane functions are based on time delays. It's convenient to use the z-plane expressions as an intermediate step because they are much closer to the operations of a digital system than are the s-plane expressions, and thus are easier to convert to the final time-domain expressions for which you can write a program.

For each s-plane function, an equivalent z-plane function exists; refer to **Table 1** for an abbreviated list of s-plane functions and their z-plane counterparts. Before you can convert the s-plane functions to the z plane, however, you must first select the sample time (cycle time), T, of the system. The value of T is somewhat arbitrary, but as a general guideline, select a value of T such that the sample frequency is at least 10 times the system bandwidth.

The 100-Hz lowpass filter mentioned in step 1 serves as a good example of how to use **Table 1**. Beginning with the first stage,

$$H(s) = 628.3/(s + 628.3).$$

If you select a 1-kHz sample rate, then T=0.001; replacing this value in entry 3 of **Table 1** yields

$$H(z) = z(1 - e^{-0.6283})/(z - e^{-0.6283})$$
$$= 0.4665z/(z - 0.5335).$$

TABLE 1—S-PLANE/Z-PLANE COUNTERPARTS

ENTRY NO	S-PLANE EXPRESSION	Z-PLANE COUNTERPART
1	INTEGRATOR: $1/s$ ⟷	$Tz/(z-1)$
2	DIFFERENTIATOR: s ⟷	$(z-1)/Tz$
3	REAL POLE: $a/s+a$ ⟷	$z(1-e^{-aT})/(z-e^{-aT})$
4	REAL ZERO: $(s+a)/a$ ⟷	$(z-e^{-aT})/(z(1-e^{-aT}))$
5	COMPLEX POLES: $\dfrac{\omega^2}{s^2+2\alpha\omega s+\omega^2}$ ⟷	$\dfrac{z^2(1-2\times e^{-\alpha\omega T}\times\cos(\sqrt{1-\alpha^2}\times\omega T)+e^{-2\alpha\omega T})}{z^2-2\times z\times e^{-\alpha\omega T}\cos(\sqrt{1-\alpha^2}\times\omega T)+e^{-2\alpha\omega T}}$
6	COMPLEX ZEROS: $\dfrac{s^2+2\alpha\omega s+\omega^2}{\omega^2}$ ⟷	$\dfrac{z^2-2\times z\times e^{-\alpha\omega T}\cos(\sqrt{1-\alpha^2}\times\omega T)+e^{-2\alpha\omega\cdot T}}{z^2(1-2\times e^{-\alpha\omega T}\cos(\sqrt{1-\alpha^2}\times\omega T)+e^{-2\alpha\omega T})}$

WHERE a =1/TIME CONSTANT OF POLE
α=DAMPING RATE
e=EXPONENT
T=SAMPLE TIME
ω=NATURAL FREQUENCY $(2\pi f)$

If the function is very complex, you can break down the full s-plane function into two or more simpler subfunctions, each of which is represented by one of the s-plane functions in **Table 1**. The final z-plane function is therefore the product of all the z-plane counterparts of the s-plane subfunctions.

In **Table 1,** the term T, although defined as the sample time of the system, also implies a relationship to dc gain (an integrator is a good example: Doubling the sample rate doubles the final count). The inclusion of gain terms is advantageous because it eliminates the need to adjust the overall gain of your filter at the end of the design process. You'll find that many z-transform tables do not include dc-gain terms, and therefore they differ from **Table 1**. However, you can use any set of transform tables to obtain subfunctions of a complex s-plane function, provided that you use them correctly and take into account any additional steps (such as gain adjustment) that they may require.

Once you've converted your function to the sample-data (z-plane) domain, you can then move on to the final design stage of the digital implementation, converting from the sample-data domain to the time domain. In order to do so, it's important that you understand that, because data is normally updated once every cycle, the variables in the system are only "snapshots." Consequently, data is represented either as new or as delayed by some integer number of samples.

Normally you add a subscript to a function to indicate, in shorthand form, the number of delay cycles. For example, f_k indicates the most recent value of f(t) (that is, in the current cycle). The expression f_{k-1} indicates the value of f(t) delayed by one sample period (that is, the value of f(t) during the previous cycle).

One of the basic properties of the z plane is that dividing a value by z yields the value you'd obtain after a delay of one sample time. Thus, the goal of this stage is to rewrite the z-plane function, replacing each z with a delay. You can accomplish the conversion to the time domain by performing the following steps:

1. Write the transfer function in the z plane as a function of output to input.

2. Multiply out the equation so that no "z"s appear in any denominator.

3. Divide the terms in the equation by the highest power of z that appears in the equation.

4. Replace the z-plane functions with functions that represent a delay of one sample period for each negative power of z. For example, replace $z^{-2}\times$out(z) with out_{k-2}.

5. Move the undelayed output term to the left side of the equation and move all other terms to the right side.

Use the steps to implement a lowpass filter

Felicitously, the 100-Hz lowpass filter is simple enough to provide a complete demonstration of the entire digital-implementation process:

- stage 1 (write the s-plane function):
  $H(s)=2\pi f/(s+2\pi f)=628.3/(s+628.3)$
- stage 2 (convert to z-plane function):
  $H(z)=0.4665z/(z-0.5335)$
- stage 3 (convert to time domain):
  step 1: $OUT(z)/IN(z)=0.4665z/(z-0.5335)$
  step 2: $OUT(z)\times(z-0.5335)=IN(z)\times0.4665z$
  step 3: $OUT(z)-0.5335\times OUT(z)/z=0.4665\times IN(z)$
  step 4: $OUT_k-0.5335\times OUT_{k-1}=0.4665\times IN_k$
  step 5: $OUT_k=0.5335\times OUT_{k-1}+0.4665\times IN_k$.

You can now write a Basic program that simulates the function of a lowpass filter with the characteristics specified in step 5. The program (**Listing 1**) simulates the action of driving the filter with a 25-Hz sine wave and displays the filter's first 200 outputs. When you run the program, you'll see that the output is attenuated by 3% of the input and that it lags the input by a delay of 1 to 2 msec, corresponding to phase angles between 10° and 20°. A lowpass filter driven at 25% of its break

LISTING 1—SIMULATION OF LOWPASS FILTER

```
1 REM   100-HZ SINGLE-POLE LOWPASS FILTER WITH INPUT OF 25 HZ.

4 REM   OUT₀ AND IN₀ ARE THE MOST RECENT VALUES OF

6 REM   OUT AND IN.

8 REM   OUT₁ IS OUT DELAYED BY ONE SAMPLE TIME.

10  TIME=0
20  T=0.001
30  OUT1=0
40  PRINT "  TIME        INPUT       OUTPUT"
50  FOR K=1 TO 200
60      TIME=TIME+T
70      IN0=SIN(6.283*25*TIME)
80      OUT1=OUT0
90      OUT0=(0.4665*IN0) + (0.5335*OUT1)
100     PRINT USING " #.###  ####.###  ####.###",TIME,IN0,OUT0
110 NEXT K
120 END
```

frequency (as this one is) should theoretically provide 3% attenuation and 14° of lag—which correlates well with the experimental result.

You can apply steps to complex functions

You can apply the step-by-step design procedure to transfer functions much more complicated than the lowpass filter in the previous example. For instance, consider an integrator with lead compensation. Assume that the lead zero is set to 10 Hz, the pole is set to 40 Hz, and the dc gain is 0.25. The integrator is to have a gain of 100 at 1 rad/sec, and the sample time is 0.001 sec. Applying the 3-stage design procedure to the integrator yields the results of **Fig 1**.

From these results, you can write a Basic program that simulates the operation of the filter when it receives a 20-Hz input (**Listing 2**). From the definition of H(s), the gain of the transfer function is −8 dB at 20 Hz, and the output lags the input by 53.1°. When you run the program, you'll find that if you eliminate (by subtraction) the dc portion of the gain, the output is 40% of the input (an attenutation of about 8 dB), and the output lags the input by 7 msec (equivalent to approximately 50° at 20 Hz). These results correlate well with the s-plane design characteristics.

Limit the input frequency to avoid aliasing

When designing digital filters, you must take care to avoid aliasing effects. Aliasing is the name of a phenomenon that causes input frequencies greater than half the sampling frequency to appear in the output transformed into frequencies less than half the sampling rate. **Fig 2** shows the effects of aliasing on a system with a sample rate of 100 Hz. You'll see that all input frequencies greater than 50 Hz (which is half the sampling rate) appear in the output as frequencies between 0 and 50 Hz.

For integral harmonics of the sampling rate, the

STAGE 1:
$$H(s) = \frac{s+62.83}{s+251.3} \times \frac{100}{s}$$
$$= \frac{s+62.83}{62.83} \times \frac{251.3}{s+251.3} \times \frac{62.83}{251.3} \times \frac{100}{s}$$

STAGE 2:
$$H(z) = \frac{z-0.9391}{0.0609z} \times \frac{0.2222z}{z-0.7778} \times 0.25 \times \frac{100\times0.001z}{z-1}$$
$$= 0.09122 \times \frac{(z-0.9391)z}{(z-0.7778)(z-1)}$$

STAGE 3:
STEP 1: $$\frac{OUT(z)}{IN(z)} = 0.09122 \times \frac{(z-0.9391)z}{(z-0.7778)(z-1)}$$

STEP 2: $OUT(z)\times(z^2-1.778z+0.7778)=0.09122\times IN(z)\times(z^2-0.9391z)$

STEP 3: $OUT(z)\times(1-1.778/z+0.7778/z^2)=0.09122\times IN(z)\times(1-0.9391/z)$

STEP 4: $OUT_k\times1.7778\times OUT_{k-1}+0.7778\times OUT_{k-2}=0.09122\times IN_k-0.08567\times IN_{k-1}$

STEP 5: $OUT_k=1.778\times OUT_{k-1}-0.7778\times OUT_{k-2}+0.09122\times IN_k-0.08567\times IN_{k-1}$

Fig 1—For just about any frequency-domain function you want to digitize, this simple 3-stage design procedure will work. In the first stage, you write the function in its s-plane form. In the second stage, you transform the expression to the sample-data (z-plane) domain. The third stage transforms the expression to the time-domain form that you can implement digitally. The example presented here is a digital implementation of a lead-compensated integrator.

apparent frequency is 0. All other frequencies are transformed to the difference between f (the input frequency) and xn, where n is the sampling rate and x is an integer representing the nearest integral harmonic of the sampling rate. Thus, in **Fig 2**, an input frequency of 230 Hz appears as an apparent output frequency of $230-(2\times100)=30$ Hz; an input of 270 Hz would appear as $(3\times100)-270=30$ Hz. Aliasing continues indefinitely as you raise the input frequency.

Thus, to avoid spurious output signals, you must limit the maximum input frequency to a value that is no greater than half the sampling rate of the system. You can achieve this limit by raising the sampling frequency so that aliasing will not begin until a frequency occurs that is higher than that of any expected signal; this is

LISTING 2—SIMULATION OF LEAD-COMPENSATED INTEGRATOR

```
10  REM   LEAD-COMPENSATED INTEGRATOR WITH AN INPUT AT 20 HZ.

20  REM   OUT0 AND IN0 ARE THE MOST RECENT SAMPLES OF OUT AND IN.

40  REM   OUT1 AND IN1 ARE OUT AND IN DELAYED BY ONE SAMPLE TIME.

60  REM   OUT2 IS OUT DELAYED BY TWO SAMPLE TIMES.

80   DEFDOUBLE I,O,T
90   DEFINT K
100  TIME=0.0
110  T=0.001
130  IN1=0.0
140  OUT1=0.0
150  OUT2=0.0
160  PRINT "   TIME      INPUT      OUTPUT"
170  FOR K=1 TO 200
180      TIME=TIME+T
190      OUT2=OUT1
200      OUT1=OUT0
210      IN1=IN0
220      IN0=SIN(6.283*20*TIME)
230      OUT0=(1.778*OUT1)-(0.7778*OUT2)+(0.09122*IN0)-(0.08567*IN1)
240      PRINT USING " #.###  ####.###  ####.###",TIME,IN0,OUT0
250  NEXT K
260  END
```

the preferred (and least expensive) method. If it is impractical (or otherwise undesirable) to raise the sampling rate, you can insert an analog lowpass filter in the signal path before the digitizing circuitry.

Procedure suits many applications

The 3-stage design procedure presented here is suitable for a wide variety of s-plane functions, including notch filters and PID compensators in servo systems. Not only does it produce more accurate break frequencies than some other popular methods (for example, the bilinear transformation or the w-plane transform), it is also a good deal more straightforward. You can depend on the procedure to produce accurate digital implementations of traditionally analog filters, with minimal complications.

However, in certain circumstances, stage 3 does not

always produce the optimum result with respect to arithmetic noise, to which integrators are very sensitive. You may, therefore, find it desirable to separate an integrator from other functions and design it for minimum noise.

Likewise, for higher-order functions, you may wish to break up the frequency-domain functions into parallel (not cascaded) subfunctions and implement each part separately, using the 3-stage design procedure for each subfunction. And finally, if you find that the computing time imposes an undue delay between the instant at which the data is sampled and the instant at which the corresponding output value becomes available, you may want to rewrite the equations in a manner that allows the processor to perform much of the background computation before the data cycle begins.

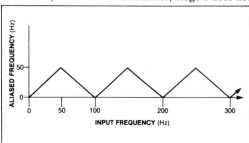

Fig 2—Aliasing is a phenomenon of sampled-data systems and results in spurious output signals. Input frequencies that are greater than half the sampling rate appear in the output as frequencies between 0 and half the sampling rate. To avoid aliasing effects, you must place an upper limit on the input signal frequency.

70

22 Amplitude-locked loop speeds filter test

ALL tests filter cutoff frequency

Before reading this article, I had never heard of an ALL – an amplitude lock loop – and I guess that goes for a lot of other people, too. Here, it is used as the basis of a useful item of production test equipment, enabling a completely unskilled worker to check filter cut-off frequencies.

Steven C Hageman
Calex Manufacturing Co Inc, Pleasant Hill, CA

The circuit shown in **Fig 1** finds, locks to, and displays the cutoff frequency of an audio-frequency lowpass filter. The circuit compares the rms input to the filter-under-test with the filter's rms output. Based on the results of this comparison, the circuit adjusts a VCO to achieve a null at the desired input-to-output attenuation of the filter. Hence, its operation is similar to that of a phase-locked loop.

The AD536 rms-to-dc converter connected to the filter input acts as a reference to the LT1013 servo amplifier. You set the null-voltage potentiometer to the desired input-signal attenuation, such as −3 dB. The servo loop adjusts the VCO's frequency until the output of the filter's rms-dc converter equals the null voltage.

The ICL8038 waveform generator is connected as a sine-wave oscillator with a wide-sweep input range of 1000 to 1. The values given in **Fig 1** provide you with a sweep range of 20 Hz to 20 kHz. The LT1042 window comparator senses when the null voltage and the filter output voltage are within ±15 mV of each other and causes the loop-locked LED to turn on. When the loop reaches lock, you can read the filter's cutoff frequency from the frequency counter.

The loop's bandwidth is 16 Hz, and it has 50° of phase margin. The circuit acquires lock in less than one second with frequency repeatability of better than 0.1%. You can increase the loop bandwidth—at the expense of accuracy—by reducing the value of the integration capacitor, C_1, and the values of the averaging capacitors around the rms-dc converters.

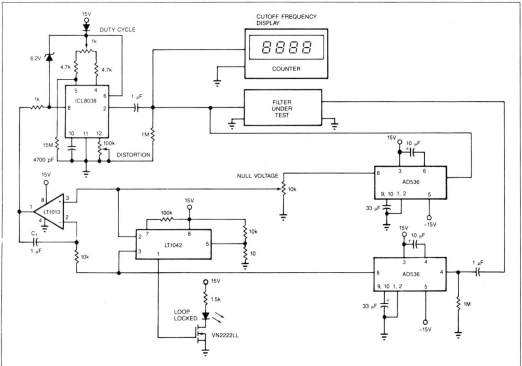

Fig 1—You can use this amplitude-locked-loop circuit *to find the cutoff frequency of a lowpass filter.*

23 Power MOSFETs and IGBTs

> ## Power MOSFETs and IGBTs
>
> A useful staff-written review of power MOSFETs and IGBTs. I take issue however with BT's strictures on die. Sure, 'die' is singular, but the plural is surely 'dice', like the things used for board games and gambling. 'Dies' is the plural of a tool used for cutting external threads, or of a mould used in diecasting.

Bill Travis, *Contributing Editor*

The quest for the perfect switch proceeds relentlessly. This switch will have zero on-resistance and infinite off-resistance, and will require no activation power. Further, the switch will commutate instantaneously and will be capable of switching at an infinite repetition rate. Electromechanical switches, of course, provide the closest approximation to the ideal on-and off-resistances. For fast switching speeds and high rep rates, though, you're obliged to use a solid-state solution—thyristors, bipolar transistors, MOSFETs, or IGBTs (insulated-gate bipolar transistors). MOSFETs and IGBTs are rapidly supplanting thyristors and bipolar transistors in fast-switching applications.

High speed, ease of application, and switching efficiency are three of the factors that endear power MOSFETs and IGBTs to designers. Further, the steadily growing number of MOSFET suppliers is nurturing keen competition, in both price and performance. As a result, the once-significant cost advantage that bipolar transistors have traditionally had over MOSFETs is dwindling. Speaking of cost, you must consider total system cost when you're choosing a switching device. In many cases, the less-complex drive circuitry needed to control a MOSFET (compared with that needed to control a bipolar device) more than offsets the MOSFET's higher purchase price.

Denser geometries, processing innovations, and packaging improvements are resulting in power MOSFETs that have ever-higher voltage ratings and current-handling capabilities, as well as volumetric power-handling efficiency. The same holds true for IGBTs. In addition to making steady improvements in voltage and current ratings, manufacturers are adding various features that bear on the devices' survivability, ease of use, and—in some cases—their "smartness" (for example, overtemperature protection). Before considering these peripheral improvements, it's useful to get an overview of the technological trends in raw voltage and current ratings.

Resistance fighters battle $r_{DS(on)}$

The current-carrying capabilities of a power MOSFET are, naturally, related to the device's on-resistance, or $r_{DS(on)}$. The conducted current times this resistance represents the on-state power, and this power is the limiting factor for the transistor. You can easily determine the maximum allowable current for a given MOSFET by using the specs for the junction-to-case or junction-to-ambient thermal resistance (R_{thJC} or R_{thJA}) of the device. You'd use the former spec in systems that have perfect heat sinking; the latter, in systems without any heat sinking.

The criterion for determining a MOSFET's maximum allowable current is the 150°C limit on junction temperature. If the case (and junction) temperature is 25°C at no power, the allowable junction-temperature rise when power is applied is 125°C. Consider the

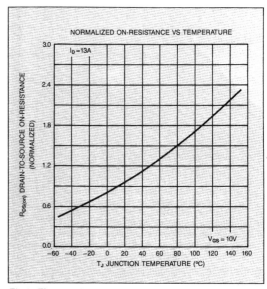

Fig 1—The positive temperature coefficient of $r_{DS(on)}$ in a power MOSFET makes it necessary to derate operating currents at elevated temperatures. That requirement can be beneficial; it prevents thermal runaway. (Courtesy International Rectifier)

These hermetic packages from Motorola resemble the plastic TO-220 and TO-247. These housings let you replace the old, bulky TO-3 in environments requiring hermeticity.

calculation for the ubiquitous IRF450, a 500V device that was developed by International Rectifier (IR) and is now available from many vendors. Its $r_{DS(on)}$ is 0.4Ω, and its R_{thJC} is 0.83°C/W. This figure produces a maximum-allowable-power spec of 150W. When you use the equation $P = I^2R$ and work backwards, you apparently obtain a current limit of 19.4A.

Note, however, that the 0.4Ω $r_{DS(on)}$ is valid at 25°C only. **Fig 1** shows the typical variation in $r_{DS(on)}$; at a 150° junction temperature, the on-resistance is 2.2 times the 25°C value, or 0.88Ω. A new calculation yields a 13A current limit, the value given by the manufacturer. Most data sheets do specify the maximum allowable current; the point of this calculation exercise is to allow you to determine this current in situations in which the heat sinking is less than perfect. The important thing to know is the *case* temperature in any given application.

This said, consider the state of the art in terms of $r_{DS(on)}$ for available power MOSFETs. Starting with 50V devices, Siliconix and SGS-Thomson both offer TO-220-packaged power MOSFETs that spec 23-mΩ max on-resistance. The secret to getting the resistance down is to pack as many parallel-connected cells as possible onto a die. For example, the $1.30 (OEM qty) STVHD90 from SGS has a density of 2.3 million cells/in$_2$. Such packing densities don't come without a price—the input capacitances (C_{iss}) for the mentioned types are 3500 and 3000 pF max, respectively. By contrast, 50V devices having 0.1Ω on-resistance have C_{iss} specs lower than 1000 pF.

IXYS and Siliconix offer 100V devices that spec the lowest $r_{DS(on)}$ figures in the industry. The $17.50 (50) IXTH75N10 from IXYS has 20-mΩ max on-resistance, handles 70A, and comes in a plastic TO-247 (also called TO-3P) package. Its 4200-pF typ C_{iss} is indicative of the high-density architecture used in the company's process, dubbed MegaMOS. Housed in a hermetic TO-3 package, Siliconix's 25-mΩ, 75A SMM70N10 costs $14.40 (100). And remember the VLSI nature of these powerhouses—Siliconix uses a Class-1 wafer-fabrication facility for the devices. To keep prices to a reasonable level, the company fabricates the parts on 6-in. wafers.

For applications requiring somewhat lower current-handling capabilities, Siliconix has recently introduced two companion devices housed in the venerable TO-220 plastic package. The SMP40N10 and SMP30N10 have $r_{DS(on)}$ specs of 40 and 60 mΩ, respectively. Again, C_{iss} inversely tracks the on-resistance—the transistors spec 3000 and 1500 pF typ, respectively, and cost $9.60 and $4 (100).

1000V MOSFETs proliferate

Bipolar transistors have always been available with very high voltage ratings, and those ratings don't carry onerous price penalties. Achieving good high-voltage performance in power MOSFETs, however, has been problematical, for several reasons. First, the $r_{DS(on)}$ of devices of equal silicon area increases exponentially with the voltage rating. To get the on-resistance down, manufacturers would usually pack more parallel cells onto a die. But this denser packing causes problems in high-voltage performance. Propagation delays across a chip, as well as silicon defects, can lead to unequal voltage stresses and even to localized breakdown.

Manufacturers resort to a variety of techniques to produce 1000V, low-$r_{DS(on)}$ power MOSFETs that offer reasonable yields (and therefore, affordable prices). Advanced Power Technology (APT), for example, deviates from the trend toward smaller and smaller feature sizes in its quest for low on-resistance. Instead, the company uses large dies to get $r_{DS(on)}$ down. The rationale is twofold. First, the relatively large geometries make the chips more tolerant of defects than are VLSI-based devices, and this tolerance manifests itself in higher yields. Second, the company claims the large chip sizes provide for efficient heat transfer to package headers.

A striking example of APT's large-die power MOSFETs is a 1000V device that uses a 388×588-mil chip. The $177.65 (1000) APT5010FN specs 0.5Ω $r_{DS(on)}$, a figure that gives the device a 22.5A usable-current rating. According to Terry Bowman, APT's marketing and sales manager, this high current rating makes it easy to design with this part, because it reduces the number of parallel MOSFETs required in high-power systems.

Housed in a hermetically sealed F-pack (called "Mighty MOS" by APT), the APT5010FN can dissipate 595W at 25°C case temperature. The package measures $1.5 \times 2 \times 0.325$ in. It's impressive for its power-handling capability, but also for the fact that it provides four leads for the MOSFET connections. A source-sense lead allows you to maximize switching speed. **Fig 2a** shows a traditional 3-lead connection. Here, a voltage $L_S di/dt$ appears at the source, effectively reducing the gate-drive potential. In **Fig 2b**, the added source-sense lead provides for an essentially floating gate drive. The resulting full gate-drive potential improves the device's fall time.

Other F-pack units from APT, rated from 400 to 800V, have corresponding $r_{DS(on)}$ specs ranging from 0.07 to 0.3Ω. The maximum C_{iss} for these large MOSFETs is 6300 pF. A number of less-expensive 1000V devices can still provide impressive $r_{DS(on)}$ figures, because they use smaller silicon dies. The

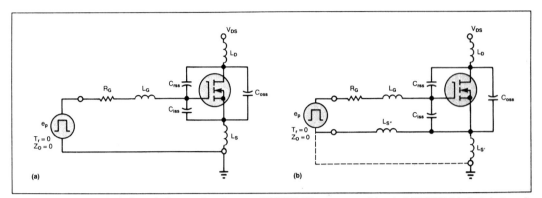

Fig 2—A source-sense terminal speeds the operation of a power MOSFET. When you use a 3-terminal MOSFET (a), the inductance in the source line degrades switching performance. In b, the fourth terminal allows the full potential of the driving source to develop between the gate and the source.

IXTH12N100 from IXYS Corp, for example, comes in a plastic TO-247 or a hermetic TO-3 package and specs 1Ω on-resistance. The unit has a C_{iss} of 4500 pF max and costs $26.71 (50).

Speaking of large MOSFETs, note that a family of huge-die units (available in die form) from APT is poised to hit the market. These range from the 1000V/43A APT10020DN to the 350 and 400V/120A APT3503DN and APT4003DN. These giants, connected in a full-bridge configuration, allow designers to break the 4-device, 2-kW barrier (in fact, to 10 kW).

Even lower in price than IXYS's IXTH12N100 is the company's 2Ω, 2800-pF IXTM5N100A, which comes in a plastic TO-247 or a hermetic TO-3 package and costs $14.06 (50). Note that APT, too, offers smaller-die units in TO-3 packages; the parts spec on-resistances from 1 to 3.5Ω. APT claims its process yields C_{iss} figures lower than those for other equivalent-rated units in the industry. Its 1 and 2Ω units, for example, spec 2450 and 1750 pF, respectively, while the IXYS devices with the same ratings spec 4500 and 2800 pF. Note that International Rectifier, the universally acknowledged leader among MOSFET suppliers, introduced 2 to 11.5Ω 1000V MOSFETs last year. Finally, watch for the imminent announcement of a 0.7Ω, 1000V device from SGS-Thomson.

Ruggedness catches on

Some years ago, General Electric (Syracuse, NY) introduced the concept of "ruggedness" specs to the MOSFET world. Ruggedness, for a MOSFET, is the ability to withstand an avalanche current (at the breakdown voltage) caused by the flyback effect that an unclamped inductive load produces. A MOSFET's ruggedness is certainly of interest to designers, because it determines whether or not a given application will need external protective circuitry.

Fig 3a shows the unclamped, inductive switching test circuit that appears in IR's power-MOSFET data sheets. With minor variations, it's the same circuit adopted by most MOSFET manufacturers. The timing diagram in **Fig 3b** shows what happens when the input pulse falls and tries to turn the device off. The flyback

effect of the inductor sustains the MOSFET current at I_L, and the MOSFET undergoes avalanche at its breakdown voltage, BV_{DSS}. The equation in **Fig 3** gives the avalanche energy in Joules.

Among several manufacturers, ruggedness specs are becoming an integral part of power-MOSFET data sheets. What's needed are standardized test methods and conditions. According to IXYS marketing director Rich Fassler and other authorities, DESC will soon issue such standards. To see an example of how ruggedness specs vary from manufacturer to manufacturer, consider the IRF450 workhorse (a 500V/13A part) and the IRFP040 (a 50V/40A device).

For both devices, International Rectifier specifies the nonrepetitive avalanche energy at 760 mJ and the avalanche current (the value at the time of attempted shutoff) at 14A. The repetitive energy (the duty cycle is <1%) listed in the IR sheet is 18 mJ. Further, that spec sheet gives a curve of avalanche energy vs starting junction temperature. For its identically rated IXTH12N50, IXYS specifies only the nonrepetitive avalanche energy (it's 800 mJ). For its ruggedized IRF450R, RCA specs the energy at 860 mJ and gives the inductor value (9.2 mH) for the test circuit.

In the data sheet for its 50V/40A MTM50N05E, Motorola specifies nonrepetitive energy at 55 mJ with the conditions $I_L = 160A$ and $V_{DD} = 25V$. Further, the sheet lists the energy in a repetitive test as 100 mJ at a 25°C case temperature ($I_L = 50A$), and as 35 mJ at a 100°C case temperature ($I_L = 20A$). For its same-rated IRFP040, IR specs I_L at 4.3A and gives no energy figures. These examples illustrate that, at the moment, it's somewhat difficult to compare the ruggedness of devices from different manufacturers. The situation will change with the advent of the DESC standards.

Another object of scrutiny by the military establishment is commutating safe operating area (CSOA). This area is bounded by the recovery characteristics (dV/dt) of the intrinsic source-drain diode. Motorola, for example, gives CSOA curves in its MOSFET data sheets. The rectangular areas in the curves impose limits on drain current and drain-to-source voltage with the con-

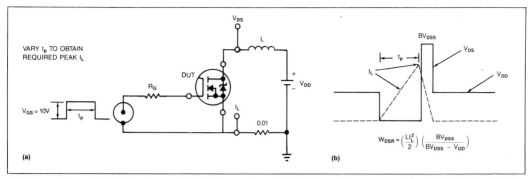

Fig 3—An unclamped inductive load proves a MOSFET's ruggedness. *The inductance, L, in* ***a***, *causes a flyback action (****b****) when the falling input signal tries to shut the MOSFET off. Avalanche energy is a function of the peak drain-source current, the voltage levels, and the inductor value.*

dition of a specified maximum rate of change of the source current. Motorola's product-marketing manager, Bob Bailey, states that JEDEC specs for dV/dt will appear this year.

One example of the emphasis MOSFET manufacturers are placing on the ruggedness issue is IR's introduction of 400 and 500V devices this year; the product announcements stress avalanche and dV/dt ratings. The $6.69 (1000) IRFP448, a 500V/11A MOSFET, specs the nonrepetitive and repetitive avalanche energy at 550 and 17 mJ, respectively, and gives peak diode-recovery dV/dt as 3.5V/nsec. The $23 (1000) IRFP360 is a 400V/25A device; its corresponding ruggedness specs are 980 and 30 mJ and 4V/nsec. Finally, be aware that, for its 30, 40, and 70A MOSFETs, Siliconix specs the repetitive avalanche current at 30, 40, and 70A (continuous).

Fast-recovery diodes

Speaking of dV/dt, manufacturers are devoting a lot of development effort to improving the recovery characteristics of the intrinsic source-drain diode. For example, the 1.2-μsec max recovery time for the IRF450's diode places a severe limitation on the attainable repetition rate in inductive-load applications, and often creates the need for external snubbers and clamps. A number of available devices address the diode-recovery issue.

As for Siliconix's 30, 40, and 70A MOSFETs, note that these devices spec respective recovery times of 130, 120, and 125 nsec typ. For its TMOS IV Series ruggedized MOSFETs, Motorola specs low (70 to 300 nsec typ) diode-recovery times. SGS's 50V/52A STVHD90 specs a recovery time of 70 nsec typ.

Siemens started the fast-recovery ball rolling some years ago by introducing its line of FREDFETs (fast-recovery epitaxial-diode FETs). Philips-Amperex has joined the fray by offering the BUK600 Family of FREDFETs. These devices spec ratings to 400V/14A and 1000V/9A.

Sensing makes sense

The technique of current mirroring for source-current-sensing purposes, which was introduced a few

years ago, involves connecting a small fraction of the cells in a power MOSFET to a separate sense terminal. The current in this terminal is a fixed fraction of the source current feeding the load. This Kelvin-like configuration is useful for monitoring and in closed-loop-feedback applications. It's also valuable if you must squeeze the maximum switching speed from a MOSFET. For example, you can use the sense terminal as described in **Fig 2** to eliminate the effects of source-lead inductance in high-speed switching applications.

A couple of examples of such sense-terminal MOSFETs come from IXYS's recent line of Mirror-FETs. Housed in a TO-247 package, the IXTH39N08MB specs 80V/39A and costs $9.26 (50). Also in a TO-247 package is the IXTH20N60MB, which handles 600V/20A and costs $18.53 (50). IR, Motorola,

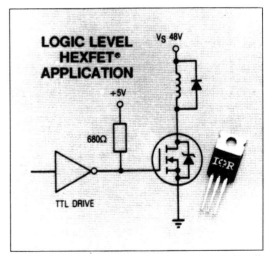

Logic-level MOSFETs from International Rectifier derive drive directly from TTL or CMOS logic.

and Philips-Amperex also offer a wide variety of source-sensing power MOSFETs; they're called HEXSense, SenseFETs, and SensorFETs, respectively.

Another subdivision of the rapidly diversifying

power-MOSFET market is a class of devices called logic-level FETs. Before the advent of these units, drive circuitry had to supply gate-source turn-on levels of 10V or more. The logic-level MOSFETs accept drive signals from CMOS or TTL ICs that operate from a 5V supply. Suppliers of these types include IR, GE, IXYS, Philips-Amperex, and Motorola.

Some recent offerings from IR exemplify what's available in logic-level MOSFETs. One family of TO-220-packaged units, for example, has voltage ratings of 60 and 100V, and handles continuous currents from 5.7 to 35A. In keeping with the present spirit of ruggedness, IR specifies avalanche and dV/dt parameters for the devices. The parts' prices range from $0.34 to $2.39 (1000).

A recent series of units from Philips-Amperex rounds out the company's 50, 100, and 200V logic-level product line. The new devices increase continuous-current ratings from 8.5 to 40A for 50V units, and 3.5 to 12A for 200V MOSFETs. Motorola's logic-level line spans the range from 60V/15A to 150V/10A. Speaking of these two companies, something's afoot in the way power MOSFETs will be specified in the future. The Philips-Amperex devices are specified for operation at a 175°C junction temperature vs the classical 150°C. Motorola plans to specify all its <250V MOSFETs the same way. And note that certain of IR's HEXSense devices are also specified at 175°C.

This increase in allowable junction temperature allows you to squeeze about 10% more current out of a MOSFET of a given die size. Motorola's Bob Bailey attributes the spec loosening to improvements in molding compounds; earlier plastics suffered a glass transition and became brittle at approximately 165°C.

The way to make logic-level MOSFETs is to reduce the thickness of the gate oxide. This reduction, of course, makes the gate more susceptible to voltage breakdown. Motorola ensures the breakdown-proof properties of its power MOSFETs by using what the company dubs the "Bullet-Proof" process. To guarantee gate-breakdown integrity, Motorola applies a 200-msec pulse to the gates of all its production units. The amplitude of the pulse is 60V for ≥400V devices, 40V for <400V units, and 20V for logic-level MOSFETs.

Killing two birds with one stone, IXYS both achieves logic-level operation in its LIMOFET line and lowers input-drive requirements by incorporating two chips in a single package. An internal CMOS driver has a totem-pole output section that can switch the Mega-MOS chip at rates as high as 500 kHz. A side benefit of the 2-chip solution is the low input capacitance—about 50 pF vs thousands of picofarads for large, unassisted MOSFETs. Note that although the input of the tandem operates from TTL levels, the driver requires a separate 7 to 15V supply. These are big devices; packaged in large, hermetic packages called Z-Pacs, they span the range from 100V/67A to 1000V/11A. They cost $118.78 to $163 (10).

Making MOSFETs spaceworthy

Some military and space applications require that their electronic parts be immune to radiation. Al-

though, thanks to the physics of their technology, power MOSFETs are relatively immune to the effects of radiation exposure, they do tend to undergo self-enhancement in the presence of large doses. To counteract this self-turn-on tendency, you need to supply a negative gate-source bias voltage in your application. There are also some parts from GE/RCA and IR that don't have this proclivity for self-enhancement.

Rad-hard MOSFETs from IR, first announced last year in TO-3 packaging, have voltage ratings of 100, 250, and 500V, and respective current ratings of 38, 19, and 10A. A series of units housed in TO-254 (hermetic TO-220) packages, which the company announced shortly thereafter, have identical ratings. These MOSFETs are guaranteed to be immune to radiation doses as high as 1M rad (S_i). Further, they can survive short-term doses as high as 10^{12} rad (S_i)/sec. The TO-3 devices cost $493.84 to $609.78 (1000); the TO-254 units sell for $519.83 to $576 (10).

Similar rad-hard MOSFETs are available from GE/RCA. Rated to withstand steady doses as high as 1M rad, they're available in 100V (14 and 38A) and 200V (9 and 30A) versions. These TO-3-packaged units, too, display survivability to 10^{12} rad (S_i)/sec. In addition, their data sheets claim they can survive exposures of 2×10^{12} neutrons.

These rad-hardened MOSFETs could be considered specialty items. To a lesser degree, you could also consider p-channel power MOSFETs to be specialties. Although a healthy market exists for them, it pales in comparison with the market for n-channel devices. It takes so much more silicon to achieve a given rating in a p-channel device, that first, equally rated units cost much more; and second, in a given package, the current limit for a p-channel MOSFET is usually ½ to ¼ of the limit for n-channel devices. As a result, designers often resort to quasicomplementary output structures, and—when the need exists for a high-side switch—they resort to charge-pump techniques to generate the necessary gate drive for an n-channel MOSFET.

Nevertheless, most of the manufacturers cited here do make p-channel MOSFETs to complement their n-channel devices. New-product announcements are few and far between, however. One exception, and a recent one, is Siliconix's family of MOSFETs housed in JEDEC TO-254 (hermetic TO-220) packages. Designated 2N7071 through 2N7080, the series comprises eight n-channel and two p-channel MOSFETs. The n-channel units have ratings of 100V/24A and 100V/30A; 200V/16A and 200V/28A; 400V/9A and 400V/15A; and 500V/7A and 500V/13A. The two p-channel devices have ratings of 100V/17A; and 200V/9.5A (minus signs are omitted for clarity). Prices range from $48.37 to $75.60 (100).

Another exception to the paucity of p-channel announcements is a series of low-cost devices from Motorola, appropriate as complements to the company's (and many others') 3055-type n-channel MOSFETs. The MTD/MTP Series is rated at 60V/12A, and costs $0.60 (1000). The parts are available in a surface-mount

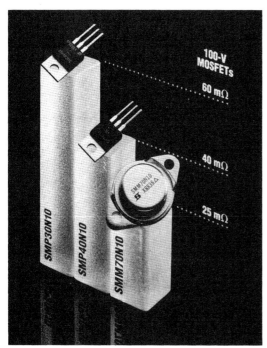

These low-resistance 100V MOSFETs from Siliconix have 25-, 40-, and 60-mΩ on-resistance specs.

or insertion-mount miniature plastic package called the D-Pack, or in a TO-220 package.

A final specialty item worthy of note is a series of temperature-protected power MOSFETs from Siemens. These products each contain a power-MOSFET chip and a temperature sensor having a thyristor (SCR) characteristic. When the MOSFET's junction temperature exceeds 150°C, the sensor places a short circuit across the gate and source, thereby shutting the MOSFET off. To reset the device, you bring the gate to 0V, then reapply the gate signal.

The BTS Series of temperature-protected MOSFETs covers the range from 50V at 12, 14, 25, 27, and 58A; and 60V at 24A. The 50V/58A device comes in a TO-218 package; all the others are housed in TO-220 packages. In addition to these n-channel units, a 50V/8A p-channel device in a TO-220 package is available.

Finally, although they're somewhat beyond the scope of this report (because they're ICs, and not discrete devices or assemblies thereof), some "smart" power devices are worthy of mention. The BTS412A from Siemens and the MPC1510 from Motorola, for example, are 30V/12A high-side power switches that incorporate such features as short-circuit and overtemperature protection and a charge-pump circuit to provide gate drive for the output stage.

For motor control, medium-frequency (50 kHz or so) switching power supplies, and other applications requiring a low-loss switch, IGBTs (insulated-gate bipolar transistors) are a viable alternative to bipolar transistors and power MOSFETs. Their MOS-like input characteristics and bipolar-like output traits would seem to make them attractive indeed to designers.

However, their slow fall times (several microseconds) and their propensity to latch when overcurrent conditions occur have seemingly proved an impediment to their popularity in the marketplace.

Well, they're improving, and the improvements are coming from companies outside of the original IGBT three (GE with its IGT, RCA with its COMFET, and Motorola with its GEMFET). The companies that are announcing the improved products are International Rectifier, SGS-Thomson, Philips-Amperex, and IXYS.

IR's recent IRG Series, for example, is a 600V/11 to 30A family that carries on the company's policy of specifying avalanche energy (as high as 100 and 12.5 mJ nonrepetitive and repetitive, respectively) in unclamped inductive-switching situations. Housed in a TO-220 package, the parts dissipate 74W and exhibit 3V max saturation voltage at rated current. The fall time is a respectable 420 nsec typ. The IRGBC20, -30, and -40 spec current ratings (at 25°C) of 11, 18, and 30A, respectively, and cost $3.60, $5.10, and $9.40 (1000). Also watch for IR's imminent announcement of the industry's first 1200V IGBT.

Also extending its IGBT voltage ratings is IXYS, which now offers 1000V units. Housed in TO-247 packages, the parts spec 25°C currents of 20, 40, and 50A. The fall time is 500 nsec typ, 1 µsec max. The 40A IXGH20N100A and 50A IXGH25N100A come in TO-247 packages and cost $9.98 and $14.98 (1000). The 20A IXGP10N100A, in a TO-220 package, costs $4.99 (1000). The company also offers 800 and 900V versions of the devices.

As with its power-MOSFET line, IXYS offers high-density IGBTs, dubbed MegaMOS IGTs. These parts have higher current-handling specs than those of the company's standard line of IGBTs. For example, the 600V IXGH40N60A handles 75A (by comparison, the IXGH30N60A offers 60A). The fall time is 0.8 µsec, and the saturation voltage is 3.2V at rated current. Housed in a TO-247 package, the device costs $15.84 (10).

Both IR and IXYS claim their IGBTs provide latch-free operation. That claim is substantiated by the data sheets, which guarantee enormous peak-current capabilities for the devices. For instance, IXYS's IXGH40N60A IGBT can withstand 150A at a 150°C junction temperature without latching. And IR's 600V family specs 72A peak-current capability.

Also housed in a TO-220 package, SGS-Thomson's STHI Series has ratings of 500V/7A and 500V/10A. The STHI07N50 and STHI10N50 spec a 2.7V max saturation voltage at rated current, and a 1.5-µsec max fall time. Finally, although details are sketchy, Philips-Amperex has an IGBT family in the offing. The BUK800 family will comprise 500, 800, and 1000V devices, and will be available in various packages.

New packages proliferate

Just a couple of years ago, MOSFET makers had a very limited list of options for packaging their high-power devices. The list included the hermetic TO-3 (which has since been renamed "TO-204" for reasons unknown), the plastic TO-218 and TO-247 (also called

TO-3P) for high-wattage devices, and the venerable TO-220 for medium-power chips. Unfortunately, the only workable hermetic package was the bulky, difficult-to-mount TO-3.

Now, the situation has changed dramatically. Hermetically sealed equivalents exist for both the TO-247 and the TO-220. The TO-258 replaces the TO-218 (or TO-247), and the TO-257 is a hermetic TO-220. Another hermetic package, the TO-254, lies between the TO-257 and TO-258 in terms of dimensions. In addition to these standard package types, several manufacturers have developed special packages to accommodate their dies. Especially striking is the advent of very large, high-current packages that accept very large dies or multiple chips.

Consider, for example, Advanced Power Technology's Mighty MOS package, also called the F-Pack. This 4-lead, isolated package handles 595W (the nonisolated TO-3 is limited to about 250 or 300W). As a bonus, the F-Pack has an enormous cavity that accommodates chips whose total area exceeds 1 in². Another large hermetic package is IXYS's Z-Pac, which occupies roughly the same area that a TO-3 package does. This 300W housing has five axial leads that egress from opposing edges of the package. Another example of power packaging is SGS-Thomson's IsoTop, which also occupies about as much space as a TO-3 does. It holds as many as four chips and accommodates currents as high as 100A. Philips-Amperex also produces power products in the IsoTop.

A specialist in plastic packaging, Motorola offers its MOSFETs in the small, surface-mountable D-Pack.

This package measures about 240×260 mils and accepts chips as large as 112×112 mils. Although it's much smaller than the TO-220, the D-Pack can dissipate nearly 80% as much power. IR also produces a wide range of MOSFETs in the D-Pack. Another plastic package from Motorola is the isolated, metal-backed IcePack. This 12-lead package accommodates multiple chips for such applications as H-bridge drivers (for example, the MPM3002 H-bridge power module).

Motorola is also making progress with its hermetic packaging. The MO-78 is a 5-pin hermetic package that resembles the TO-257 and TO-258. And, in a symbiotic relationship with Omnirel, a hybrid-circuit manufacturer and packaging specialist, Motorola is developing a larger version of the D-Pack—a surface-mountable replacement for the TO-220. Further collaboration with Omnirel will help Motorola expand its penetration of the military/high-reliability MOSFET market. This collaboration involves standard TO-257 and TO-258 packages, as well as large, multipin packages for power hybrids.

Finally, note that virtually all the companies mentioned here are producing power modules. These modules combine power-MOSFET chips, rectifiers, and other devices in such configurations as half or full H-bridges. Omnirel takes power-module manufacture one step further by hermetically sealing all its large power packages. Gentron is another company that produces high-power, hermetically sealed modules; it also makes a broad line of large plastic power modules. Yet another manufacturer is ABB Semiconductor (formerly Brown Boveri), which combines IGBTs, for example, in sextuples in a large plastic package for a 3-phase motor drive.

"Die" and other atrocities

How many times have you seen the word "die" used as a plural? "Company X offers a full range of power MOSFET die," people have been heard to say. Well, the plural of the singular word "die" is "dies." To point out this incorrect usage might seem like nitpicking, but I'm convinced that there are those among EDN's readership who object to our industry's systematic massacre of the English language. After all, would you say "I bought three new shirt last week"?

Consider, for example, "verbizing"—the art of creating new verbs from nouns. (Of course, there's no such word as "to verbize;" it's the editorial world's contribution to the massacre.) In the electronics industry, verbizing is rampant: "You can input

the signal to pin 1, you can interface the data to the bus, you can leverage the stock deal—there's an inductive load, let's freewheel-diode the output." Sometimes it's easier to use such nouns as verbs, and difficult to come up with the correct equivalent phrase, but that's no excuse for incorrect grammar.

Finally, note the industry's propensity for obfuscation, the fine art of using jargon either to hide the fact that you don't know what you're talking about, or to make sure the reader or listener will never be able to figure out what you're trying to say. This art—born, nurtured, and perfected in Washington, DC—is catching on like wildfire in high-tech circles. The following example is taken from an interview

that appeared in another publication (we'll leave it unnamed here):

Q: Can you give us an example of how such total integration might be achieved using expert systems?
A: Let's look at a hypothetical greenfield situation. To begin with, the integration process will have to be both top-down and bottom-up. In other words, it will involve incremental expansion of the corporate-level knowledge infrastructure at the same time that individual expert systems are being developed and put on-line to provide productivity solutions at the level of the component life-cycle phases.

I rest my case.—BT

24 Amplifier has infinite time constant

Effectively infinite time constant

This ingenious pulse comparator circuit uses integrated positive feedback to enable it to cope with input pulses of any duration. It also provides some hysteresis, to assist in noise rejection.

M U Khan
Systronics, Ahmedabad, India

An ac-coupled pulse amplifier built around an ECL triple line receiver is shown in the **figure**. Transistors Q_1 and Q_2 form a high-impedance preamplifier; Q_3 and Q_4 constitute an ECL-to-TTL translator. The usual limitation of this type of circuit is its inability to faithfully reproduce pulses of very long duration, because of the finite time constant R_1C_1. Feedback through resistor R_F, however, remedies the problem by suitably controlling the amplifier's threshold.

Once the pulse's positive leading edge crosses the threshold, the feedback lowers the threshold below the signal's average value. This done, only the negative trailing edge can cross the new threshold. The circuit thus faithfully amplifies a pulse of infinitely long duration. The feedback poses no problem for short-duration pulses—in fact, it helps in discriminating against the base-line noise of low-duty-cycle pulses. It might be necessary to initialize the threshold for these pulses, but thereafter the circuit automatically tracks all duty-cycle variations. Note that R_FC_2 should be less than $0.1R_1C_1$.

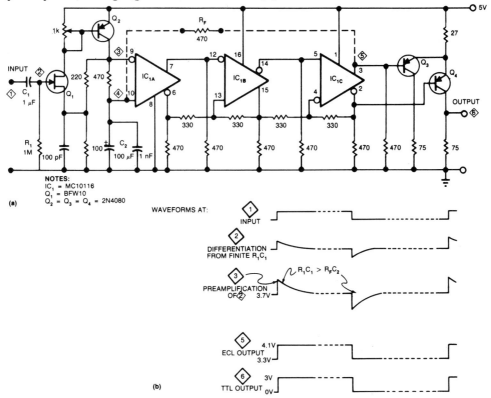

Amplify pulses of any duration with this ECL-based circuit. It uses feedback to set the amplifier's threshold so that only the negative trailing edge of the input pulse triggers the amplifier's threshold.

25 Voltage divider switch adds range to DPM

Accuracy maintained

Here is another brilliantly simple idea. It lets you use solid state switches to select ranges on a DPM, without incurring inaccuracies due to switch resistance on the more extreme division ratios.

Don Sherman
Maxim, Sunnyvale, CA

You can extend the range of many currently available digital-panel-meter (DPM) chips and modules by adding a voltage divider switch to the DPM's input (**Fig 1**). If you use mechanical switches, the contacts' resistance won't affect the divider's ratio. However, if you use solid-state switches, you need to include the switch resistance in your voltage-divider equations. Unfortunately, an analog switch's exact resistance varies with temperature and the power-supply voltage.

Fig 1's circuit overcomes this problem by using the differential inputs of the DPM to remove the analog switch's IR drop which is in series with the divider resistor. The second analog switch in each pair carries no current. This switch connects the INPUT LO pin to the bottom of the precision voltage-divider resistor, and causes the divider to ignore the voltage drop in the companion, current-carrying switch.

You must supply the analog switch, in this case the DG509A analog multiplexer, with both a positive and negative voltage if you want it to pass positive- and negative-going voltages. **Fig 1** generates the negative voltage using the MAX138's internal charge-pump; the V⁻ pin can supply as much as 0.5 mA. You can build the precision divider with discrete 1% resistors, or purchase a precision resistor network. As **Fig 1** shows, you can control the voltage-divider switch by using a microprocessor and the select pins of the multiplexer.

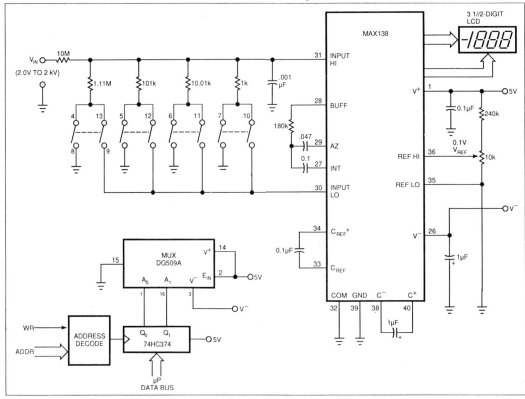

Fig 1—To extend the range of a digital-panel-meter chip or module, you can add a precision voltage divider to the device's input.

26 Trouble shooting is more effective with the right philosophy

> ## Circuit not working? Here's how to tackle it
>
> This was the first in a series of a dozen articles by that well-known circuit doyen, Bob Pease of National Semiconductor Corporation. I found some of them more interesting than others, but I have certainly saved the lot. They generated a raft of interesting correspondence, some of which was published in *EDN*, May 10 1990. The series of articles have been revised and published as another book in the EDN series: *Troubleshooting Analog Circuits*.

Robert A Pease, *National Semiconductor Corp*

If you recall that the most *boring* class in school was a philosophy class, and you think this article will be boring that way, well, WRONG. We are going to talk about the real world and examples of how we can recover from mistakes, goofs, and all the nasty problems the world tries to inflict on us. We are talking about Trouble with a capital T, and how to overcome it.

Here at National Semiconductor, we decided a couple of years ago to write a book about switching power supplies. Within the applications and design groups, nearly all of the engineers volunteered to write chapters, and I volunteered to do a chapter on troubleshooting. At present, the status of the book is unclear. But, the troubleshooting chapter is going strong, and EDN readers are the first to benefit.

Although I am probably not the world's best analog-circuit troubleshooter, I am fairly good; and I just happened to be the guy who sat down and put all these stories in writing. (Ed Note: *For a better insight into how Bob happened to tackle this assignment, see **box**, "Who is Bob Pease, anyway?"*) Furthermore, the techniques you need to troubleshoot a switching power supply apply, in general, to a lot of other analog circuits and may even be useful for some basic digital hardware. You don't have to build switchers to find this article useful—if you design or build any analog circuits, this article is for you.

Perhaps EDN readers who are more knowledgeable than I am about computers, microprocessors, and software will contact the editors about contributing articles on troubleshooting those types of products. If you don't have enough troubleshooting ideas to produce a full-length article but do have some good tips that you don't see in this series, send them to the Design Ideas editor at EDN. No doubt, EDN will print some of them. (Be sure to include a copy of the design entry blank included in each issue's Design Ideas section.)

Why are we interested in troubleshooting? Because even the best engineers take on projects whose requirements are so difficult and challenging that the circuits don't work as expected—at least not the first time. I don't have data on switching regulators; but I read in an industry study that when disk drives are manufactured, the fraction that fails to function when power is first applied ranges from 20 to 70%. Of course, this fraction may occasionally fall as low as 1% and rise as high as 100%. But, on the average, production engineers and technicians must be prepared to repair 20, 40, or 60% of these complex units.

Switching-regulated power supplies can also be quite complex. If you manufacture them in batches of 100, you shouldn't be surprised to find some batches with 12 pieces that require troubleshooting and other batches that have 46 such pieces. The troubleshooting may, as you well know, be tough with a new product whose bugs haven't been worked out. But, it can be even tougher when the design is old and the parts it now uses aren't quite like the ones you once could buy. Troubleshooting can be tougher still when there is little documentation describing how the product is supposed to work and the designer isn't around anymore. If there's ever a time when troubleshooting isn't needed, it's just a temporary miracle.

You might avoid troubleshooting . . . for a while

And, what if you decide that troubleshooting isn't necessary? You may find that your first batch of products has only three or four failures, so you decide that you don't need to worry. The second batch has a 12% failure rate, and all of the rejects have the same symptoms as those of the first batch. The next three batches have failure rates of 23, 49, and 76%, respectively. When you finally take the time to study the problems, you will find that they would have been relatively easy to fix if only you had started a couple of months earlier. That's what Murphy's Law can do to you if you try to slough off your troubleshooting chores—we have all seen it happen.

If you have a bunch of analog circuits that you have to troubleshoot, well, why don't you just look up the troubleshooting procedures in a book? The question is excellent, and the answer is very simple: Almost nothing has been written about the troubleshooting of such circuits. The best write-up I have found is a couple pages in a book by Jiri Dostal (**Ref 1**). He gives some basic procedures for looking for trouble in a fairly straightforward little circuit: a voltage reference/regulator. As far as Dostal goes, he does quite well. But, he does not offer much advice, and there is much to explain beyond what he has written. Another book that has several pages about the philosophy of troubleshooting is by John I Smith (**Ref 2**). Smith explains some of the foibles of wishing you had designed a circuit correctly when you find that it doesn't work "right." What's missing, though, is general information.

You'll probably use general-purpose test equipment

What equipment can you buy for troubleshooting? I'll cover that subject in considerable detail in the next installment. For now, let me observe that if you have several million dollars worth of circuits to troubleshoot, you should consider buying a $100,000 tester. Of course, for that price you only get a machine at the low end of the line. And, after you buy the machine, you have to invest a lot of time in fixturing and software before it can help you. Yes, you can buy a $90 tester that helps locate short circuits on a pc board; but, in the price range between $90 and $100,000, there isn't a lot of specialized troubleshooting equipment available. If you want an oscilloscope, you have to buy a general-purpose oscilloscope; if you want a DVM, it will be a general-purpose DVM. Now, it's true that some scopes and some DVMs are more suitable for troubleshooting than others (and I will discuss the differences in the next part of this series), but, to a large extent, you have to depend on your wits.

Your wits: very handy to use—your wits—but, then what? One of my favorite quotes from Jiri Dostal's book says that troubleshooting should resemble fencing more closely than it resembles wrestling. When your troubleshooting efforts seem most like wrestling in the mud with an implacable opponent (or component), then you are probably not using the right approach. Do you have the right tools, and are you using them correctly? I'll discuss that in the next issue. Do you know how a failed component will affect your circuit, and do you know what the most likely failure modes are? I'll deal with components in subsequent installments. Ah, but do you know how to think about Trouble? That is to-day's main lesson.

One of the first things you might do is make a list of all the things that could be causing the problem. This idea can be good—up to a point. I am an aficionado of stories about steam engines, and this story comes from the book, *Master Builders of Steam* (**Ref 3**). A class of new 3-cylinder 4-6-0 (four little wheels in front of the drive wheels, six drive wheels, no little wheels in back) steam engines had just been designed by British designer W A Stanier, and they were "perfect stinkers. They simply would not steam." So the engines' designers made a list of all the things that could go wrong and a list of all the things that could not be at fault; they set the second list aside.

The designers specified changes to be made to each new engine in hopes of solving the problem: "Teething troubles bring modifications, . . . and each engine can carry a different set of modifications." The manufacturing managers "shuddered as these modified drawings seemed to pour in from Derby (site of the design facility—the Drawing Office), continually upsetting progress in the works." (Lots of fun for the manufacturing guys, eh?)

In the end, the problem took a long time to find because it was on the list of "things that couldn't go wrong." Allow me to quote the deliciously horrifying words from the text: "Teething troubles always present these two difficulties: that many of the clues are very subjective and that the 'confidence trick' applies. By the latter I mean when a certain factor is exonerated as trouble-free based on a sound premise, and everyone therefore looks elsewhere for the trouble: whereas in fact, the premise is not sound and the exonerated factor is guilty. In Stanier's case this factor was low superheat. So convinced was he that a low degree of superheat was adequate that the important change to increased superheater area was delayed far longer than necessary. There were some very sound men in the Experimental Section of the Derby Loco Drawing Office at that time, but they were young . . . and their voice was only dimly heard. Some of their quite painstaking superheater test results were disbelieved." But, of course nothing like that ever happened to anybody you know—right?

Another thing you can do is ask advice only of "experts." After all, only an expert knows how to solve a difficult problem—right? Wrong! Sometimes, a major reason you can't find your problem is because you are too close to it—you are blinded by your familiarity. You may get excellent results by simply consulting one or two of your colleagues who are not as familiar with your design; they may make a good guess at a solution to your problem. Often a technician can make a wise (or lucky) guess as easily as can a savvy engineer. When that happens, be sure to remember who saved your neck. Some people are not just lucky—they may have a real knack for solving tricky problems, for finding clues, and for deducing what is causing the trouble. Friends like these can be more valuable than gold. (For more on clues, see **box**, "Learn to recognize clues.")

At National Semiconductor, we usually submit a newly designed circuit layout to a review by our peers. I invite everybody to try to win a Beverage of Their Choice by catching a real mistake in my circuit. It's fun because if I give away a few pitchers of brew, I

Learn to recognize clues

There are four basic questions that you or I should ask when we are brought in to do troubleshooting on someone else's project:

- Did it *ever* work right?
- What are the symptoms that tell you it's not working right?
- When did it start working badly or stop working?
- What other symptoms showed up just before, just after, or at the same time as the failure?

As you can plainly see, the clues you get from the answers to these questions might easily solve the problem right away; if not, they may eventually get you out of the woods. So even if a failure occurs on your own project, you should ask these four questions—as explicitly as possible—of yourself or your technician or whoever was working on the project. Similarly, if your roommate called you to ask for a lift because the car had just quit in the middle of a freeway, you would ask whether anything else happened or if the car just died. If you're told that the headlights seemed to be getting dimmer and dimmer, that's a *clue*.

The telephone is sometimes a good troubleshooting tool; at other times, however, it is just another wretched part of the problem.

When you ask these four questions, make sure to record the answers in a notebook. As an old test manager I used to work with would tell his technicians, "When you are taking data, if you see something funny, record the amount of funny." A few significant notes can save you hours of work. Clues are where you find them; they should be saved and savored.

Ask not only these questions but also any other questions suggested by the answers. For example, a neophyte product engineer will sometimes come to see me with a batch of ICs that have a terrible yield at some particular test. I'll ask if the parts failed

any other tests, and I'll hear that nobody knows because the tester doesn't continue to test a part after it detects a failure. A more experienced engineer would have already retested the devices in the RUN ALL TESTS mode.

Likewise, if *you* are asking another person for advice, you should have all the facts laid out straight—at least in your head—so that you can be clear and not add to the confusion. I've worked with a few people who tell me one thing and a minute later start telling me the opposite. Nothing makes me lose my temper faster! Nobody can help you troubleshoot effectively if you aren't sure whether the circuit is running from +12V or ±12V and you start making contradictory statements.

And, if I ask when the device started working badly, *don't* tell me, "At 3:25 PM." I'm looking for clues, such as, "About two minutes after I put it in the 125°C oven," or, "Just after I connected the 4-Ω load." So just as we can all learn a little more about troubleshooting, we can all learn to watch for the clues that are invaluable for fault diagnosis.

---

get some of my dumb mistakes corrected—mistakes that I might not have found until a much later, more painful, and more expensive stage. Furthermore, we all get some education. And, you can never predict who will find the little mistakes or the occasional real killer mistake.

You can make Murphy's Law work for you

Murphy's Law is quite likely to attack even our best designs: "If anything can go wrong, it will." But, I can make Murphy's Law work for me. For example, according to Murphy's Law, if I drive around with a fire extinguisher, I will make sure that I never have a fire in my car. When you first hear it, the idea sounds dumb. But, if I'm the kind of meticulous person who carries a fire extinguisher, I may also be neat and refuse to do the dumb things that permit fires to start. Similarly, when designing a circuit I leave extra safety margins in areas where I cannot surely predict how the circuit will perform. When I design a breadboard,

I might tell the technician, "Leave 20% extra space for this part because I'm not sure that it will work without modifications. And, please leave extra space around this resistor and this capacitor because I might have to change those values." When I design an IC, I leave little pads of metal at strategic points on the chip's surface, so that I can probe the critical nodes as easily as possible. To facilitate probing when working with 2-layer metal, I bring nodes up from the first metal through vias to the second metal. Sometimes I leave holes in my Vapox passivation to facilitate probing dice.

The subject of testability has often been addressed for large digital circuits, but the underlying ideas of design for testability are important regardless of the type of circuit you are designing. You can avoid a lot of trouble by thinking about what can go wrong and how to keep it from going wrong before the ensuing problems lunge at you. By planning for every possibility, you can profit from your awareness of Murphy's

Law. Now, clearly, you won't think of *every* possibility. (Remember, it was something that *couldn't* go wrong that caused the problems with Stanier's locomotives.) But, a little forethought can certainly minimize the number of problems you have to deal with.

Recently, we had so many nagging little troubles with band-gap reference circuits at National, that I decided (unilaterally) to declare myself, "Czar of Band Gaps." The main rules were that (**a**) all successful band-gap circuits should be registered with the Czar so that we could keep a log book of successful circuits; (**b**) all unsuccessful circuits, their reasons for failure, and the fixes for the failures should likewise be logged in with the Czar so that we could avoid repeating old mistakes; and (**c**) all new circuits should be submitted to the Czar to allow him to spot any old errors. So far, we think we've found over 50% of the possible errors, and we're gaining. In addition, we have added Czars for start-up circuits and for trim circuits, and we are considering other czardoms. It's a bit of a game, but it's also a serious business to use a game to try to prevent expensive errors.

I haven't always been a good troubleshooter, but my "baptism of fire" occurred quite a few years ago. I had designed a group of modular data converters. We had to ship 525 of them, and some foolish person had bought only 535 pc boards. When less than half of the units worked, I found myself in the troubleshooting business because nobody else could imagine how to repair them. I discovered that I needed my best-triggering scope and my best DVM. I burned a lot of midnight oil. I got half-a-dozen copies each of the schematic and the board layout. I scribbled notes on them—of what the dc voltages ought to be, what the correct ac waveforms looked like, and where I could best probe the key waveforms. I made little lists of, "If this frequency is twice as fast as normal, look for Q47 to be damaged, but if the frequency is $\frac{1}{10}$ normal, look for a short on bus B." I learned where to look for solder shorts, hairline opens, cold-soldered joints, and intermittents. I diagnosed the problems and sent each unit back for repair with a neat label of what to change. When they came back, did they work? Some did—and some still had another level or two of problems. That's the Onion Syndrome: You peel off one layer, and you cry; you peel off another layer and cry some more . . . By the time I was done, I had fixed all but four of the units, and I had gotten myself one hell of a good education about troubleshooting.

After I found a spot of trouble, what did I do about it? First of all, I made some notes to make sure that the problem really was fixed when the offending part was changed. Then I sent the units to a *good, neat* technician who did precise repair work—much better than a slob like me would do. Lastly, I sent memos to the manufacturing and QC departments to make sure that the types of parts that had proven troublesome were not used again, and I confirmed the changes with ECOs (engineering change orders). It is important to get the paperwork scrupulously correct, or the alligators will surely circle back to vex you again.

I once heard of a similar situation where an insidious problem was causing nasty reliability problems with a batch of modules. The technician had struggled to find the solution for days. Finally, when the technician went out for lunch, the design engineer went to work on the problem. When the technician came back from lunch, the designer told him, "I found the problem; it's a mismatch between Q17 and R18. Write up the ECO, and when I get back from lunch I'll sign it." Unfortunately, the good rapport between the engineer and the technician broke down: there was some miscommunication. The technician got confused and wrote up the ECO with an incorrect version of what should be changed. When the engineer came back from lunch, he initialled the ECO without really reading it and left for a two-week vacation.

When he came back, the modules had all been "fixed," potted, and shipped, and were starting to fail out in the field. A check of the ECO revealed the mistake—too late. The company went bankrupt. It's a true story and a painful one. Don't get sloppy with your paperwork; don't let it happen to you.

Troubleshooting by phone—a tough challenge

These days, I do quite a bit of troubleshooting by telephone. When my phone rings, I never know if a customer will be asking for simple information or submitting a routine application problem, a tough problem, or an insoluble problem. Often I can give advice just off the top of my head because I know how to fix what is wrong. At other times, I have to study a while before I call back. Sometimes, the circuit is so complicated that I tell the customer to mail or transmit the schematic to me. On rare occasions, the situation is so hard to analyze that I tell the customer to put the circuit in a box with the schematic and a list of the symptoms and ship it to me.

Sometimes the problem is just a misapplication. Sometimes parts have been blown out and I have to guess what situation caused the overstress. Here's an example: In June, a manufacturer of dental equipment complained of an unacceptable failure rate on LM317 regulators. After a good deal of discussion, I asked, "Where did these failures occur?" Answer: North Dakota. "When did they start to occur?" Answer: In February. I put two and two together and realized that the climate in a dentist's office in North Dakota in February is about as dry as it can be and is conducive to very high electrostatic potentials. The LM317 is normally safe against electrostatic potentials as high as 3 or 4 kV, but walking across a carpeted floor in North Dakota in February can generate even higher voltages. To make matters worse, the speed-control rheostat for this dental instrument was right out in the handle. The wiper and one end of the rheostat were wired directly to the LM317's ADJUST pin; the other end of the rheostat was connected to ground by way of a 1-kΩ resistor located near the IC.

The problem was easily solved by placing the resistor in series with the IC's ADJUST pin and relocating it to the instrument's handle. By moving the resistor and connecting the rheostat wiper to ground, much less current would take the path to the ADJUST pin and the diffused resistors on the chip would not be damaged or zapped by the current surges.

A similar situation occurs when you get a complaint from Boston in June, "Your op amps don't meet spec for bias current." The solution is surprisingly simple: Usually a good scrub with soap and water works better than any other solvent to clean off the residual contaminants that cause leakage under humid conditions.

When computers replace troubleshooters, look out

Now, let's think—what *needs* troubleshooting? Circuits? Television receivers? Cars? People? Surely doctors have a lot of troubleshooting to do—they listen to symptoms and try to figure out the solution. What is the natural temptation? Letting a computer do all the work! After all, a computer is quite good at listening to complaints and symptoms, asking wise questions, and proposing a wise diagnosis. Such a computer system is called an expert system—part of the general field of artificial intelligence. But, I am still in favor of *genuine* intelligence.

I won't argue that the computer isn't a natural for this job; it will probably be cost effective, and it won't be absent minded. But, I am definitely nervous because if computers do all the routine work, soon there will be nobody left to do the thinking when the computer gives up and admits it is stumped. I sure hope we don't let the computers leave the smart troubleshooting people without jobs, whether the object is circuits or people.

My concern is shared by Dr. Nicholas Lembo, the author of a study on how physicians make diagnoses, which was published in the *New England Journal of Medicine*. He recently told the *Los Angeles Times*, "With the advent of all the new technology, physicians aren't all that much interested (in bedside medicine) because they can order a $300 to $400 test to tell them something they could have found by listening." An editorial accompanying the study commented sadly:

Who is Bob Pease, anyway?

For the record, Bob Pease is a senior scientist in industrial linear-IC design at National Semiconductor Corp in Santa Clara CA; he has worked at National since 1976. He is also one of the best-known analog-circuit designers in the world—he's been creating practical, producible analog products for fun (his) and profit (both his and his employers') and writing about analog topics for over a quarter of a century.

As you might expect, though, there's a lot more to Bob Pease than his impressive credentials. Following untrodden paths to discover where they lead is one of Bob's avocations. He's done it on foot, on skis, and on a bicycle— sometimes by himself and sometimes with his wife and two sons—mostly along abandoned railroad beds throughout the US. Aside from the peace and quiet and the thrill of the journey itself, the reward for these wanderings is observing vistas of America that few people have seen. The curiosity that motivates Bob's exploration of old railroad routes is reflected in many of his other activities both at and away from work.

For example, another of Bob's hobbies is designing voltage-to-frequency converters (VFCs). Most people who design VFCs do

it as part of a job. Although Bob sometimes designs VFCs for use in National products, he often does it just for fun and because he finds the activity educational and challenging. A while ago, on such a lark, he put together a VFC that used vacuum tubes. The device proved that the company where he spent the first 14 years of his career, George A Philbrick Researches, (now Teledyne-Philbrick of Dedham, MA) could have gone into the VFC business in 1953—eight years before Pease received his BSEE from MIT. Fifteen years after he designed it, one of Bob's first

solid-state VFCs, the 4701, continues to sell well for Teledyne-Philbrick.

Pease pontificates prolifically

Bob also loves to write—he clearly enjoys communicating to others the wisdom he has acquired through his work. He has published 46 magazine articles (not including this series) and holds eight patents. Bob takes great delight in seeing his ideas embodied in the work of others. For example, one of his proudest accomplishments is a seismic preamplifier that he designed for an aerospace company during his coffee break. After many years of service, the amplifier is still at work on the moon, amplifying and telemetering moonquakes.

National has taken advantage of Bob's penchant for providing ideas that others can use. In his role of senior scientist, Bob's responsibilities—besides designing voltage references and regulators, temperature sensors, and VFC ICs—include consulting with coworkers, fielding applications questions that have stumped other engineers, and reviewing colleagues' designs. In a similar vein, Bob is a long-time EDN contributing editor who reviews design-idea submissions in the analog area.—*Dan Strassberg*

"The present trend . . . may soon leave us with a whole new generation of young physicians who have no confidence in their own ability to make worthwhile bedside diagnoses." Troubleshooting is still an art, and it is important to encourage those artists.

No problems? No problem . . . just wait

Now, let's skip ahead and presume we have all the necessary tools and the right receptive attitude. What else do we need? What is the last missing ingredient? That reminds me of the little girl in Sunday School who was asked what you have to do to obtain forgiveness of sin. She shyly replied, "First you have to sin." So, to do troubleshooting, first you have to have some trouble. But, that's usually not a problem; just wait a few hours, and you'll have plenty. Murphy's Law implies that if you are not prepared for trouble, you will get a lot of it. Conversely, if you have done all your homework, you may avoid most of the possible trouble.

I've tried to give you some insights on the philosophy of how to troubleshoot. Don't believe that you can get help on a given problem from only one specific person. In any particular case, you can't predict who might provide the solution. Conversely, when your buddy is in trouble and needs help, give it a try—you could turn out to be a hero. And, even if you don't guess correctly, when you do find out what the solution is, you'll have added another tool to your bag of tricks.

References

1. Dostal, Jiri, *Operational Amplifiers*, Elsevier Scientific, The Netherlands, 1981.
2. Smith, John I, *Modern Operational Circuit Design*, John Wiley & Sons, New York, NY, 1971.
3. Bulleid, H A V, *Master Builders of Steam*, Ian Allan Ltd, London, UK, 1963, pgs 146-147.

27 Op amp provides phase-locked loop

Op amp PLL

Lab bench audio sinewave generators typically include a sync input, by means of which the output frequency can be locked to a given frequency low level signal, if manually tuned to approximately the same frequency. In the case of a squarewave generator, the locking action can be described in terms of a phase-locked loop, as this article shows. Note that if a squarewave output is desired, the mean DC level at the input must be ground: alternatively, the input may be DC blocked.

Ralph Wilbur
Vega Electronics, El Monte, CA

Equaling the performance of a classical phase-locked loop in some applications, this oscillator is frequency-modulated directly by the input signal's phase relation to the oscillator output, obviating the usual separate phase comparator, integrator and linear voltage-controlled oscillator.

To picture this "loop," first consider the operation of the basic oscillator (**Fig 1**). The op-amp output is a square wave formed by R_F charging C_F to the hysteresis voltage at the noninverting input. When the inverting input crosses this noninverting input, the output changes state accordingly; R_F must now charge C_F in the opposite direction. When the output's state changes, the voltage at the noninverting input moves in the same direction—it takes time for the voltage on C_F to cross it again. The time for two such crossings constitutes one cycle period.

Applying an input signal equal to the oscillator's free-running (center) frequency at R_{IN} (**Fig 2a**) aligns the output's phase relation so that the input's influence on the charging of C_F half aids the output (in phase) and half hinders it (out of phase). The net effect is zero. If the input frequency decreases, the input tends to lag the center-frequency phase (**Fig 2b**), hindering the charging and resulting in a corresponding decrease in output frequency. With an increase in input frequency, the phase tends to lead, pulling the output frequency with it. A 90° input lead or lag exerts the maximum influence; beyond 90° the influence cannot hold phase lock.

Phase lock occurs within one cycle and has no overshoot. The phase settles to equilibrium with a time constant inversely proportional to lock range. The lock range equals the capture range and is proportional to input amplitude;

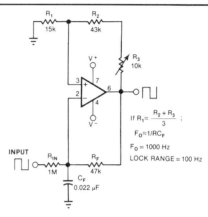

If $R_1 \approx \dfrac{R_2 + R_3}{3}$;

$F_0 \approx 1/RC_F$

$F_0 = 1000$ Hz

LOCK RANGE = 100 Hz

Fig 1—This oscillator circuit *is frequency-modulated by the phase relation of its input signal to its output signal.*

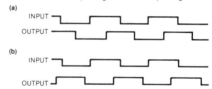

Fig 2—An input signal *of the same frequency as the oscillator's frequency aligns the phase relationships so that the net effect is zero (a); decreasing the input frequency hinders C_F's charging, causing a decrease in the oscillator's frequency (b).*

it varies as an inverse function of R_{IN}.

Response to odd harmonics in this circuit is the same as to the fundamental, but response to odd subharmonics drops off in lock range in proportion to the square of the frequency.

Response to waveforms other than a square wave is similar, but generally weaker. For a given frequency and lock range, the normalized settling time constant is 1 for square waves, 1.5 for sine waves and 2 for triangle waves.

Temperature stability, from −30 to +70°C, is better than 0.2% of F_0 for film resistors, a ceramic C_F and a CA3130 op amp. This variation can be largely compensated by a diode network in place of R_1 or R_F.

28 Failure analyses and testing yield reliable products

Enhancing product reliability

Product reliability is only achieved by attention to detail at all stages. It must be designed in from the outset, demonstrated by testing, and maintained in production by inspection and using only components from reliable manufacturers. This useful article covers all those areas and indicates the steps taken in a large company to ensure reliable products. Some of them may be beyond the reach of a small company, in which case conservative design becomes all the more important.

Arthur F Upham, *Hewlett-Packard Co*

Design guidelines developed from statistical analyses of past failures, combined with a thorough program of environmental testing during all phases of design, will help you produce a reliable, maintainable product. These analyses will alert you to some common stress factors for specific components, and they'll reveal vendors that have a history of questionable reliability. In addition, some of the standard techniques used when designing reliability into automatic test equipment can now prove useful in all fields of electronic design.

Like many companies, Hewlett-Packard has been collecting statistical data on warranty repairs for several years. Where necessary, the company has augmented these statistical failure analyses with data collected by the military, which has also been keeping failure records for many years *(MIL Handbook 217C)*. HP studied this data to identify component failures that could be associated with a part's use.

Based on an assessment of device failure modes, you can develop a rigid set of design guidelines, and you can implement procedures to ensure that the guidelines are followed. At HP, for instance, a reliability engineer is assigned to a project at the outset. This member of the engineering team verifies the design and appropriate use of components as the work progresses and serves as a resource for the design engineers.

To ensure compliance, individual engineers review their initial designs. They must fill out a computer form on every part and every circuit to make certain that the guidelines are obeyed. A computer-generated form for each component class lists a component's part number and the guidelines for that part. On the same line as a part's guidelines, the engineer must fill in the values of certain critical parameters for that part as it's used in the design. You can use these same guidelines in your design by adhering to the limits expressed in **Tables 1** through **7**. These graphs and charts are straightforward and easy to use. They show the relative failure rates of common components vs both power dissipated and ambient temperature.

Another useful aspect of failure-analysis data is the information it can provide about vendors of unreliable components. Traditionally, US companies rely on multiple sources to provide alternative parts, many of indeterminate reliability. This approach maintains many sources of supply to ensure that components are readily available to keep the production lines running.

The development of reliable vendors is another approach—one endorsed by Japanese companies. Failure analyses can reveal vendors whose products show abnormally high failure rates. You might choose to avoid these vendors and work with those showing more manageable rates. Or you can help vendors understand where their products are failing and work with them to increase reliability. HP provides this aid through instruments and analysis capabilities—scanning electron microscopes, chemical analysis, and spectroscopy, for example—that might not be readily available to vendors.

Merely following guidelines is only the first step toward producing reliable equipment. You must test and characterize each component and the entire design to verify the guidelines. HP performs environmental-stress tests at the breadboard, prototype, and pilot-run stages of a project.

Every component in a design is subjected to a stress analysis under worst-case conditions. The tests determine the maximum voltage across every capacitor, the power dissipated by every resistor, the junction temperature of every semiconductor, and the maximum current through each inductor. Proper component selection plays a major role here. Note, for example, that the reliability curves in **Table 3**'s graph vary dramatically for different types of capacitors. (On no account should you use the older, unreliable wet-slug tantalum capacitors.)

Not included in the **tables** are charts for switches,

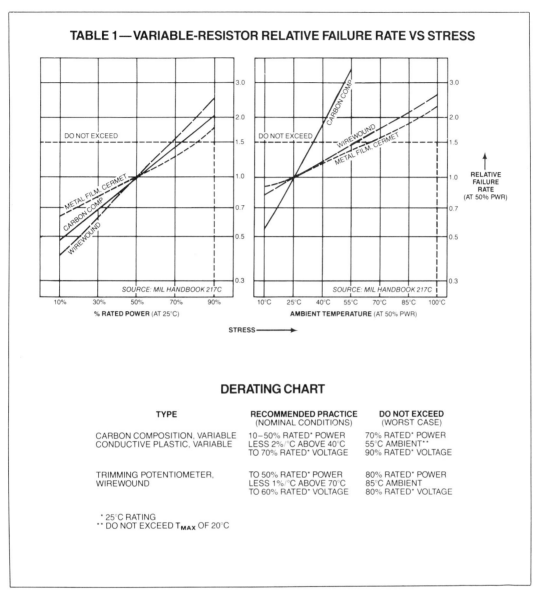

TABLE 1—VARIABLE-RESISTOR RELATIVE FAILURE RATE VS STRESS

SOURCE: MIL HANDBOOK 217C

% RATED POWER (AT 25°C)

RELATIVE FAILURE RATE (AT 50% PWR)

SOURCE: MIL HANDBOOK 217C

AMBIENT TEMPERATURE (AT 50% PWR)

STRESS ———→

DERATING CHART

TYPE	RECOMMENDED PRACTICE (NOMINAL CONDITIONS)	DO NOT EXCEED (WORST CASE)
CARBON COMPOSITION, VARIABLE CONDUCTIVE PLASTIC, VARIABLE	10–50% RATED* POWER LESS 2%/°C ABOVE 40°C TO 70% RATED* VOLTAGE	70% RATED* POWER 55°C AMBIENT** 90% RATED* VOLTAGE
TRIMMING POTENTIOMETER, WIREWOUND	TO 50% RATED* POWER LESS 1%/°C ABOVE 70°C TO 60% RATED* VOLTAGE	80% RATED* POWER 85°C AMBIENT 80% RATED* VOLTAGE

* 25°C RATING
** DO NOT EXCEED T_{MAX} OF 20°C

relays, and other electromechanical and mechanical components. No statistically valid data is available for these components; you'll have to depend on your own experience and testing.

For example, HP recently developed a more reliable version of the 8640 RF signal generator—the 8642—for ATE applications. Historically, the least reliable component in any RF instrument has been its attenuator. This presents a problem because, according to HP's research, ATE can cycle the 8642's solenoid-operated attenuator as many as 3 million times per year.

The company established a lifetime specification of 10 million cycles for attenuators used in ATE equipment. It built computer-controlled test equipment capable of cycling an attenuator and measuring its contact resis-

tance at every step at the rate of approximately a million cycles per day. The company took existing attenuator designs, stress-tested them to failure by cycling them at elevated temperatures, disassembled them to determine what failed, and then strengthened or redesigned the respective parts.

You should test all components—electronic and electromechanical—not just at room temperature, but also at your maximum specified temperature (55°C in Model 8642's case). You should then derate each component, on the basis of this worst-case analysis, to 50% of its maximum rating. The net effect is a double derating that yields components unlikely to be stressed in any way during normal operation of the product.

TABLE 2—FIXED-RESISTOR RELATIVE FAILURE RATE VS STRESS

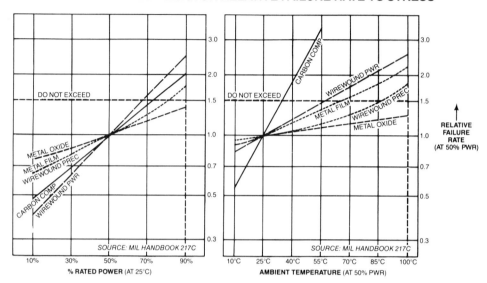

SOURCE: MIL HANDBOOK 217C

% RATED POWER (AT 25°C)

AMBIENT TEMPERATURE (AT 50% PWR)

STRESS⟶

RELATIVE FAILURE RATE (AT 50% PWR)

DERATING CHART

TYPE	RECOMMENDED PRACTICE (NOMINAL CONDITIONS)	DO NOT EXCEED (WORST CASE)
CARBON COMPOSITION FIXED	10–50% RATED* POWER LESS 2%/°C ABOVE 40°C TO 70% RATED* VOLTAGE	70% RATED* POWER** 55°C AMBIENT 90% RATED* VOLTAGE
METAL FILM, FIXED METAL FILM, NETWORK	10–50% RATED* POWER LESS 1%/°C ABOVE 70°C TO 70% RATED* VOLTAGE	80% RATED* POWER*** 85°C AMBIENT 90% RATED* VOLTAGE
METAL OXIDE, FIXED	TO 50% RATED* POWER LESS 0.5%/°C ABOVE 70°C TO 70% RATED* VOLTAGE	90% RATED* POWER 100°C AMBIENT 90% RATED* VOLTAGE
WIREWOUND, PRECISION (≤ ± 0.1%), GENERAL PURPOSE	TO 50% RATED* POWER LESS 1%/°C ABOVE 70°C TO 60% RATED* VOLTAGE	80% RATED* POWER 85°C AMBIENT 80% RATED* VOLTAGE
WIREWOUND, POWER (≥ 2W)	TO 50% RATED* POWER LESS 0.5%/°C ABOVE 55°C TO 70% RATED* VOLTAGE	70% RATED* POWER 75°C AMBIENT 90% RATED* VOLTAGE

  * 25°C RATING (MAY BE SAME AS 70°C RATING)
 ** PEAK POWER LESS THAN 30 TIMES AVERAGE RATING
*** PEAK POWER LESS THAN 10 TIMES AVERAGE RATING

TABLE 3—CAPACITOR RELATIVE FAILURE RATE VS STRESS

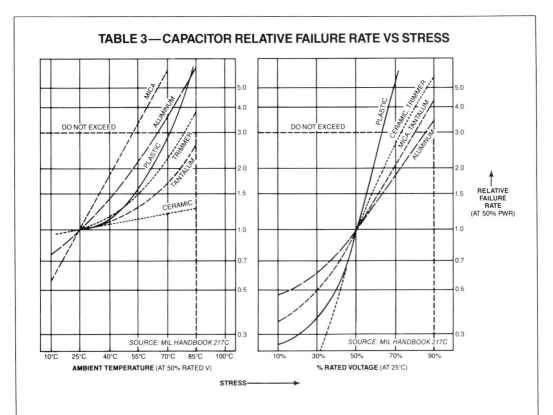

DERATING CHART

TYPE	RECOMMENDED PRACTICE (NOMINAL CONDITIONS)	DO NOT EXCEED (WORST CASE)
MICA, FIXED	TO 50% RATED* VOLTAGE LESS 2%/°C ABOVE 45°C	75% RATED* VOLTAGE 55°C AMBIENT
CERAMIC, FIXED	TO 50% RATED* VOLTAGE LESS 2%/°C ABOVE 55°C	70% RATED* VOLTAGE 80°C AMBIENT
PLASTIC FILM, FIXED (MYLAR, POLYCARBONATE, POLYPROPYLENE)	TO 40% RATED* VOLTAGE LESS 2%/°C ABOVE 55°C	60% RATED* VOLTAGE 70°C AMBIENT
ELECTROLYTIC (ALUMINUM)	20–60% RATED* VOLTAGE LESS 2%/°C ABOVE 55°C TO 1V REVERSE BIAS	80% RATED* VOLTAGE 65°C AMBIENT 1.5V REVERSE BIAS
ELECTROLYTIC (SOLID TANTALUM)	TO 50% RATED* VOLTAGE LESS 1%/°C ABOVE 55°C TO 5% REVERSE BIAS	75% RATED* VOLTAGE 80°C AMBIENT 10% REVERSE BIAS AT 25°C 5% REVERSE BIAS AT 70°C

*25°C RATING

91

TABLE 4—DIODE RELATIVE FAILURE RATE VS STRESS

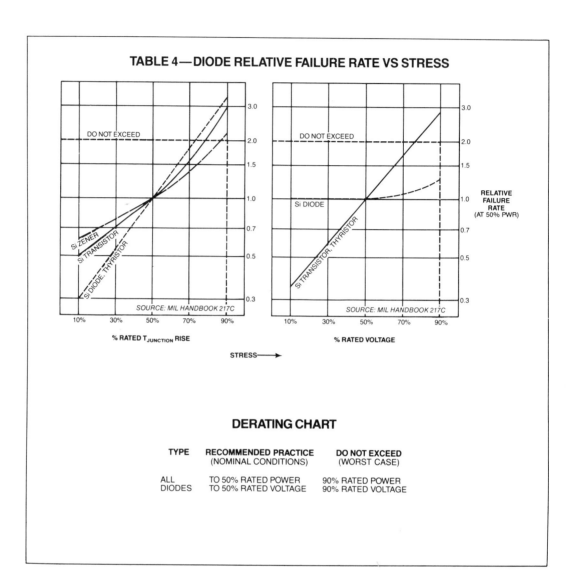

DERATING CHART

TYPE	RECOMMENDED PRACTICE (NOMINAL CONDITIONS)	DO NOT EXCEED (WORST CASE)
ALL DIODES	TO 50% RATED POWER TO 50% RATED VOLTAGE	90% RATED POWER 90% RATED VOLTAGE

TABLE 5—TRANSISTOR RELATIVE FAILURE RATE VS STRESS

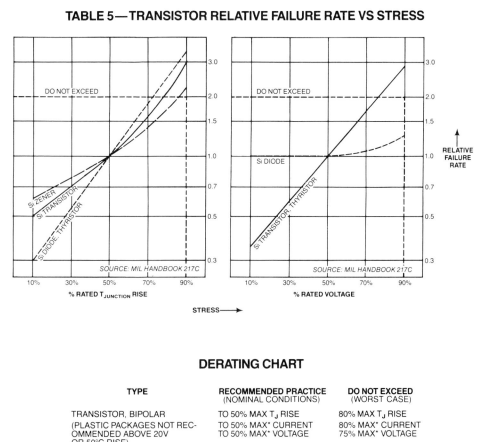

DERATING CHART

TYPE	RECOMMENDED PRACTICE (NOMINAL CONDITIONS)	DO NOT EXCEED (WORST CASE)
TRANSISTOR, BIPOLAR	TO 50% MAX T_J RISE	80% MAX T_J RISE
(PLASTIC PACKAGES NOT REC-	TO 50% MAX* CURRENT	80% MAX* CURRENT
OMMENDED ABOVE 20V	TO 50% MAX* VOLTAGE	75% MAX* VOLTAGE
OR 50°C RISE)		
TRANSISTOR, FIELD EFFECT	TO 50% MAX T_J RISE	80% MAX T_J RISE
(PLASTIC PACKAGES NOT REC-	TO 50% MAX* VOLTAGE	75% MAX* VOLTAGE
OMMENDED)		

*25°C RATING

TABLE 6—SILICON-IC RELATIVE FAILURE RATE VS STRESS

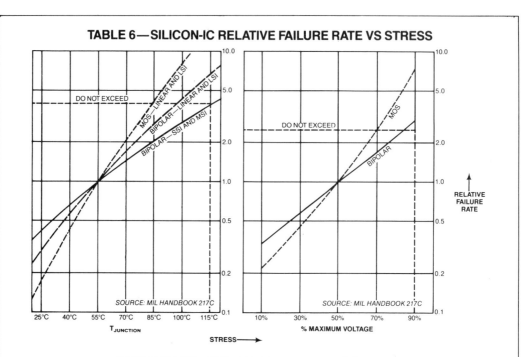

IC PACKAGES—AVERAGE THERMAL RESISTANCE

PINS	PACKAGE TYPE	MATERIAL	θ_{JC}* (°C/WATT)	θ_{JA}** (°C/WATT)
8–12	METAL	TO-99,100,101	60	200
8	PLASTIC	DUAL-IN-LINE	50	125
	CERAMIC		40	110
14–18	PLASTIC	DUAL-IN-LINE	40	100
	CERAMIC		30	90
20–24	PLASTIC	DUAL-IN-LINE	35	75
	CERAMIC		25	60
40	PLASTIC	DUAL-IN-LINE	30	60
	CERAMIC		20	45

* θ_{JC} ASSUMING EUTECTIC DIE ATTACHMENT; EPOXY DIE ATTACHMENT WILL INCREASE VALUE.
** θ_{JA} ASSUMING COPPER LEAD FRAME AND PC MOUNT; ADD 25% IF USING ALLOY 42 LEADS OR SOCKET.

TYPE	RECOMMENDED PRACTICE (NOMINAL CONDITIONS)	DO NOT EXCEED (WORST CASE)
BIPOLAR LINEAR	TO 55°C $T_{JUNCTION}$	100°C** $T_{JUNCTION}$
	TO 65% MAX* LOAD	85% MAX* LOAD
	TO 65% MAX* VOLTAGE	85% MAX* VOLTAGE
MOS, JFET LINEAR	TO 55°C $T_{JUNCTION}$	85°C $T_{JUNCTION}$
	TO 50% MAX* CURRENT	70% MAX* CURRENT
	TO 50% MAX* VOLTAGE	70% MAX* VOLTAGE

* OF 25°C RATING
** DO NOT EXCEED 85% OF ABSOLUTE MAX RATING

94

TABLE 7—DIGITAL-IC RELATIVE FAILURE RATE VS STRESS

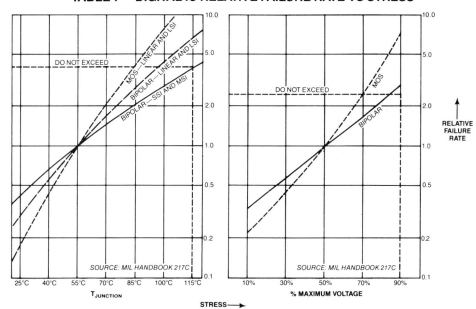

SOURCE: MIL HANDBOOK 217C

T$_{JUNCTION}$

% MAXIMUM VOLTAGE

STRESS ⟶

RELATIVE FAILURE RATE

DERATING CHART

TYPE	RECOMMENDED PRACTICE (NOMINAL CONDITIONS)	DO NOT EXCEED (WORST CASE)
BIPOLAR DIGITAL SSI/MSI	TO 55°C T$_{JUNCTION}$ TO 65% MAX* LOAD TO 65% MAX FREQUENCY	120°C T$_{JUNCTION}$*** 85% MAX* LOAD 85% MAX FREQUENCY
BIPOLAR DIGITAL LSI	TO 55°C T$_{JUNCTION}$ TO 65% MAX* LOAD TO 65% MAX* VOLTAGE**	100°C T$_{JUNCTION}$*** 85% MAX* LOAD 85% MAX* VOLTAGE**
MOS DIGITAL MSI/LSI	TO 55°C T$_{JUNCTION}$ TO 50% MAX* CURRENT TO 50% MAX* VOLTAGE	85°C T$_{JUNCTION}$*** 70% MAX* CURRENT 70% MAX* VOLTAGE

* OF 25°C RATING
** WHERE APPLICABLE (OC OUTPUTS)
*** DO NOT EXCEED 85% OF ABSOLUTE MAX RATING

IC JUNCTION-TEMPERATURE ESTIMATION

$$T_{JUNCTION} = T_{AMBIENT} + \Delta T_{JC} + \Delta T_{CA} = T_A + \Delta T_{JA}$$
$$= T_{CASE} + P_{DISS} (\theta_{JC}) = T_A + P_D (\theta_{JA})$$

IF THE THERMAL RESISTANCE (θ_{JC}) OF THE PACKAGE IS NOT KNOWN ACCURATELY, IT MAY BE MODELED USING THE HP *THERMAL DESIGN HANDBOOK*, OR THE FOLLOWING APPROXIMATE VALUES:

PINS	PACKAGE TYPE	MATERIAL	θ_{JC}* (°C/WATT)	θ_{JA}** (°C/WATT)
8–12	METAL	TO-99,100,101	60	200
8	PLASTIC CERAMIC	DUAL-IN-LINE	50 40	125 110
14–18	PLASTIC CERAMIC	DUAL-IN-LINE	40 30	100 90
20–24	PLASTIC CERAMIC	DUAL-IN-LINE	35 25	75 60
40	PLASTIC CERAMIC	DUAL-IN-LINE	30 20	60 45

* θ_{JC} ASSUMING EUTECTIC DIE ATTACHMENT; EPOXY DIE ATTACHMENT WILL INCREASE VALUE.
** θ_{JA} ASSUMING LEADS SOLDERED INTO PRINTED CIRCUIT; SOCKET WILL INCREASE θ_{JA} TO 25%.

Junction temperature kills ICs

Note that the data on digital ICs in **Table 7** lists only junction temperature and not power dissipation or impressed voltage. This is because excessive junction temperature is the dominant failure-causing stress factor in digital ICs. Most designers err in considering only fan-out specs when applying digital ICs. You should check the digital ICs' junction temperatures as well. You may find that some digital ICs need heat sinks.

Another aspect of temperature control is air movement. Put simply, when it comes to fans, bigger is better—the bigger the fan, the better the convective cooling. A little ingenuity will probably yield a means of positioning or orientation that will permit incorporation of a larger fan than was first thought possible. The larger fan in turn can compensate for the effects of heat-generating components. For example, the 8642 has a linear power supply that specs no better than 50% efficiency. Despite this inefficiency, the power supply doesn't exceed the 55°C max temperature spec. This is not because the supply has especially large heat sinks; it does, rather, benefit from a large flow of cooling air.

Unexpected failures crop up

No matter how much design effort goes into selecting components for a product, something unexpected will almost always occur. Therefore, it's wise to put the product through stress testing and shake the problems out of it early.

You might, for example, use small, cart-mounted environmental chambers that perform cooling and heat tests. Each engineer can roll one of these units up to his bench to cycle his subassembly or prototype up and down in temperature. Before the advent of these mobile chambers, design engineers had to secure test-chamber time from the quality-control department. Weeding out circuit problems at the initial design stage rather than at the production stage ultimately saves significant amounts of development time: Conducting elevated temperature/humidity tests is the fastest way to reveal problems. Such tests require a full-blown environmental test chamber, however, and can't be done with the mobile units.

No random failures

When any failure occurs, you must try to figure out what caused it. Attributing it to "random" component failure is not good enough, because there's no such thing as a random failure—all failures have a cause. The fault might lie with the component's manufacturer, with your manufacturing practices, or with the design itself; the design might be stressing the component in some way you didn't predict.

For example, wet electrolytic capacitors can fail simply from sitting on a shelf for too long without any voltage impressed on them. Also, electrolytics often cannot stand even the slightest reverse voltage. In many cases, you can't avoid momentary reverse voltages across decoupling capacitors. You could, as a consequence, encounter unexpected failures if you use elec-

trolytic caps for decoupling.

It may also not be enough simply to test the product at specified temperature and humidity extremes. You should put your product on a shake table to see what can happen to it during shipment. Companies lacking shake tables should consider renting one or putting the product into the hands of a test laboratory that has one.

Because automatic test equipment must meet rigorous requirements for operating time and reliability—it's typically up and running 24 hours a day—advanced self-test capabilities and good resistance to high levels of stress must be designed into the equipment. The 8642 RF signal generator, for example, has built-in software-controlled testing and calibration capabilities. Though circuits like these are currently common only in high-end ATE, you might find that this approach suits your designs, because the cost for these self-test circuits is dropping dramatically.

The 8642's control section contains a 10-bit A/D converter that's hooked to an analog multiplexer. The multiplexer has a line to each of the instrument's eight internal modules. Inside six of these modules are other analog multiplexers, which select individual test points within the modules. Using this circuitry, the instrument's 68000 μP can obtain a digital readout from a total of 54 critical test points inside the modules. Two other inputs to the multiplexer include one for the built-in power meter and another for an external probe that's used for guided-probe testing of additional circuit nodes.

The 10-bit A/D converter acts as a 2½-digit DVM. In the 8642's case, its front-panel LCD shows the A/D converter's scaled output in volts just as a DVM would; in your design, the readings could be part of a self-test routine or reported over some interface to a diagnostic instrument. Built-in analog-test capability gives you the means to troubleshoot your product remotely without removing it from its installation or even taking off its cover. This capacity could save far more in warranty charges or downtime than the added circuitry costs.

Software calibration

Another ATE design technique can replace one of the least reliable components known: trimming potentiometers. These low-cost components don't usually receive much attention from designers, but they can be the source of problems. Many trimming potentiometers are sensitive to moisture and dirt. Wherever possible, you should replace these and other mechanical components with electrical ones. One of the best ways to do this is to substitute software calibration for conventional manual calibration.

With software calibration, you replace the variable resistors with D/A converters. A D/A converter that's operating as a variable resistor is more reliable than its mechanical counterpart. You can store the calibration information in electrically erasable PROMs (EEPROMs). If your design is modular, every replaceable module should have its own EEPROMs, which store the calibration constants for that module.

Finally, installation instructions should clearly indicate any special mounting requirements for proper air circulation. Extra care taken in documentation of all kinds pays off in reduced warranty service.

Making a reliable product doesn't stop once the designing has stopped. Striving for maximum reliability means keeping track of the failure data gathered by the warranty service people, finding out what caused the failure, and correcting it.

29 Replace exclusive ORs with resistors

Simple twelve-bit comparator

EDN readers have fertile imaginations, and here is another circuit gem. If one of the counts is fixed or can be presettable, then that counter can be replaced by hardwired straps or DIL switches.

George Breindel
Custom Chronograph Co, Tonasket, WA

Designers commonly need a signal that indicates when counter outputs are identical. You could employ exclusive-OR gates to provide this indication; however, a more economical solution requires only two CMOS counters, such as the 4040 12-bit binary devices shown in the **figure**. Tie the respective outputs together via resistors; a transistor emitter-base junction supplies power to the counters and monitors their current consumption. When the outputs of both counters are identical, no current flows in the resistors. Because CMOS circuits inherently consume only microamperes, the transistor lacks base drive and turns off, producing a negative-going pulse.

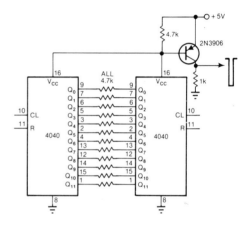

No current flows *through the resistors when the counter's outputs are identical.*

30 MOSFETs provide low-loss rectification

Low-loss rectification

I first saw active devices, notably bipolar transistors, proposed as low-loss rectifiers many years ago. Here is a low-loss rectification scheme implemented using MOSFETs.

William Chater
The Aerospace Corp, Los Angeles, CA

Rectifiers strongly affect the efficiency of a low-voltage power supply. Silicon diodes, for example, carry a 0.7V forward-voltage penalty. You can avoid much of the power dissipation and heat burden associated with diode rectifiers by using the high-efficiency MOSFET rectifiers shown in **Fig 1**. This approach is especially useful in vacuum work, where the lack of convection cooling limits the allowable power dissipation.

The secondary of the transformer shown in **Fig 1** maintains opposite-polarity V_{DS} voltages across the MOSFETs Q_1 and Q_2; it reverses these polarities once per input cycle. With each change of polarity, the secondary voltage also toggles the MOSFETs' on/off states by causing the output of each comparator (IC_{1A} and IC_{1B}) to switch between the comparators' supply rails. As a result, a unidirectional and nearly constant current flows from the transformer's center tap through the load and back through each MOSFET in turn.

In **Fig 2**, note how an IRFF110 MOSFET's familiar first-quadrant curves extend into the less familiar third quadrant. In particular, note that the channel is off for V_{GS} less than 3V (first quadrant) and fully on for V_{GS} in the 4 to 6V range (third quadrant). Thus, by switching the V_{GS} level you can simulate a diode with very low on-resistance and low forward bias. What's more, this approach avoids activating the MOSFET's parasitic diodes, which usually prevent the application of MOSFETs as rectifiers.

In the circuit shown in **Fig 1**, the comparators' open-collector outputs provide a rapid transition to the low state, but the 1-kΩ pullup resistors produce a slower transition to the high level. The MOSFETs thus avoid conduction overlap by turning off rapidly and turning on slowly. Diodes D_1 and D_2 offer protection by clamping the comparators' inverting-input voltages with respect to the negative supply voltage (pin 4). These diodes are normally superfluous, however, because the MOSFETs' low forward drop won't allow the diodes to turn on.

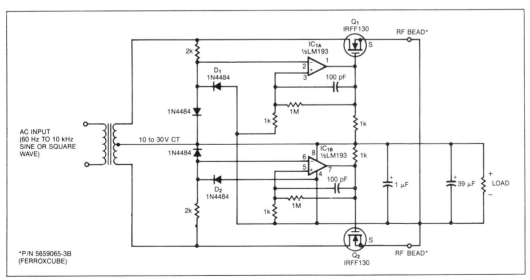

Fig 1—Using MOSFET switches *in place of diode rectifiers, this full-wave rectifier circuit produces a 5V, 1A output at 97% efficiency.*

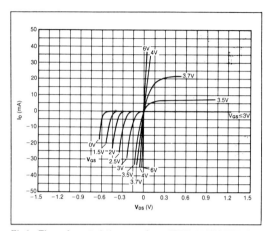

Fig 2—These characteristic curves for an IRFF110 MOSFET show how it can simulate a nearly ideal diode when you simultaneously switch its V_{DS} and V_{GS} voltages.

Using a square-wave input, this circuit can produce a 5V, 1A output with 97% efficiency (resistive losses are 60 mW, and each transistor dissipates another 60 mW). For even lower losses, you can parallel two MOSFETs for each switch. Using diode rectifiers, the efficiency would be about 90%. The use of a sine-wave input also lowers the circuit efficiency but not to the level of a diode-rectifier version: The duty cycle of the switches in **Fig 1** goes from almost 50% with a square-wave input to about 20% with a sine-wave input. Consequently, the switches deliver greater-amplitude current pulses to the load filter, which increases the power dissipation.

31 Predictive coding improves ADC performance

Enhance the ADC process

As a mainly analog engineer, I found this a useful primer on an important topic on the borderland between the analog and digital worlds. The linear nature of predictive encoding is ideal where the next stage is DSP, in contrast to non-linear coding schemes such as the mu-law and A-law companding methods used in the US and European telephone networks respectively.

Richard J Karwoski, Consultant

By shortening digital-word size without sacrificing digital resolution or accuracy, predictive coding and companding can both improve the efficiencies of analog-to-digital conversions. While differing in their basic concepts (see **box**), both methods find use in applications requiring greater conversion accuracy than is available with current low-cost ADCs. By using predictive coding or companding, you can extend a system's dynamic range so that shorter data words maintain the signal-to-quantizing noise ratio of longer ones.

Highly correlated signals are redundant

Predictive coding achieves this constant accuracy with reduced word size (or increased accuracy with the same word size) because a sampled signal is usually full of redundant information. Any sample can be closely estimated by examining its neighbors; the samples of a redundant signal correlate with one another, and the accuracy of any prediction rises with the degree of correlation.

Specifically, highly correlated sequences, such as voice or music waveforms, contain much redundant information and exhibit relatively small sample-to-sample variations. By contrast, you can expect wild

---

Companding versus predictive coding

Essentially a bipolar logarithmic technique, companding can reduce rates in digital data-transmission systems. With a compandor, an analog input signal receives very high-resolution quantization around 0V.

As the input amplitude to a companding ADC increases, the quantization becomes more coarse. This process maintains a relatively constant signal-to-noise ratio over a wide input-signal range **(figure).** Companding proves quite effective in servo systems, where nulling accuracy is important.

Both companding and predictive coding are well suited to voice-signal digitization. The choice between the techniques generally hinges on the ultimate application. For example, predictive coding proves ideal for digital filtering or FFT applications because predictor output codes are linear; the logarithmic nature of a compandor's output code precludes simple interfacing with digital signal-processing software or hardware. On the other hand, companding is simpler to realize in LSI circuitry, as the many recently introduced inexpensive codec chips demonstrate.

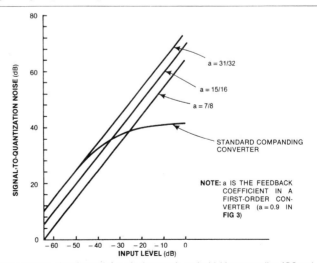

Curves plot the signal-to-noise performance of a typical 8-bit companding ADC and three predictive ADCs with different feedback coefficients.

fluctuations in sample values for sequences exhibiting little correlation. Each sample at the output of a digital noise generator, for example, is statistically independent of its neighbors. For such a signal, predictability is out of the question.

Correlated time sequences have frequency spectra with energies that are concentrated at the low end and fall off at the high end of the frequency range. In the example shown in **Fig 1**, signal energy is concentrated well below half the sampling frequency (f_s). A standard linear ADC converts signals in its full input range at frequencies up to $f_s/2$ (the Nyquist frequency); the ADC thus has full-power bandwidth up to $f_s/2$.

But in the conversion of most naturally generated signals, this capability is not necessary. To obtain maximum signal-to-noise efficiency from the ADC, input signals should have a *flat* frequency spectrum so that the total ADC input range is always used up in the conversions (**Fig 2**).

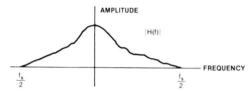

Fig 1—Most real-world signals *concentrate their energy at frequencies far below the Nyquist frequency (half the sampling frequency).*

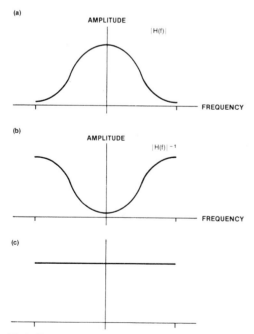

Fig 2—To get the most out of an ADC's dynamic range, *the input spectrum (a) should be modified by a filter with the inverse spectrum (b) so that the resulting ADC input is flat (c).*

You can re-examine this principle by remembering that most of a natural signal's energy occurs far below the Nyquist frequency. Thus, for low-frequency components of the input signal, many more samples than necessary are made. For example, for a signal band-limited to 16 kHz, sampling at 32 kHz avoids aliasing. This sampling rate provides two samples per cycle of 16-kHz input—the minimum number necessary. For a 1-kHz input, however, 32 samples are taken per input cycle—16 times the number needed. If the signal is digitized, you can improve the quantization accuracy per sample for a given word length by "stealing" information contained in previous samples.

Removing redundancy

The key to predictive coding is the removal of signal redundancy—a process termed decorrelation. For example, a simple first-order predictor might use nine-tenths of the most recent sample as its estimate for the next sample. The predictor output would then be the difference between the prediction and the actual signal value (**Fig 3**). This simple predictor has a frequency response computable by means of Fourier techniques. Because its output has contributions from its input and a delayed version of that input, the network function is

$$Y(j\omega)/X(j\omega) = 1 - 0.9\exp(-j\omega T).$$

The predictor has a frequency response similar to H^{-1} depicted in **Fig 4a**. For a 100%-efficient predictor, the input spectrum would have to be the inverse of the predictor's frequency response (**Fig 4b**).

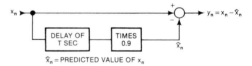

Fig 3—This predictor *uses nine-tenths of the present sample as its estimate of the next one.*

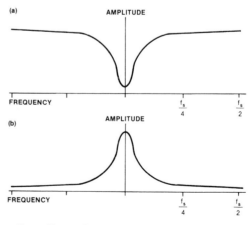

Fig 4—The predictor *shown in* **Fig 3** *has a frequency response close to that depicted in (a). It closely resembles the inverse of the spectrum shown (b) and is typical of many real-world phenomena, such as voice and video images.*

Obviously, real-world data exhibits time-varying frequency spectra. But for most data sources, you can predict the worst-case frequency spectrum; a predictor designed with that spectrum in mind offers a substantial fidelity enhancement. The system shown in **Fig 3**, for example, closely matches the spectrum of **Fig 4b**—a spectrum fairly typical of many real-world data sources such as audio and image signals.

Using predictors in encoders and decoders

To construct a predictive encoder, embed a predictor in an ADC feedback loop (**Fig 5**). To maintain a flat output frequency response when the digital data is finally recovered, you must also incorporate an inverse predictor in the DAC circuit. Such encoding and decoding circuits offer enhancement of conversion accuracies. The transfer function of the circuit depicted in **Fig 5** is $y/x = 1 - P$—the standard transfer function for a predictive encoder.

In the encoder, the ADC output produces an error with each conversion because of its inherent resolution limit. For reasonable input levels, the errors prove independent of the signal output y and are also limited by feedback to values within $\pm\frac{1}{2}$ LSB of the true value of y. Conversion errors are generally unrelated to each other and produce a random, uncorrelated sequence. The frequency power spectrum of such a sequence is very flat, and its total power is $\sigma^2 = q^2/12$, where σ is the value of an ADC LSB in volts.

Because the quantization errors are uncorrelated, you can model the ADC output as the input signal plus

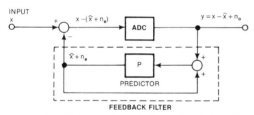

Fig 5—**A predictive encoder** *embeds a predictor in the ADC feedback loop. Here, x is the input signal, x̂ the predicted value for x, n_o the ADC noise and n_e the error-signal noise.*

noise $(y + n_o)$. The noise term (n_e) appearing at the ADC input results from the output noise (n_o) passing through the feedback filter containing the predictor. Because of this feedback, both n_o and n_e are constrained to a value within $\pm\frac{1}{2}$ LSB of the theoretical value of the signal $(s - \hat{s})$. Feedback corrects any tendency of signals to cross this boundary. For another—possibly simpler—explanation of the process, see the nearby **box**.

A matching decoder (**Fig 6**) has the transfer function $r/y = 1/(1 - P)$, where r is the reconstructed output. The complete encoding/decoding process thus yields the original input signal: $r/x = (1 - P)/(1 - P) = 1$. The noise of the reconstructed output is about 3 dB greater than that generated by the ADC itself. However, the decoder has signal gain, so the total system signal-to-noise ratio is improved over the ADC's inherent accuracy.

Predictive coding transmits differences

Quantization error in a predictive encoder won't exceed $\pm\frac{1}{2}$ LSB because the loop continually monitors the conversion process and adjusts the present-sample value to compensate for the previous one.

To understand the process, examine the **figure,** a relabeled version of **Fig 5.** Here, linear analysis is possible because the quantization is small. The feedback voltage (e_p) is expressed in terms of the input voltage via two loop equations:

$$e_o = e_i - e_p$$
$$[P/(1-P)]\,e_o = e_p.$$

Combining these equations yields $e_p = Pe_i$. In other words, e_p is the predicted value of the input. If the predictor is performing well, e_p will be a good estimate of e_i, and the ADC will quantize the difference $e_i - e_p$. If the ADC's total input range is devoted to quantizing $e_i - e_p$, the relative digital error for e_i will decrease when the signal is reconverted to the analog domain.

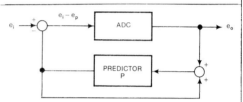

The ADC *in this encoder converts the difference between the prediction and the input signal.*

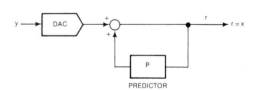

Fig 6—**A predictive decoder** *unfolds the encoder loop.*

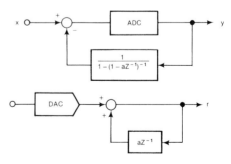

Fig 7—**The predictor** *depicted in Fig 3 can serve in both encoder and decoder circuits. Here, a equals the feedback coefficient (0.9 in Fig 3) and Z^{-1} denotes a delay of one sample time.*

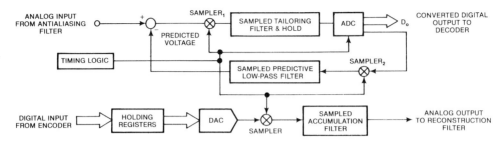

Fig 8—A predictive-encoder/decoder system *divides into several subsystems, shown in detail in* **Fig 9.**

The example predictor shown in **Fig 3** works well in both encoding and decoding circuits (**Fig 7**). The decoder gain formula in this case is

$$r/y = 1/(1 - 0.9\exp(-j\omega T)).$$

For low frequencies (below 300 Hz), gain is approximately 10, corresponding to more than three additional bits of ADC accuracy; an 8-bit converter used in **Fig 7** thus achieves the accuracy of an 11-bit converter.

An actual circuit provides an example

Putting all this theory together produces the circuits diagrammed in **Fig 8** and broken down into components in **Fig 9**. Illustrating the basic principles of predictive coding, this 8-bit system breaks neatly into several subcircuits.

The ADC (Fig 9a). The ADC used in the system is a typical successive-approximation type, using an 8-bit, fast-settling DAC, an SAR and a comparator. The sample/hold circuit that usually precedes the ADC's comparator can be incorporated in a tailoring filter used to adjust frequency response and full-power bandwidth, as in the case here.

The predictor (Fig 9a). The predictive filter and sampler 2 form the heart of the scheme. The sample/hold circuit is timed to sample the DAC output after the converter has completed the successive-approximation routine and has settled to the comparator voltage ($e_c \pm \frac{1}{2}$ LSB). The connected filter is essentially a linear hold circuit and low-pass-filter combination. The sampled input turns the combination into a "leaky" discrete accumulator.

After going through a bit of mathematics, you can find that a portion of the present sample of e_i is used as the estimate of the next value of e_i. This single-sample estimation process is termed a first-order prediction. A predictive filter used to perform this estimation is usually a very low-bandwidth discrete filter or integrator with a time constant much greater than the sampling interval.

The decoder (Fig 9b). In the decoder, holding registers store a digital word, which is converted by an 8-bit DAC into an analog voltage. To avoid DAC bit-transition glitches, a sample/hold circuit samples the DAC output and feeds it into the final subcircuit, the accumulator.

The accumulator (Fig 9b). Essentially the low-pass filter used in the ADC feedback loop, this circuit has a time constant matching that of the predictor to ensure the encoder's exact inverse frequency response.

System handles 32-kHz sampling rate

As with any analog-to-digital conversion system, DAC settling times and analog sampling limitations determine this system's conversion rates. This circuit handles a sampling rate of 32 kHz (31-μsec conversion time). The series of scope photos shown in **Fig 10** illustrates the effectiveness of predictive coding in reducing quantization errors. **Figs 10a, 10b** and **10c** show various points in the successive-approximation routines, while **Fig 10d** illustrates a 2.5-kHz reconstructed sine wave after it has passed through a 7-pole Butterworth signal-reconstruction filter with a cutoff frequency of 12 kHz.

Standard conversion systems have trouble with low input levels. Emphasizing the quantization error in conversion, **Fig 11a** shows a 750-mV-pk 500-Hz sine wave in a predictive system without an output accumulator. The LSB jumps are plainly visible at the tops and bottoms of the sine wave, indicating severe digital noise contamination. **Fig 11b** depicts the same signal after it has passed through the output accumulator. The photo shows barely noticeable quantization error.

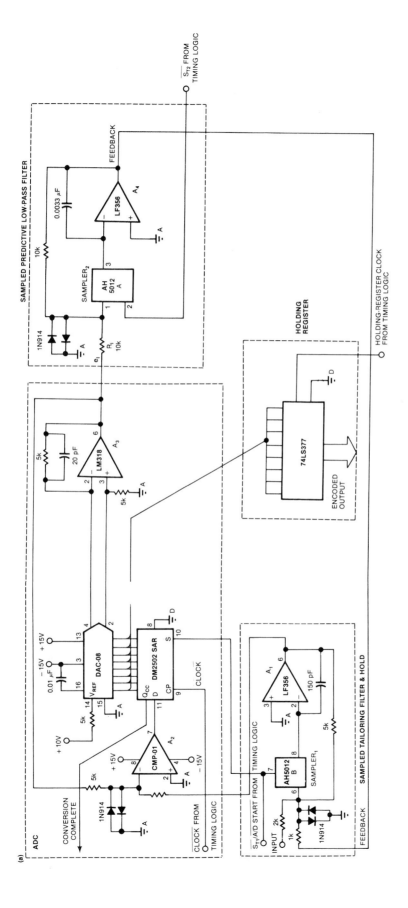

Fig 9—An encoder (a) uses hybrid sample/hold units, as does a decoder **(b)**. Timing logic **(c)** controls both subsystems with signals sequenced as in **(d)**.

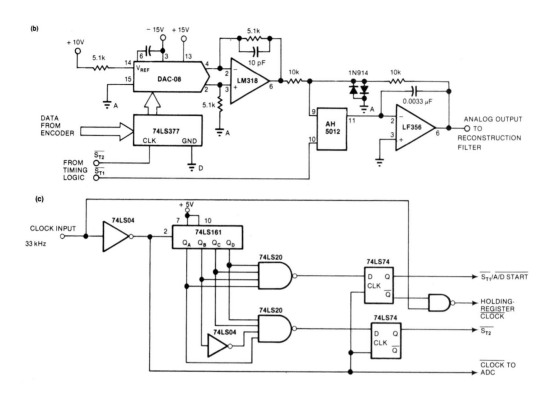

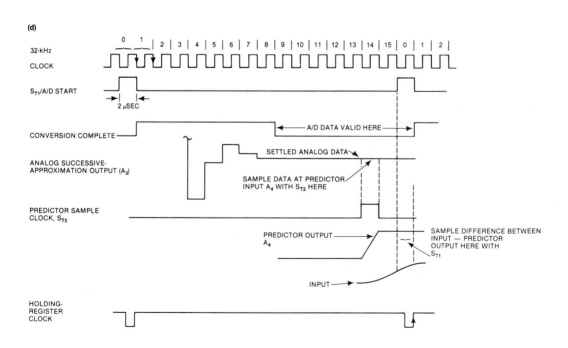

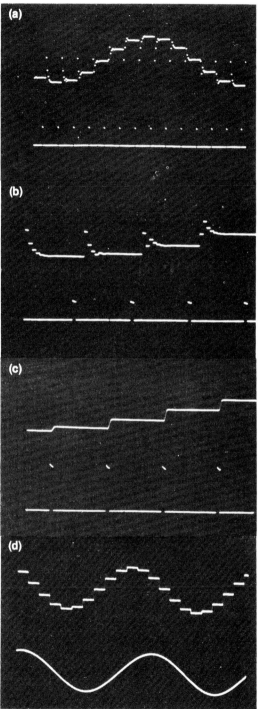

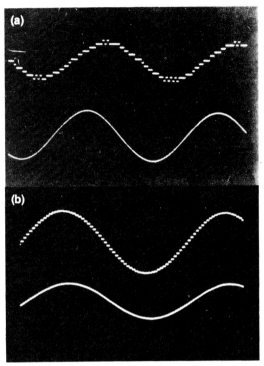

Fig 11—**With a 750-mV, 500-Hz sine-wave input,** *a system without prediction suffers from severe quantization errors when encoding a small input* **(a)**. *With prediction, quantization is much more accurate* **(b).** *The lower trace in* **(b)** *is a filtered version of the upper one.*

Fig 10—**Observe** *the successive-approximation process* **(a)**; *the sample signal appears along the bottom of the trace. Expanding the time axis,* **(b)** *offers a magnified view of the sine-wave conversion. An expanded view of the sampled-and-held results of each approximation appears in* **(c).** *The top trace in* **(d)** *is the encoded 2.5-kHz sine wave as it appears before (above) and after (below) passing through a 7-pole, 12-kHz Butterworth filter.*

Use predictive coding to save money

Most applications of predictive-coding systems take advantage of the technique's digitization efficiency, which can produce savings in hardware, memory, channel bandwidth and converter cost.

Video and image-processing systems use predictive coding to minimize data and enhance accuracy. In voice communications, predictive converters can minimize the data rate of multiplexed transmissions.

Predictive coding can also be applied in the field of professional audio equipment. Audio circuitry that handles music signals has always required the best signal-to-noise performance out of a digital system; predictive coding minimizes memory requirements for digital reverberation systems while achieving 90-dB S/N ratios.

A more subtle advantage of predictive coding relates to current data-conversion technology. Fast 12-bit ADCs are relatively inexpensive and common, but longer-word-length converters (14 and 16 bits) are either slow or expensive. Predictive coding, in conjunction with today's 12-bit converters, enhances conversion accuracy. A 12-bit predictive encoder, for example, can generate a 14-bit output word when the encoder runs at a rate faster than that necessary to avoid aliasing. Converting signals band-limited to 10 kHz at a 160-kHz rate and then *digitally* resampling at twice the Nyquist frequency (20 kHz) can then yield about three additional bits of accuracy.

32 Op amp reduces transformer droop

Extended LF response

Negative feedback to the rescue again. I once used a similar idea for the 600 Ω output of a highly accurate standard 1 mW telephony signal source. To avoid problems with the tempco of the transformer's output winding, I wound it with constantan resistance wire, which then formed part of the instrument's 600 Ω output source resistance.

Don Holly and **Tom Lovell**
University of Wisconsin Dept of Physics, Madison

Coupling a signal through an audio transformer can break ground loops or shift the signal's dc level. The transformer's low frequency droop, however, degrades signals with frequencies lower than a few hundred hertz. The circuit shown in **Fig 1** provides a simple means of extending a transformer's low-frequency response while reducing its distortion.

While one leg of the center-tapped primary excites the secondary, the other leg provides feedback to linearize the output. The op amp forces the feedback voltage—and thus the secondary voltage—to follow the input signal. As an added benefit, the circuit maintains constant input impedance so long as the op amp remains within its linear range.

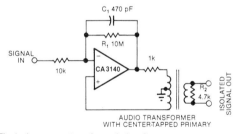

Fig 1—Improve a transformer's low-frequency response *and reduce its distortion with the help of an op amp.*

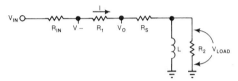

Fig 2—An equivalent circuit *aids calculation of L/R time.*

C_1 and R_2 provide ac stability by rolling off the op amp's response and damping transformer resonance; R_1 supplies a dc feedback path. The range over which the scheme extends the transformer's response depends on signal amplitude—response is limited by the output-voltage swing required to maintain the transformer's secondary voltage.

Fig 2's circuit is equivalent to **Fig 1**'s. To determine this circuit's L/R time, assume the transformer couples to the output side just as it couples to the feedback side, and further assume that the op amp has infinite gain.

From the equivalent circuit depicted in **Fig 2**,
$$\mathbf{V}- = V_{IN}(R_1/(R_1+R_{IN})) + V_O(R_{IN}/(R_1+R_{IN})) = -V_{LOAD}$$
$$I = (V_O - V_{LOAD})/R_S = (V_{LOAD}/R_2) + (1/L)\int V_{LOAD}dt.$$
Combining, you obtain
$$-V_{IN} = V_{LOAD}((2R_{IN}/R_1) + ((R_{IN}R_S)/(R_2R_1)) + 1) + (R_{IN}R_S/R_1L)\int V_{LOAD}dt.$$
Thus, the circuit's L/R time is
$$t = R_1L/R_{IN}R_S.$$

33 Designed-in safety features ease compliance

How to design equipment to comply with national safety standards

Most electronic equipment offered for sale must comply with one or other of various safety standards, depending upon where it is being sold – these are defined by the OSHA in the USA, CSE in Canada, IEC in Europe, etc. Thus, a manufacturer with world-wide sales may need to collect a whole sheaf of approvals, although things are simplified in much of Europe, since throughout the member countries of the EEC at least, a single standard prevails. Alas, a world-wide standard still looks a very long way off.

Glen Dash, *Dash, Straus & Goodhue Inc*

Incorporating safety-related features into your electronic-equipment design should be far more than a peripheral or "by the way" consideration. Whether you're designing a circuit, a pc board, or an enclosure, considering safety early in the product design cycle will save you time, money, and inconvenience.

Any electronic system destined for use in the workplace must comply with standards dictated by organizations such as OSHA (in the US), CSA (in Canada), and IEC (in Europe) (see the **boxes**, "There's no such thing as voluntary compliance," and "Safety approvals differ from country to country"). Depending on the target market for your product, you'll have to take into account one, two, or all three of these organizations' standards. And finally, proof of testing may shield you against civil and criminal liability if injury

does occur.

Considering that compliance is a requirement, it makes sense for you to consider safety aspects early on. Choosing the best components from the beginning—that is, those that already comply with their own individual standards—may save you from performing specialized tests. Including in your design items such as impedance-protection circuitry, thermal cutoff devices, and interlocking mechanisms can prevent possible redesign and retrofit later on. Ultimately, designed-in safety features that ensure compliance or make testing much easier will lighten an expensive load in your production department.

What are the four harms?

The purpose of all safety standards is to prevent the

There's no such thing as voluntary compliance

To many manufacturers, it's unclear whether they are legally compelled to submit their equipment to a listing agency. Some manufacturers are under the impression that it is voluntary. In fact, it's mandatory. Any device intended for the workplace has to comply with OSHA regulation, section 1910.399: "Electronic equipment . . . is acceptable . . . if it is . . . listed . . . by a nationally recognized testing laboratory . . . ."

The use of unlisted equipment can result in a host of federal penalties, including fines and imprisonment. And, even though criminal liabilities for unlisted products can be significant, civil liabilities are equally scary. Worse, even if the injured party chooses not to sue, his or her insurance company might. For example, if an injured person applies for workmen's compensation, the insurer for the compensation plan might try to recoup its losses from an equipment manufacturer under the legal

principle of "subrogation."

Standards such as UL 478 represent a benchmark for the due care required of all manufacturers under product-liability law. Failure to meet the appropriate standard can itself be construed as proof of negligence if compliance could have prevented the injury. A listing thus serves as a shield (albeit an incomplete one) for the manufacturer, and failure to achieve listing provides a sword for the plaintiff.

possibility of property loss or injury. More specifically, you want to avoid the so-called "four harms": electrical shock, fire, mechanical hazards, and exposure to high energy levels. Except for the mechanical hazards, the harms stem from exposure to electrical levels (volts, amperes, Joules) that can give rise to hazardous conditions.

The US OSHA standards explicitly define these four harms:

- Electrical shock—potential for risk arises when an operator is exposed to circuitry whose voltage exceeds 30V rms, 42.4V peak, and whose current can exceed 5 mA through a 1.5-kΩ resistor.
- Fire—danger occurs when temperature increases exceed prescribed limits, and in circuits whose voltage and current capabilities exceed 42.4V, 8A peak.
- Mechanical hazards—physical danger is caused by moving parts, sharp corners and edges, and products that can tip over.
- High-energy levels—situation becomes risky when a potential of 2V or more between adjacent parts can produce a continuous volt-ampere level exceeding 240 VA, or in which reactive components can produce energy levels exceeding 20J. Such energy levels can produce metal meltdown, resulting in the splattering of flaming material.

Two of the most widely followed US standards that address protection against these hazardous conditions are UL 478, which covers electronic data-processing (EDP) equipment, and UL 1459, which covers telecommunications equipment. When the two equipment categories overlap (for example, in the case of modems), the somewhat-more-stringent UL 478 takes precedence. In Canada, the EDP and the telecommunications standards are CSA C22.2 Nos 220 and 0.7, respectively. In general, the Canadian specs accept all tenets of the UL standards, even though separate approvals are required. For most of Europe, IEC 950 covers EDP equipment (see **box**, "IEC 950: UL 478's European counterpart").

In addition to these end-equipment safety standards, a number of individual standards apply to the components used in EDP and telecomm equipment (**Table 1**). Components that fall under these separate regulations should meet both the individual standards and the end-equipment standard. For example, a power supply for an EDP application must satisfy both UL 1012 and UL 478.

The more familiar you are with the specific aspects of designing equipment with safety approvals in mind, the better your chances of designing acceptable equipment. First of all, be sure to read the spec very carefully; there are many specific definitions.

For instance, don't confuse "Roman numeral" Class I and Class II circuitry with "Arabic numeral" Class 1 and Class 2 devices. Class I circuits and devices are those housed in metal enclosures; Class II are housed in plastic. These definitions are completely unrelated to the definitions for Class 1 and 2 devices, which refer to a circuit's voltage and current rating. Class 2 circuits receive their power from supplies whose maximum peak open-circuit voltage is 42.4V and whose short-circuit current capability is lower than 8A.

You should also be aware of different definitions for different types of insulation. Double insulation refers to a part's basic insulation plus an additional layer (supplemental insulation) that protects against shock. Reinforced insulation serves the same purpose as double insulation, but is a single layer.

Safety and testing specifications for UL 478, as is the case with most UL standards, fall into two categories: construction specs and performance specs. As you learn more about designing-for-safety, you'll find that the terms used to describe a piece of equipment's packaging and protective covering have specific meanings. The typical assembly in **Fig 1**, for example, is labeled according to the UL nomenclature. The enclosure (A) provides basic protection against fire- and shock-related injuries. During the approval process, the external housing (B) undergoes investigation either as an enclosure if it protects against fire or shock, or as a guard if it protects against mechanical injury. The operator-access door is labeled C; hazardous areas inside the enclosure thus need barriers (E). A bottom panel (D) must meet its own strict criteria. Enclosures, guards, and barriers must use materials that are not combustible. These include steel, corrosion-protected aluminum, or heat-resistant glass that's tempered, wired, or laminated.

Any plastic materials that you use must meet UL-standard flame ratings:

- 94HB material can burn but only at some specified maximum rate. It is acceptable for use in cabinets and guards.
- 94V-5 material can flame or glow, but it can't release flaming or glowing particles. It is acceptable for enclosures and barriers for floor-mounted equipment.
- 94V-0 and 94V-1 material can release particles, as long as these don't ignite surgical cotton. These materials are acceptable for table- or rack-mounted equipment.

TABLE 1—INDIVIDUAL COMPONENT STANDARDS

COMPONENT	UL STANDARD NO
POWER-SUPPLY LINE CORDS	817
TRANSFORMERS	1585, 1310
POWER SUPPLIES	1012
EMI FILTERS	1283
FUSES	198
FUSE HOLDERS	512
SWITCHES	20, 1054
WIRE AND CABLE	486A, 486B, 83
PRINTED-CIRCUIT BOARDS	796
PLASTIC PARTS	746C
PLUGS AND RECEPTACLES	498
CATHODE-RAY TUBES	723
CIRCUIT BREAKERS	489
MOTORS	519

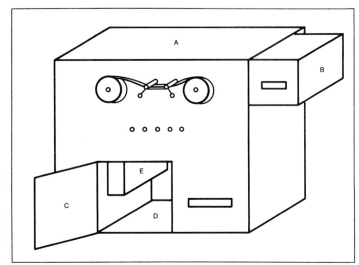

Fig 1—A typical piece of equipment for EDP applications has several protection mechanisms. The enclosure (A) provides basic protection against fire and shock dangers. The housing (B) protects personnel from fire, shock, and mechanical injury. The internal barrier (E) prevents access to hazardous areas inside the equipment. The bottom panel (D) keeps flaming material inside the equipment.

- 94V-2 material can release flaming particles that ignite surgical cotton.
- 94HF-1 plastic-foam material does not ignite surgical cotton.
- 94HF-2 plastic-foam material can ignite surgical cotton.
- 94HBF plastic-foam material burns at a specified maximum rate.

If you plan to use conductive coating for EMI suppression, you have to get UL approval for the paint and plastic, as well as the facility that applies the coating. In addition, all the parts used in EDP equipment (except for Class 2 circuits), including pc boards, wiring, and connectors, must have ratings of 94V-2, 94HF-2, or better. Externally mounted air filters must satisfy the more relaxed 94HB or 94HBF ratings.

Keep hazardous parts out of reach

Equipment that has to have openings—for ventilation for example—also has strict regulations. In general, you have to test the openings by using a finger-like IEC articulated probe (Fig 2). You should not be able to insert the probe into an opening in such a way that it touches any hazardous parts—those that move, are sharp, are hot, or may be exposed to voltages higher than 42.4V.

Moreover, you have to ensure that items such as coins and paper clips, which present a risk of short-circuit-induced fire, can't fall inside the equipment. The openings in the top and on the sides of the enclosure must measure less than $^3/_{16}$ in. Louvers can be longer than $^3/_{16}$ in., but you must design them so that they deflect falling parts (Fig 3).

Bottom panels have strict regulations because they must provide protection against falling, flaming parts. In general, bottom panels should be closed, but openings are permitted under wires, receptacles, or impedance-protected or thermally protected motors. In addition, $^1/_4$-in. openings are acceptable under materials

that have a flame rating of 94V-1 or better, or in cases where the openings are covered by a second barrier consisting of a stainless-steel mesh screen made of 0.018-in. min diameter wire.

Fig 2—An articulated probe emulates the human finger. You use the probe to test the protective qualities of the openings in an enclosure. The IEC articulated test probe shown (you can also build your own from IEC-published schematics) is available from Compliance Design (Boxborough, MA).

In some EDP applications, an operator might have to reach inside the enclosure—to make adjustments or to replace lamps, for example. To make sure the equipment is powered down in these instances, you have the option of using an interlocking mechanism. If you use an interlock, you'll be able to waive some UL 478 accessibility requirements, provided that the mechanism meets certain other safety standards, For instance, it must not be possible for someone to open the interlock with an IEC articulated probe, and the interlock must require an intentional adjustment before it can be bypassed. The interlock should also be

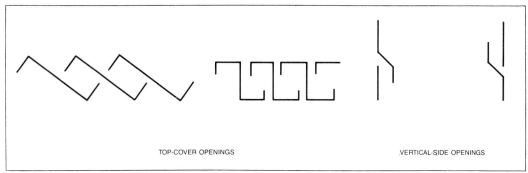

TOP-COVER OPENINGS   VERTICAL-SIDE OPENINGS

Fig 3—Openings in an enclosure must deflect falling parts. These drawings show cross sections of acceptable types of openings that keep out small metal parts that could otherwise cause short circuits and fires.

mechanical and must open all current-carrying conductors. A solid-state relay may be unacceptable because a single short circuit in the device can render the interlocking mechanism ineffectual. Finally, the interlock must be capable of 100,000 operations.

You'll find that the construction spec governing most of the hazardous conditions associated with EDP equipment is the one that governs the unit's connection to the ac-supply mains. The ac line cord must be permanently attached to the equipment unless it is of an acceptable, detachable form. The line cord must not be longer than 15 ft, and its plug must have a rating of at least 125% of the rated current. A permanently attached line cord must include a bushing and strain-relief feature. For low-power equipment, you can use ac adapters as long as they have component recognition under UL 1310.

The nature of the internal wiring also requires attention, and must be "so routed and secured that neither it nor related electrical connections are likely to be subject to stress or mechanical damage." Specifically, you must ensure that the wiring is properly rated for voltage breakdown and temperature. For wiring that passes through metal guides, you must provide either smooth surfaces or bushings. Any wire that's subject to motion must have some form of auxiliary mechanical protection, such as helical wraps.

The wire must be insulated with PVC, PFE, BTFE, FEP, or neoprene, and it must be marked with a rating of VW1. Splices are permitted, but you must mechanically secure them prior to soldering. In addition, wires that connect to screw terminals must do so by means of a solder lug. You can use the frame of the equipment to carry secondary current, but hinges or conductive coatings are prohibited for this purpose. If planned operator servicing entails possible operator contact with the wires, you must provide a second layer of insulation, such as tubing, or else provide an interlocking mechanism.

Spacings between components and uninsulated conductors (pc-board traces, for example) must meet their own particular requirements (**Table 2**). These specs apply to primary circuitry; to secondary circuitry that operates at more than 100V, 200 VA; and to secondary

TABLE 2—REQUIRED CIRCUIT SPACINGS

| VOLTAGE PRESENT | | SPACING | |
V RMS	V PEAK	IN.	MM
0 TO 50	0 TO 70.7	3/64	1.2
51 TO 125	72.1 TO 176.8	1/16	1.6
126 TO 250	178.2 TO 353.5	3/32	2.4

circuitry such as interlock circuits that is intended as safety protection. The spacing requirements don't apply to circuitry whose series impedance is greater than 20 kΩ. For secondary circuits with a rating lower than 100V, 200 VA, the necessary spacing is determined according to the results of a performance test.

Another important construction consideration is your grounding technique. UL grounding regulations apply mainly to Class I devices. Part of the shock protection in a Class I device comes from grounding all exposed metal. Ground wires must be green in the US and green-yellow in Europe. You must use a terminal to connect the ground line to the mandatory 3-wire plug, and you should secure this terminal to the equipment frame by a screw (or welded stud, nut, or lockwasher) that won't be removed during normal servicing. Don't rely on either hinges or conductive coatings to carry fault current.

Class II units are those encased in insulated housings; the case itself, rather than the grounded metal, serves as protective insulation. Double or reinforced insulation, or a minimum amount of through-air spacing, is required between any hazardous parts and the operator. **Table 3** lists the minimum spacings required for double-insulated Class II devices. In some instances, it's impossible to separate live parts from operator access by using through-air spacing and plastic. In these cases, an extra-thick section of plastic, which serves as reinforced insulation, is acceptable.

Devices that fall under the Class II category use a 2-wire ac line cord. If you use metal clamps for strain relief, you must provide a form of supplementary insulation at least $1/32$ in. thick between the clamp and the cord's insulation. You should securely fasten the wire and use screws, along with lockwashers, so that loosening will not compromise the double insulation.

Class 2 circuits relax UL rules

In EDP and telecomm equipment, Class 2 circuitry operates from relatively low voltage and current levels, so it does not present a high risk of fire or shock; therefore, UL standards make Class 2 circuitry exempt from certain safeguards. You can install fuses in the power supply's secondary circuit to limit current to Class 2 levels. For supplies of 21.2V max, these fuses must have a rating of 5A max, and for supplies of 21.3 to 42.4V, they must have a rating of 3.2A max. UL specs can also dictate the use of an isolation transformer in the power supply. Transformers satisfying UL 1310 or 1411, or double-insulated transformers (or those with reinforced insulation) meeting UL 1485, are satisfactory.

Underwriters Laboratories considers Class 2 circuits so free of hazards that it finds operator access acceptable, provided that two levels of protection exist between hazardous voltages and points of possible operator access. You can meet this requirement by providing an interlocking mechanism or by ensuring that Class 2 circuits are separated from other hazardous areas by double insulation.

TABLE 3—SPACING FOR <125V CLASS II DEVICES		
SPACING TYPE	**IN.**	**MM**
THROUGH-AIR OR OVER-SURFACE SPACING BETWEEN: LIVE PARTS AND INACCESSIBLE DEAD METAL	1/16	1.6
LIVE PARTS AND ACCESSIBLE DEAD METAL	1/8	3.2
LIVE PARTS AND INSIDE SURFACE OF SUPPLEMENTARY INSULATION (ENCLOSURE)	1/32	0.8
SPACING THROUGH INSULATING MATERIAL: SUPPLEMENTARY INSULATION	1/32	0.8
REINFORCED INSULATION	5/64	2.0

Motors and switches deserve special thought

You need to give special design-for-safety considerations to particular types of components such as motors, switches, and CRTs. Motor-related problems usually arise from locked rotors or from overheating during loaded conditions. To prevent these problems, you usually have to provide thermal-cutoff devices or impedance protection. In addition, motors should satisfy the individual safety standards, UL 519 and UL 547. Fuse ratings must not exceed 250% of the full-load current (300% for inductive loads). Switch ratings must equal or exceed the levels of their intended loads (200% for inductive loads), and the switches must disconnect all ungrounded connections.

In a system with motors of ⅓ hp or more, you are required to have a separate switch to control each motor. If you provide a convenience receptacle, it must be properly rated and wired—that is, its third wire must be grounded, and its silver lead must be connected to neutral. The receptacle should have a marking indicating the maximum output current. Finally, the receptacle should have its own fuse, in accordance with the National Electrical Code; examples are a cartridge-type fuse, such as that found in household wiring boxes, or a listed circuit breaker.

CRTs present two hazards: x-rays and implosion. First, a CRT must meet its own individual component-recognition standard, UL 1418. In addition, the projected area (**Fig 4**) of an enclosure opening through which flying parts might reach the CRT must measure less than 0.2 sq in. The UL standard limits x-ray radiation to 0.5 mrad/hr, averaged over 10 sq cm at a distance 5 cm from the CRT. You must perform the radiation test with the controls set to their worst-case settings. It's also necessary to check for worst-case radiation by alternately opening and shorting components in the CRT's high-voltage circuitry.

UL standards also require that you affix several warning and cautionary labels to your equipment. In fact, the labels themselves must undergo UL component recognition under UL 969. Words such as "DANGER," "CAUTION," and "WARNING" must be typeset at least ³⁄₃₂ in. high. In addition to the manufacturer's information, you must specify voltage, current, frequency, and a symbol for alternating or direct current on each label. Other types of labels are also required; two examples are "Operators or service personnel may come in contact with hot surfaces," and "Service personnel may be exposed to capacitors that won't discharge according to UL standards."

In general, the safety requirements described here are designed to protect an equipment operator; the UL standards assume that a serviceperson is aware of potential hazards during equipment repair and maintenance. Nonetheless, some standards mandate the incorporation of protective measures for service people as well.

For example, if service personnel must reach over, under, or around uninsulated electrical parts or moving parts while a piece of equipment is energized, you must place all live parts that present shock or fire hazards in such a way that contact or bridging is unlikely during servicing. You have to make sure that power-supply capacitors discharge to less than 50V, 20J in 1 sec, or else provide service-personnel warning labels. You must also affix warning labels on parts that service personnel would expect to be at ground potential but are not, and on parts that can become energized by a single fault. If you use an interlocking mechanism as protection for a serviceperson, it must be capable of 6000 operations. This requirement is less stringent than that for equipment operators.

In addition to all these safety specs governing the construction of EDP equipment, UL specs cover a series of power-on performance tests. The first and simplest of these tests applies to a unit's current consump-

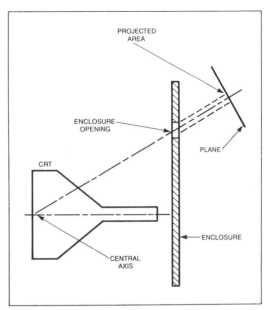

Fig 4—To prevent flying parts from reaching a CRT, the projected area of enclosure openings must not exceed 0.2 sq in. The purpose of this requirement is to prevent implosion of the CRT.

tion and its power cables. The maximum current for any equipment must not exceed 110% of the rating on the equipment label. Strain reliefs attached to the unit's power cable must withstand a 35-lb pull from any angle; the UL standard does not allow for any movement of the power cable.

For purposes of fire prevention, the standard specifies the maximum temperature rise permitted for all components in a unit. The components list includes transformers, motors, relays, inductors, large electrolytic capacitors, switches, fuses, and pc boards under components that provide heat. For a typical test, you would mount a number of thermocouples at key positions where you'd expect the temperature to rise. You can find the maximum permitted temperature rise for various components in Table 32.1 of UL 478 (which is too voluminous to reproduce here). In addition to internal components, the UL spec stipulates the maximum temperatures of external surfaces (**Table 4**).

Other tests are intended to evaluate the efficacy of insulation under electrical stress. Between the primary winding and ground or between the primary and secondary windings, you have to apply 1250V ac for one minute. Sudden, excessive current flow and cascading voltage drops indicate insulation breakdown—and failure. You have to apply the test voltages stipulated in **Table 5** from the secondary winding to ground or between multiple secondary windings.

Parts that either open or short-circuit in the primary circuit cause an anomaly called an "abnormal." These failures are capable of presenting a fire hazard, so UL 478 specifies a test for them. To perform the test, place the equipment over a hardwood surface covered with tissue paper, cover the unit with cheesecloth, and insert a 3A fuse in the ground return. The purpose is

TABLE 4—MAXIMUM TEMPERATURES OF EXTERNAL SURFACES

SURFACE	METAL °C	°F	NONMETALLIC °C	°F
HANDLES, KNOBS, OR SURFACES THAT ARE GRASPED FOR LIFTING, CARRYING, OR HOLDING	55	131	75	167
HANDLES OR KNOBS THAT ARE TOUCHED, BUT DO NOT INVOLVE LIFTING, CARRYING, OR HOLDING; SURFACES SUBJECT TO CONTACT DURING INTENDED USE OR MAINTENANCE	60	140	85	185
OTHER SURFACES	70	158	95	203

to determine the cause of a fire hazard, whether it be the failure of parts in the primary circuit, or whether it be a mechanical malfunction such as jammed components, wrongly set switches, or wrongly inserted connectors.

To test for abnormals, try all switch settings and initiate all possible jams of mechanical components. Further, alternately open and short each part in the primary circuit. Most of these abnormals will, in the worst scenario, simply cause the primary fuse to blow, and this result is acceptable. If the cheesecloth ignites or the 3A fuse in the ground return opens, the equipment is unacceptable. After each abnormal testing, the

TABLE 5—TEST REQUIREMENTS FOR SECONDARY CIRCUITS

VOLTAGE PRESENT IN CIRCUIT V RMS	V PEAK	TEST-VOLTAGE LEVEL
0 TO 30	0 TO 42.4	NO TEST REQUIRED
30.1 TO 333.3	42.5 TO 471.3	10 TIMES MAXIMUM VOLTAGE PRESENT IN CIRCUIT (1000V RMS MAX)
333.4 TO 1000	471.4 TO 1414	3 TIMES MAXIMUM VOLTAGE PRESENT IN CIRCUIT
1000 OR MORE	1414.1 OR MORE	1750V RMS PLUS 1.25 TIMES VOLTAGE PRESENT IN CIRCUIT

standard specifies that you perform a 1250V dielectric test between the primary winding and ground. Dielectric breakdown is considered unacceptable.

The UL spec also requires tests to verify that equipment won't tip or fall and cause operator injury. In one test, the unit must return to its starting position after being subjected to a 10° tilt. For this test, you can leave all doors on the unit closed, but you must place all casters and jacks in their most unfavorable positions.

If your equipment has any horizontal surfaces lower than 1m high, you must apply an 800N downward force to the surface to see if the unit will tip. For equipment taller than 1m and weighing more than 25 kg, apply a force equal to one-fifth the unit's weight (250N max) to points as high as 2m in every direction but up. Again, the equipment must not tip.

Another series of tests for mechanical integrity measures the equipment's reaction to impact. You have to drop handheld units onto a hardwood floor three times from a height of 3 ft. For other equipment, you have to drop a 2-in. sphere from a height of 51 in. onto the top and sides of the unit (**Fig 5**). In another test for mechanical integrity, you have to press on the enclosure with a special tool that has a ½-in. steel sphere at its tip. For metallic enclosures, the pressing force is 111N; for nonmetallic enclosures, it is 30N.

Your equipment will fail these tests if any holes appear in the enclosure large enough to allow an IEC articulated probe to make contact with live parts. Distortions can appear, but these should not cause an enclosure to come in contact with hazardous parts or permanently reduce spacings to values less than those in **Table 2**.

Because many users interrupt the ground line by using adapters, the UL standard specifies the leakage current that can flow to earth ground. **Fig 6** shows the test method. In this test, you break the ground line of the 3-wire line cord and measure the current from the enclosure's exposed metal to earth ground. Usually, UL standards stipulate that the leakage current

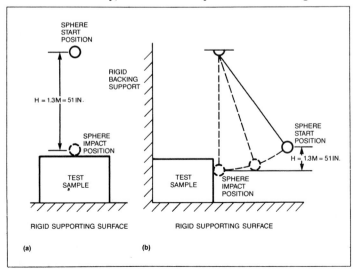

*Fig 5—Enclosures must be able to survive contact with falling objects. In these tests for the top (**a**) and sides (**b**) of an enclosure, you drop a 2-in. steel sphere from a height of 51 in. The impact must not create openings that would permit the articulated probe of **Fig 2** to make contact with live parts.*

must not exceed 0.5 mA. If your unit incorporates a line filter, the spec allows a ground-circuit current of 5 mA.

The leakage requirement for Class II devices is 250 μA max vs 5 mA for Class I units. Moreover, you must measure the insulation resistance; the UL limit is 7 MΩ min. If inaccessible dead metal exists in the enclosure, the resistance between the dead metal and the live parts must be 2 MΩ min. Between the inaccessible metal and the accessible surface, it must be a minimum of 5 MΩ. Before performing insulation tests, you must condition the equipment by exposing it to 99% relative humidity for 48 hours.

A final test necessary to satisfy UL performance requirements involves checking the motors connected to the secondary circuitry for fire hazards. This test, applicable to motors running at voltage and power lev-

els lower than 100V, 200 VA, consists of locking the rotor at full power for seven hours. You have to place cheesecloth over the equipment under test; it must not ignite. For motors running at levels higher than 100V, 200 VA, you have to apply the test for primary-circuit abnormals. Motors in Class 2 circuits and stepping motors are exempt from the locked-rotor test.

100% factory testing is required, too

All of these performance tests must, of course, be done on the sample units used in the evaluation and approval process. You should also be aware, however, that 100% factory testing is required for compliance.

IEC 950: UL 478's European counterpart

In contrast with the old days, when you had to apply for approval in each European country where you wanted to sell equipment, you can now follow the "harmonized" IEC specs, which all members of the European Economic Community accept. Because it is similar in principle and intent to UL 478, the spec of most interest here is IEC 950.

The two standards do have several differences, however. One is the acceptability of reinforced insulation in Class II devices. IEC 950 dictates that reinforced insulation is acceptable only in cases where the use of basic and supplemental insulation is clearly impractical.

IEC 950 is strict on the amount of acceptable minimum clearance (shortest distance in air between two parts) and creepage (distance over insulating surface between two parts). Primary circuits must have 3-mm min clearance and creepage between parts of opposite polarity for basic insulation and 4 mm for supplemental insulation. Parts separated by solid insulation have to be at least 1 mm thick to qualify as supplementary insulation and 2 mm thick for reinforced insulation.

The standard also mandates stringent insulation and dielectric tests. First, you have to condition the equipment at 93% relative humidity for two days. You then ap-

ply 500V dc for one minute between the secondaries and the enclosure, and then between the primaries and the enclosure. Class II devices have to be wrapped in metal foil. Resistance must exceed 7 MΩ. For the dielectric test, you apply 1250 to 3750V dc between the same points.

Another insulation test is the one governing leakage current.

This current can result from the lack of grounding of Class II equipment or from the disconnection of the ground return in Class I units. The limit for most Class I devices is 3.5 mA; for Class II equipment, it is 0.25 mA. Portable Class I machines have a 0.75-mA leakage-current limit.

IEC 950 recognizes Class 2 (note the Arabic numeral) circuits, which IEC standards de-

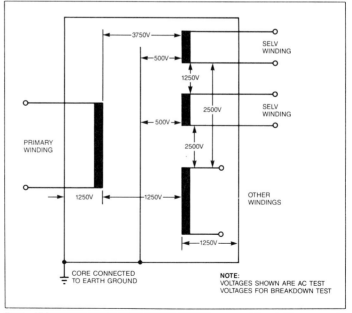

Fig A—IEC requirements for safety isolating transformers are stringent. The specs require >3750V ac breakdown between the primary and the SELV secondaries and >1250V ac breakdown between all windings and the transformer's case.

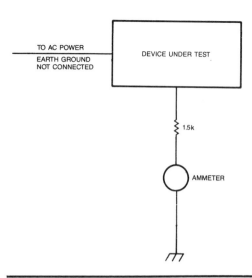

TO AC POWER

EARTH GROUND
NOT CONNECTED

DEVICE UNDER TEST

1.5k

AMMETER

Fig 6—For equipment with no earth-ground return, you must test for leakage to ground. For such ungrounded equipment, the leakage to ground must not exceed 0.5 mA. If your equipment has a line filter, UL specs allow a maximum leakage of 5 mA.

note as "SELV," or safety extra-low-voltage circuits. IEC specs for insulation and isolation are more stringent than UL specs. A SELV circuit's wires and harnesses must be double insulated (for example, with supplemental tubing). Further, the IEC specs for transformers used in SELV circuits are far stricter than the UL standards. **Fig A** shows the IEC breakdown requirements for transformers.

As is the case with UL compliance, all components in a unit have to meet IEC component specs. The use of some components requires special care. For instance, all capacitors greater than 1 µF must be marked with their voltage rating and capacitance. You should not connect capacitors across thermal-cutout devices. Across-the-line capacitors in primaries must have a value lower than 0.5 µF, or they must have a bleeder resistor in parallel that discharges the capacitor to 34V max one second after disconnection.

IEC 950 mechanical-stress tests are similar to those of UL 478. First, you press against external covers and guards with a test tool having a spherical steel surface of 30-mm diameter, using a force of 250N. Next, you drop a 0.5-kg, 15-mm diameter sphere from a height of 1.3m onto the top and sides of the equipment.

TABLE A—IEC 950 DIELECTRIC-STRENGTH TESTS		
VOLTAGE APPLIED BETWEEN	CLASS I	CLASS II
PRIMARY AND BODY	1250V	3750V
PRIMARY AND SELV SECONDARIES	3750V	3750V
PRIMARY AND NON-SELV SECONDARIES	1250V	1250V
SELV SECONDARIES AND BODY	NO TEST	NO TEST
NON-SELV SECONDARIES AND BODY	1250V*	2500V
SELV AND NON-SELV SECONDARIES	2500V	2500V

*APPLY 10 TIMES THE WORKING VOLTAGE, TO 1250V MAX.
NO TEST NEEDED IF SECONDARY OPERATES AT <30V RMS.

You drop a handheld unit in its worst-case orientation from a height of 1m onto a hardwood floor.

Finally, the equipment has to undergo a 70°C bake for seven hours. After the tests, the unit cannot have openings that permit contact with hazardous parts. In addition, you should not be able to pull the power-supply cord free from the housing, and the unit should show no compromise of its supplemental or reinforced insulation.

You'll encounter a number of IEC 950 performance tests for ensuring device safety. First, you run the device at 10% above and 15% below its rated voltage. During these tests, overload protection should not operate. Next, you test dielectrics by applying 50% of the voltages shown in **Table A** to the primary circuits. A fully loaded unit should not draw more than 110% of its rated cur-

rent. Motor-operated equipment must start smoothly three times at 85% rated voltage.

In the IEC 950 abnormals test for motors, units with thermal or impedance protection run with locked rotors for 18 and 15 days, respectively. Motors with manual reset capability run through 60 cycles with locked rotors. Temperature increases cannot exceed 150 to 215°C. A similar abnormals test for transformers uses shorted secondaries and alternately opened and shorted primaries.

Finally, the IEC spec (as well as UL) places a limit of 0.5 mrad/hr of CRT x-ray emission; the spec also limits ozone concentrations to 0.1 ppm. You should take care when you design circuitry that can generate ozone (for example, high-voltage circuits), because this gas is heavier than air and can accumulate in pockets.

34 JFET serves as low-power logic translator

Simple non-inverting logic level translator

A bipolar transistor makes a fine logic level translator, but it is inverting. This translator is not, and uses fewer components as well.

Timothy R Wolf
Herley Microwave Systems, Lancaster, PA

Fig 1 shows a simple method for translating a 5V logic signal to the 12 or 15V level required by certain CMOS ICs. Transistor Q_1 is an n-channel JFET operating in the common-gate mode. A source voltage above 1 or 2V pinches the JFET's channel off and allows R_1 to pull the drain voltage to V_S. A source voltage near 0V turns the channel on, which places the drain near 0V as well.

R_1 determines the circuit's speed and power consumption. Values from 100 kΩ to 1 MΩ draw approximately 150 to 15 µA and set a practical pulse-rate limit of about 1 MHz. This circuit consumes less power than one based on a bipolar transistor, and it does away with one part (the base resistor).

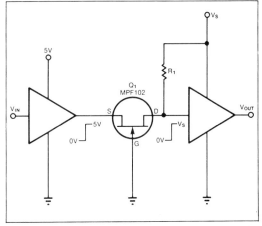

*Fig 1—This JFET, operating in the **common-gate mode**, provides low-power translation of a 5V logic signal to higher voltage levels.*

35 Floating-point math handles iterative and recursive algorithms

Floating point representation of numbers

This article reviews the various standards used to represent numbers in 32 bit form, as commonly used in computing. Whereas computer manufacturers naturally use their in-house format, semiconductor manufacturers (such as Motorola, in their DSP96002) tend to favour the IEEE format. Some DSP chips are capable of supporting more than one standard, for example IEEE and DEC.

Charlie Ashton, *Advanced Micro Devices Inc*

Many signal-processing algorithms, such as fast Fourier transforms, generate outputs whose magnitudes far exceed those of the inputs. Nevertheless, those outputs must retain the precision of the input operands if the accuracy of the computation is not to be so severely degraded as to render the results meaningless. For these and similar applications that use iterative or recursive algorithms, true floating-point operation often furnishes the only acceptable number representation.

Until recently, you needed a very good reason to give your system floating-point hardware. It was large, expensive, power-hungry, and relatively slow (although faster than the software-based implementations needed to perform comparable operations). However, the introduction of fast VLSI array processors has changed the picture. These devices (such as Weitek's 1032/1033 and AMD's Am29325) can stand alone and are implemented on one or two chips. You can now economically use floating-point hardware in applications whose size and budget constraints would previously have forced the use of fixed-point hardware or floating-point software.

The new chips won't dissipate all your potential headaches, of course. Just one of the many choices you'll have to make is which standard to support. The four most commonly used standards (IEEE, DEC, IBM, and MIL-STD-1750A) have subtly different binary representations of floating-point numbers. Each standard has advantages and disadvantages for specific types of computational problems. This series of articles covers some of the theoretical considerations you'll have to take into account, as well as some specifics on the available chips.

The manner in which a system represents floating-point numbers clearly affects both the dynamic range and the precision of the system. The most obvious way to represent numbers is to use a signed exponent and a signed fraction (**Table 1**). A large exponent field obviously supports a large dynamic range: A 2-digit exponent, for example, implies a dynamic range of 10^{100}, whereas a 3-digit exponent increases the dynamic range to 10^{1000}. Similarly, the more digits you can include in the fraction, the greater will be the precision of the number, especially if the number is normalized so that the left-most digit of the fraction is nonzero. Leading zeros in the fraction of an unnormalized number clearly reduce the precision of that number. As a general principle, then, the precision of a floating-point

TABLE 1—SIGNED vs BIASED EXPONENTS

DECIMAL NUMBER		SIGNED EXPONENT		FRACTION
−123.45	=	10^{+3}	×	−0.12345
+0.0000678	=	10^{-4}	×	0.678

DECIMAL NUMBER		BIASED EXPONENT		FRACTION
−123.45	=	$5+3=8$	×	0.12345
+0.0000678	=	$5-4=1$	×	0.678

number depends on the length of its fraction, and the dynamic range depends on the size of the exponent and the radix.

In practice, floating-point hardware generally uses a biased exponent for two reasons. First, use of a biased exponent avoids problems that follow from the need to handle negative numbers in the exponent circuitry. Second (and perhaps more important), a suitable choice of bias can ensure that you'll be able to compute the reciprocals of all the representable numbers without exponential overflow or underflow. You'll find that overflow and underflow cause plenty of problems in computing the fraction portion of the output (see **box**, "Dealing with underflow and overflow"). You certainly don't want to introduce them into exponential computations as well.

Biased exponents and normalized fractions are the features that give true floating-point representation a clear advantage over block floating-point and integer formats. To double the dynamic range of an integer word, you have to double the number of bits in it. To obtain the same result in true floating-point operation, you need to add only one bit to the exponential field. In fact, a 32-bit floating-point number in IEEE format has a dynamic range equivalent to that of a 276-bit 2's-complement integer.

Despite the high precision and large dynamic range of normalized floating-point numbers, floating-point systems do not altogether escape the effect of quantization (rounding) errors. You can think of a floating-point system as producing an infinitely precise result (ie, a fraction of unlimited length, abbreviated "IPR"), which is then rounded to fit into the destination format.

Typically, this strategy means that some of the low-order fraction bits are lost. Consequently, whenever the destination format lacks enough bits to accommodate the IPR, rounding introduces quantization errors, which in turn result in system noise. Consider, for example, the multiplication of two numbers in a 4-digit decimal system:

$$(0.8102 \times 10^3) \times (0.8001 \times 10^{-7}) = 0.6410401 \times 10^{-4}.$$

The IPR is rounded to 0.6410×10^{-4} to fit the destination format, thus introducing a quantization error. In practice, quantization errors during a long computation will be random, and the overall effect will be analogous to an increase in system white noise. If the quantization errors are *not* random, they may appear as system nonlinearities and, as a consequence, cause serious problems in such applications as spectral analysis.

Are quantization errors data dependent?

Mathematical analysis of an integer system shows that quantization errors due to rounding have a mean value of one-quarter the value of the least significant

Dealing with underflow and overflow

For the rare cases in which the result of a calculation is too large or too small to be represented, you must have previously specified the way in which your system will deal with that result. In short, your system must handle the related problems of underflow and overflow.

Underflow arises when the rounded result of an operation is a number between zero and the smallest representable normalized number. You can handle such a number in one of two ways: You can set the number to zero (sudden underflow), or you can represent the rounded result by a denormalized number (gradual underflow).

Overflow occurs when the rounded result of an operation is greater than the largest representable number. You can handle this problem by setting the result to infinity, which implicitly terminates a chain of calculations, or by saturating the result to the largest representable number (correctly signed).

It's important to know which of the various methods your system supports, because in some

applications sudden underflow or saturated overflow can destroy the accuracy of an entire series of calculations. The IEEE standard, for example, treats underflows by invoking the gradual underflow method, while the IBM and DEC standards deal with only sudden underflow.

Sudden underflow is generally the fastest method of treating underflows and is acceptable in the majority of systems because high accuracy is seldom required for very small numbers. Sudden underflow can produce quantization errors almost as large as the smallest normalized number, but usually you can treat these errors as insignificant.

The gradual-underflow method creates much smaller errors because it rounds results to a normalized number. On the other hand, gradual underflow is more difficult and more expensive to implement than sudden underflow, a drawback you'll have to weigh against the advantage of accurate results over a wider range of numbers. Gradual underflow is generally best for iterative applications in which

you drive a residual value to zero and for which you require maximum possible accuracy. When such a residual value underflows gradually to zero, you know that it's negligible compared with every normalized number.

For handling overflow, data-processing applications generally set the result to infinity, because in a high-accuracy mathematical model a saturated result could destroy the accuracy of an entire series of calculations. In real-time digital signal processing, however, it's generally preferable to saturate the result and continue the chain of calculations. In the analysis of radar returns, for example, you would certainly not want a single anomalous return to bring the entire processing sequence to a halt by introducing an operand (an infinity) that would be useless in further processing. In this and similar applications, it's often better to have an approximately correct data point than no data point at all.

TABLE 2—NUMBER REPRESENTATION
IN FOUR FLOATING-POINT STANDARDS

IEEE FORMAT

BIT	31	30	29	28	27	26	25	24	23	22	21	20	19		3	2	1	0
	S	2^7	2^6	2^5	2^4	2^3	2^2	2^1	2^0	2^{-1}	2^{-2}	2^{-3}	2^{-4}	$\cdots$	2^{-20}	2^{-21}	2^{-22}	2^{-23}

SIGN S	BIASED EXPONENT (E)	FRACTION (F)

$E = 0$ AND $F = 0$ .... $V = (-1)^S * 0 (-0, +0)$
$E = 0$ AND $F \neq 0$ .... $V = (-1)^S * 0.F * 2^{-126}$ (DENORMALIZED)
$0 < E < 255$ .... $V = (-1)^S * 1.F * 2^{E-127}$ (NORMALIZED)
$E = 255$ AND $F = 0$ ...... $V = (-1)^S * 00 (-00, +00)$
$E = 255$ AND $F \neq 0$ ...... $V = $ NaN (NOT-A-NUMBER)

(a)

DEC FORMAT

BIT	31	30	29	28	27	26	25	24	23	22	21	20	19		3	2	1	0
	S	2^7	2^6	2^5	2^4	2^3	2^2	2^1	2^0	2^{-2}	2^{-3}	2^{-4}	2^{-5}	$\cdots$	2^{-21}	2^{-22}	2^{-23}	2^{-24}

SIGN S	BIASED EXPONENT (E)	FRACTION (F)

$S = 1$ AND $E = 0$ .... $V = $ DEC RESERVED OPERAND
$S = 0$ AND $E = 0$ .... $V = 0$
$E > 0$ .... $V = (-1)^S * 0.1F * 2^{E-128}$ (NORMALIZED)

(b)

IBM FORMAT

BIT	31	30	29	28	27	26	25	24	23	22	21	20	19		3	2	1	0
	S	2^6	2^5	2^4	2^3	2^2	2^1	2^0	2^{-1}	2^{-2}	2^{-3}	2^{-4}	2^{-5}	$\cdots$	2^{-21}	2^{-22}	2^{-23}	2^{-24}

SIGN S	BIASED EXPONENT (E)	FRACTION (F)

$F = 0$ .... $V = (-1)^S * 0 (-0, +0)$
$F \neq 0$ .... $V = (-1)^S * 0.F * 16^{E-64}$

(c)

MIL-STD-1750A FORMAT

BIT	31	30	29	28	27		11	10	9	8	7	6	5	4	3	2	1	0
	-2^0	2^{-1}	2^{-2}	2^{-3}	2^{-4}	$\cdots$	2^{-20}	2^{-21}	2^{-22}	2^{-23}	-2^7	2^6	2^5	2^4	2^3	2^2	2^1	2^0

FRACTION (F)	EXPONENT (E)

.... $V = F * 2^E$

(d)

bit. The relative error at each rounding thus depends on the magnitude of the operand being rounded. Therefore, as the magnitude of the operand decreases, the relative quantization error increases. The same is true of a block floating-point system, in which denormalized operands may contain leading zeros. In integer and block-floating-point systems, therefore, the errors are data-dependent, and for this reason error analysis is both difficult and time-consuming.

In true floating-point systems, however, operands are generally normalized, so the relative quantization errors are the same, regardless of the magnitude of the operands. Quantization error analysis in floating-point systems is thus data independent and therefore doesn't require complicated worst-case simulations.

Floating-point systems can suffer from a computational drawback known as the "operand ordering problem." Consider the addition of three floating-point numbers: A ($=1$), B ($=2^{90}$), and C ($=-2^{90}$). You may find that $(A+B)+C=0$, although $A+(B+C)=1$. This result clearly violates the associative law of addition. The discrepancy occurs because the floating-point standard doesn't have enough bits to accommodate the intermediate result of the first calculation $(A+B)$. The hardware has to round the IPR, $2^{90}+1$, to the nearest representable number, which is 2^{90}. Errors of this kind are inevitable whenever the IPR has to be rounded to fit the destination format, although they would usually be considered so small as to be unimportant.

You can minimize rounding errors (although, as the previous example shows, you can't entirely remove them) by a judicious choice of rounding mode. Some floating-point standards allow you to select from among several rounding modes the one that best suits your operation. All of the commonly used floating-point standards support one or more of four modes:

- Round-to-nearest mode replaces the IPR with the closest representation that fits in the destination format. In the case of an IPR that falls exactly halfway between two representations, the IEEE standard rounds the IPR to the representation having an LSB of zero, whereas the DEC standard rounds the IPR to the representation that has the greater magnitude.
- Round-to-minus-infinity mode rounds the IPR to the closest representable value that is less than or equal to the IPR.
- Round-to-plus-infinity mode rounds the IPR to the closest representable value that is greater than or equal to the IPR.
- Round-to-zero mode is analogous to truncation; it rounds the IPR to the closest representable value with a magnitude less than or equal to that of the IPR.

As noted earlier, the various floating-point standards specify different binary representations of floating-point numbers, and you'll have to match their respective advantages and disadvantages to your own computational problems. The four of the most common binary floating-point standards, the IEEE, DEC, IBM, and MIL-STD-1750A standards, all represent single-precision, floating-point numbers by means of 32-bit words having the formats shown in **Table 2**. All four standards support double-precision data, and some of these standards also support other data types, such as single-extended and double-extended data.

The IEEE working group presented the specifications contained in proposed standard P754, draft 10.1, as a robust standard for portable floating-point software. This proposed standard has received wide acceptance, and it's likely to form the basis of a large number of future hardware implementations. P754 has several features that aren't found in other standards. In particular, $+0$, -0, and infinities are all valid operands. Operations performed on infinities signal no exceptions unless the operation itself is invalid. The standard allows the use of a special operand known as NaN (Not-a-Number). An implementation should interpret NaNs as signals rather than numbers, and it should use NaNs to indicate invalid operations or to pass status information through a series of calculations. Also, the standard accepts denormalized numbers as a representation of a result that is less than the smallest normalized number.

TABLE 3—COMPARISON OF FLOATING-POINT STANDARDS

	IEEE	DEC	IBM	1750A
LARGEST POSITIVE NUMBER	$2^{128}-2^{104}$	$2^{127}-2^{103}$	$2^{253}-2^{228}$	$2^{127}-2^{103}$
SMALLEST POSITIVE NUMBER	2^{-149}	2^{-128}	2^{-280}	2^{-129}
LARGEST NEGATIVE NUMBER	$-2^{128}+2^{104}$	$-2^{127}+2^{103}$	$-2^{253}+2^{228}$	-2^{127}
SMALLEST NEGATIVE NUMBER	-2^{-149}	-2^{-128}	-2^{-280}	-2^{-129}
DYNAMIC RANGE	2^{277}	2^{255}	2^{533}	2^{256}
PRECISION	2^{-23}	2^{-23}	2^{-20}	2^{-23}

The DEC standard is implemented in all DEC VAX minicomputers; the VAX Architecture Manual contains the full specifications of the standard. Conceptually simpler than the IEEE standard, the DEC standard has no provisions for infinities or denormalized numbers, and it has only a single representation for zero. The DEC standard does, however, incorporate DEC reserved operands, which are analogous to IEEE NaNs.

An important feature common to both the IEEE and the DEC standards is the existence of a hidden bit. Both standards specify that all operands will be normalized (except for denormalized numbers in the IEEE format). This stricture implies that the leading fraction bit must always be a one. This bit would not only be redundant if included in the 32-bit representation, but it would actually reduce the precision of the number, so its presence is assumed. In the case of IEEE denormalized numbers, the biased exponent is zero, thereby instructing the system to assume that the value of the hidden bit is also zero.

The IBM floating-point standard differs from its IEEE and DEC counterparts in several respects. It has no provision for infinities or reserved operands, although it does accept denormalized numbers. More important, however, are the absence of a hidden bit and the use of radix 16 rather than radix 2. Because the exponent of an IBM number is expressed as a power of 16, the standard has a large dynamic range. For the same reason, however, numbers are spaced farther apart than in the other formats. This increased granularity results in less precision than is provided by the IEEE and DEC formats. Also, the use of radix 16 allows as many as three leading zeros in the binary fraction of a normalized number, even though the leading hexadecimal digit is nonzero if the number is expressed in hexadecimal format. The leading binary zeros can cause the precision to vary from one operand to another. This variation is known as wobbling.

The MIL-STD-1750A standard, developed for use in military systems, allows no reserved operands, infinities, or denormalized numbers. Furthermore, the use of a 2's-complement fraction, rather than a sign-magnitude representation as in the other three formats, requires a somewhat different hardware architecture.

The applications to which each of the four standards is best suited differ quite widely. Nevertheless, you can make a simple comparison (**Table 3**) between the standards, based on factors such as the largest and smallest representable numbers, the dynamic range, and the precision. Such a comparison can be useful in selecting the most suitable format for a given application. In most cases, however, the format to be used is determined by outside constraints, such as compatibility with existing hardware or software.

VLSI floating-point μP for recursive algorithms

One example of floating-point hardware that handles recursive algorithms is the Am29325 from Advanced Micro Devices. The processor integrates a 32-bit adder/subtracter, a multiplier, and a data path on a single chip. This level of integration reduces the processing overhead incurred by chip sets comprising separate ALU and multiplier chips. The internal feedback paths facilitate the implementation of such recursive algorithms as sum-of-products and Newton-Raphson division.

The processor supports both the IEEE and DEC floating-point formats. The instruction set includes instructions that convert data from IEEE format to DEC format and vice versa, as well as instructions that convert data to and from 32-bit integer format.

Three functional blocks

The processor has three main functional blocks (**Fig A**): a floating-point ALU, a status-flag generator, and a 32-bit internal data path. The ALU is fully combinatorial, and it performs all instructions in a single cycle. The eight instructions handle floating-point R+S, R−S, R×S, and 2−S operations as well as the format conversions.

The 2−S instruction forms the core of the Newton-Raphson division algorithm, which performs division by a sequence of iterations. In this and other iterative algorithms, intermediate results are retained in the R or S register, thereby eliminating the need for any off-chip registers and minimizing the number of required data transfers.

Three programmable I/O modes allow the Am29325 to interface with a variety of systems. The 32-bit, 2-input-bus mode uses three separate 32-bit

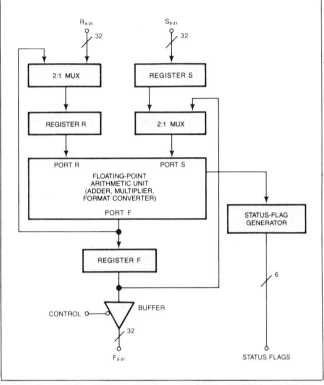

Fig A—This VLSI floating-point processor is fast because it contains all the major components for 32-bit operations on a single chip. It has one input for an external clock and 17 inputs for instruction-select and control functions.

buses (R, S, and F) for high-speed, nonmultiplexed operation; in this case, the R and S registers are configured as independent 32-bit ports. In the 32-bit, 1-input-bus mode, both the R and S registers are connected to a common 32-bit input bus; the host multiplexes operands onto this bus. In the 16-bit, 2-input-bus mode, 32-bit operands are multiplexed onto the corresponding 16-bit buses (low-order bits first).

Six flags and four modes

The status-flag generator provides six fully decoded flags. Four of these flags report exceptional conditions, as defined in

the IEEE standard. The remaining two flags identify zero-valued or nonnumerical results.

The Am29325 implements the four IEEE-mandated rounding modes: round-to-nearest, round-to-plus-infinity, round-to-minus-infinity, and round-to-zero. The same four modes are supported for the DEC standard, except that when the infinitely precise result is halfway between two representable numbers, the IEEE round-to-nearest mode rounds to the closest representation with an LSB of zero, whereas the DEC round-to-nearest mode rounds to the value with the larger magnitude.

36 Multiple technologies produce fast clock

L band clock generator

Many RF-ish ideas for designs tend to go to the magazines specializing in RF and microwave, but *EDN* gets its fair share. This example shows a clock generator whose frequency is controlled by a surface acoustic wave device. Needless to say, at this frequency, extreme attention to the detailed layout will be essential to obtain the desired results.

Michael A Wyatt
SSAvD Honeywell Inc, Clearwater, FL

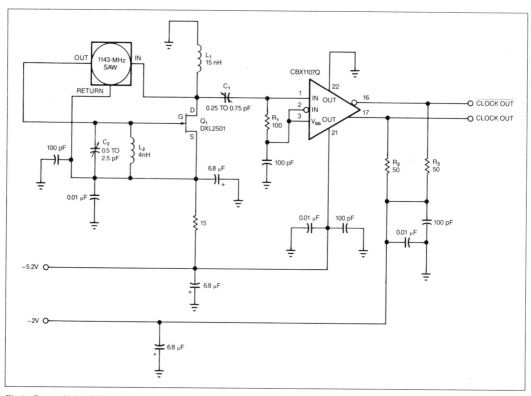

Fig 1—By combining SAW, GaAs, and ECL devices, *this circuit implements a fast, stable oscillator.*

By combining SAW, GaAs, and high-speed bipolar devices, you can achieve an ECL-compatible clock oscillator (**Fig 1**). The heart of the circuit is the SAW-stabilized network that surrounds Q_1, the DXL2401 GaAs FET from Gould Dexcel Div (Santa Clara, CA). The 1143 SAW oscillator from RF Monolithics (Dallas, TX) has 180° of phase shift at resonance and couples the

energy from Q_1's drain to its gate. L_1 and C_1 tune Q_1's drain to 1143 MHz; L_2 and C_2 tune Q_1's gate to 1143 MHz. These networks also maintain the proper phase relationship for oscillation at 1143 MHz. The frequency of oscillation and temperature drifts are strictly determined by the SAW characteristics. High-quality SAW devices typically have Qs in the neighborhood of 6000 and frequency-drift rates as low as 1 ppm/°C.

An ultrahigh-speed, bipolar, ECL-compatible decision IC, the Sony CBX1107Q, functions as a comparator and ECL-level translator. C_1 couples Q_1's output to the CBX1107Q's noninverting data input. R_1 acts as a load resistor and supplies bias voltage to pin 1 of the decision IC. The inverting data input of the CBX1107Q is directly connected to the bias voltage, V_{BB}, which configures the IC as a high-speed analog comparator with input levels around V_{BB}. R_2, R_3, and the $-2V$ supply provide the proper termination and voltage level for ECL-compatible logic from the CBX1107Q's data outputs.

37 Power isolators are bidirectional

Two-way DC isolated power supply

I have never yet needed to be able to power item A from item B or vice versa at will, while maintaining DC isolation between them. But if I ever do, I shall know how to.

John LaBelle
Logical Control Engineering, Long Beach, CA

The power isolators in **Figs 1** and **2** have the remarkable property of being bidirectional. That is, you can energize either side of the circuits with the appropriate voltage and draw regulated current from the other side.

In operation, the FETs on the powered side of the isolator drive transformer T_2 into saturation first in one direction, then in the opposite direction. T_2's winding inductance disappears when the transformer goes into saturation. Transformer T_1 provides the input-to-output power coupling during T_2's saturation. Resistors R_1, R_2, R_3, and R_4 and capacitors C_3 and C_4 control the voltage overshoot from the winding's leakage induc-

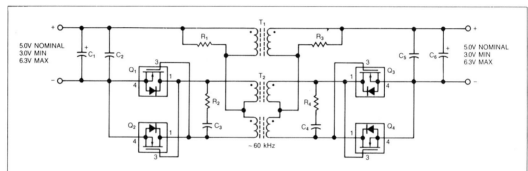

PARTS LIST

REFERENCE	DESCRIPTION
C_2, C_5	0.1 µF 50V CERAMIC CAPACITOR KEMET C320C104M5U5CA
C_1, C_6	100 µF 6.3 VDC TANTALUM CAPACITOR SPRAGUE 199D107X96R3DA1
C_3, C_4	0.0015 µF 50V CERAMIC CAPACITOR KEMET C320C152M2R5CA
R_2, R_4	3.3Ω 0.25W CARBON RESISTOR ALLEN BRADLEY RCR07-3.3
R_1, R_3	10Ω 0.25W CARBON RESISTOR ALLEN BRADLEY RCR07-10
Q_1, Q_2, Q_3, Q_4	N-CHANNEL POWER MOSFET INTERNATIONAL RECTIFIER IRFD120
T_1	2 STRANDS OF #28 AWG KYNAR INSULATED WIRE-WRAP WIRE. 7 TURNS BIFILAR WOUND ON FERROXCUBE 266T125-3E2A CORE
T_2	4 STRANDS OF #28 AWG KYNAR INSULATED WIRE-WRAP WIRE. 7 TURNS QUADFILAR WOUND ON FERROXCUBE 266T125-3E2A CORE

OUTPUT VOLTAGE VERSUS LOAD

INPUT VOLTS	INPUT AMPS	OUTPUT VOLTS	LOAD OHMS	OUTPUT AMPS	OUTPUT WATTS
5.	0.063	4.98	OPEN	0.000	0.000
5.	0.112	4.95	100	0.050	0.245
5.	0.160	4.92	50	0.098	0.484
5.	0.255	4.86	25	0.194	0.945
5.	0.439	4.74	12.5	0.379	1.80

Fig 1—This 5V, 1W power isolator *is bidirectional and provides 3750V ac isolation.*

tance. The FETs on the load side of the isolator act as rectifiers.

The isolators operate at around 60 kHz. Their output impedance is essentially the on-resistance of the two FETs in the 5V isolator—0.6Ω—or the four FETs in the 12V isolator—2.4Ω. You can obtain stepped-up or stepped-down voltages by mating one side of the 5V circuit to one side of the 12V circuit.

If you use the specified Kynar-insulated wire (0.005-

in. insulation), the transformers will provide 3750V ac rms isolation. They will also pass a 1-sec, 5000V ac rms hipot test. You can use identical transformers for T_1 and T_2 in the 5V isolator by connecting the windings of T_2 in parallel and using it as T_1.

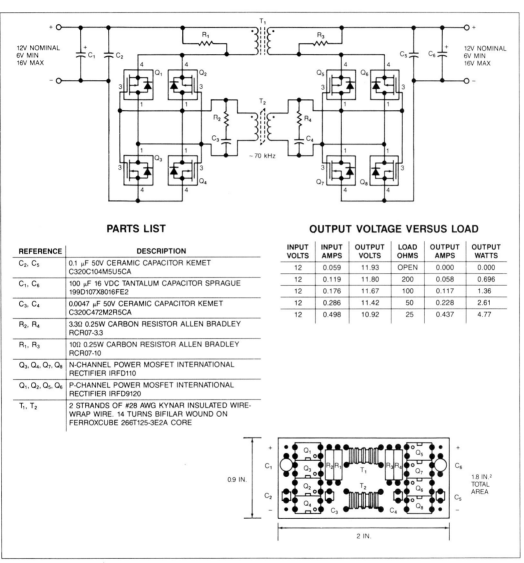

PARTS LIST

REFERENCE	DESCRIPTION
C_2, C_5	0.1 µF 50V CERAMIC CAPACITOR KEMET C320C104M5U5CA
C_1, C_6	100 µF 16 VDC TANTALUM CAPACITOR SPRAGUE 199D107X8016FE2
C_3, C_4	0.0047 µF 50V CERAMIC CAPACITOR KEMET C320C472M2R5CA
R_2, R_4	3.3Ω 0.25W CARBON RESISTOR ALLEN BRADLEY RCR07-3.3
R_1, R_3	10Ω 0.25W CARBON RESISTOR ALLEN BRADLEY RCR07-10
Q_3, Q_4, Q_7, Q_8	N-CHANNEL POWER MOSFET INTERNATIONAL RECTIFIER IRFD110
Q_1, Q_2, Q_5, Q_6	P-CHANNEL POWER MOSFET INTERNATIONAL RECTIFIER IRFD9120
T_1, T_2	2 STRANDS OF #28 AWG KYNAR INSULATED WIRE-WRAP WIRE. 14 TURNS BIFILAR WOUND ON FERROXCUBE 266T125-3E2A CORE

OUTPUT VOLTAGE VERSUS LOAD

INPUT VOLTS	INPUT AMPS	OUTPUT VOLTS	LOAD OHMS	OUTPUT AMPS	OUTPUT WATTS
12	0.059	11.93	OPEN	0.000	0.000
12	0.119	11.80	200	0.058	0.696
12	0.176	11.67	100	0.117	1.36
12	0.286	11.42	50	0.228	2.61
12	0.498	10.92	25	0.437	4.77

Fig 2—Similar to the circuit in Fig 1, this circuit handles 12V at 2W.

38 Make passive filters active with a floating synthetic inductor

Make passive filters active

Active filters are widely used, notwithstanding the ready availability and convenience in application of switched capacitor filters. This is because switched capacitor filters (and the earlier N-path type of filter which they have supplanted) are sampled data filters and must therefore in many applications themselves be preceded by a purely analog (time-continuous) filter, and because in sensitive measurement applications, there is always the possibility of spurious responses involving the clock frequency. For the realization of time continuous active filters there are several possibilities, including filters based on second order RC sections such as the active Biquad, and filters based directly on the corresponding passive version with the inductors (too lossy and expensive to be useful at low frequencies) replaced by synthetic inductors. This article takes the latter route.

Arthur D Delagrange, US Navy Dept

You can apply the floating-inductor design developed in this article to all types of filters—bandpass and bandstop versions as well as high- and low-pass configurations. The design expands on a previously presented technique (**Ref 1**), which proves useful in the creation of grounded synthetic inductors for converting passive high- and low-pass filters into active units but doesn't apply to bandpass/bandstop versions. And it overcomes the limitations of circuit-design tricks (**Ref 2**) capable of converting only certain passive bandpass/bandstop forms to their active counterparts.

Passive prototypes are well classified

Why start with passive-filter designs rather than design active units from scratch? First, the passive prototypes are extensively catalogued (**Ref 3**). And second, passive filters usually exhibit good (ie, low) sensitivities in their reactive elements—an advantage in active designs.

Consider, for example, the low-pass prototype circuit shown in **Fig 1**—a 3-pole, 2-zero, 1.25-dB-ripple, 39-dB-stopband design. (Note that all prototypes used here are normalized to the standard 1-rad/sec, 1Ω-impedance form, with values in ohms, farads and henries.) The most commonly used bandpass transformation for this design (**Ref 4**) makes the following substitution in the filter transfer function:

$$S = (S^2 + \omega_o^2) \div S.$$

This substitution geometrically moves the low-pass function, including its mirror image, up to a center frequency of ω_o. It also compresses the function by a

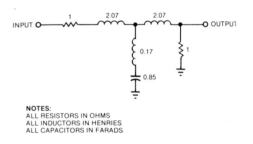

Fig 1—A prototype low-pass filter *forms the basis of this article's passive-to-active-filter conversion. It's chosen as the basis of the design method because such passive filters are well-documented.*

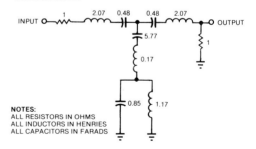

Fig 2—Adding a parallel inductor *to each capacitor in Fig 1's low-pass design and a series capacitor to each inductor transforms the design to a bandpass filter.*

factor of two, so that the bandwidth remains essentially unchanged. The circuit changes required to perform the substitution include adding a parallel inductor to each capacitor and a series capacitor to each inductor, with each LC reactance having a frequency of ω_o.

Fig 2 illustrates this conversion with $\omega_o = 1$, resulting in an approximately octave bandpass. For this value of ω_o, the L and C values in each resonator section are reciprocals. However, because they're calculated to four decimal places and then rounded down to two, they might not appear precisely so. Note that the circuit contains both floating capacitors and floating inductors and that it's not in ladder form.

Build a 1H synthetic inductor

How can you turn **Fig 2**'s passive design into an active one? Start with the circuit depicted in **Fig 3**, which appears at its terminals to be a 1H floating inductor. In this circuit, which is merely the grounded

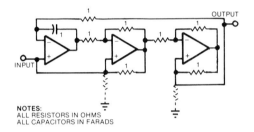

NOTES:
ALL RESISTORS IN OHMS
ALL CAPACITORS IN FARADS

Fig 3—**This floating synthetic 1H inductor** uses three op amps: The first acts as an integrator and the other two as current sources.

inductor used in **Ref 1** equipped with an added op amp, the first op amp is an integrator and the other two are current sources.

The current sources require matched resistors, readily available in DIPs in groups of seven or more. Depending on how the tolerance errors stack up, you might also need the indicated broken-line resistors for stability; for 1%-tolerance filter components, their values can be 10 to 100 times as great as those of the other resistors. Note also that if you plan to use this synthetic inductor in a circuit where one end is grounded, make that end the right-hand one, effectively eliminating the third op amp and reverting the circuit to the 2-amplifier design.

Several ICs containing quad op amps usable in this design are available. However, you should minimize the number of op amps—less because of cost than because of performance limitations. Note also that you probably couldn't devise a dual-op-amp circuit without using approximations, which introduce problems of their own.

Replacing each inductor in **Fig 2**'s design with **Fig 3**'s synthetic inductor results in an active filter. **Fig 4** shows the final circuit after frequency scaling to 1000 rad/sec (160 Hz)—achieved by first dividing all capacitor values by 10^3 and then impedance-scaling to 10 kΩ by multiplying all resistor values and dividing all capacitor values by 10^4.

The performance of **Fig 4**'s circuit with a 160-Hz center frequency appears as the virtually textbook-case solid curve in **Fig 5**. The lower notch is really deeper than it appears because oscillator harmonics come through in the bandpass.

The broken line in **Fig 5** shows the results of raising the center frequency to 1.6 kHz by reducing all capacitor values by a factor of 10 and lowering the values of the stability resistors. The resulting bandpass droops, and the upper stopband does not fall off properly.

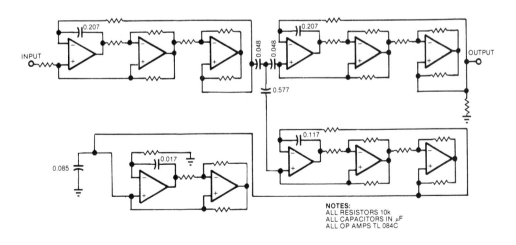

NOTES:
ALL RESISTORS 10k
ALL CAPACITORS IN μF
ALL OP AMPS TL 084C

Fig 4—**Replacing each inductor in Fig 2's circuit** with **Fig 3**'s floating synthetic inductor produces an active filter.

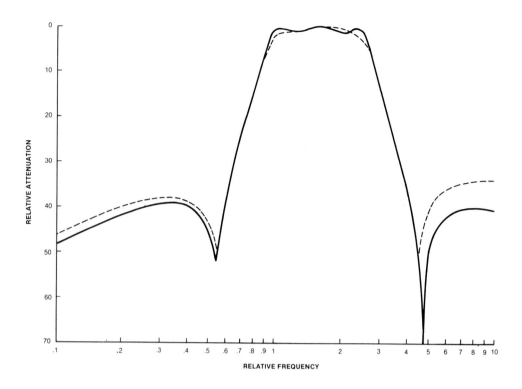

Fig 5—Performance of Fig 4's active filter *at a 160-Hz center frequency (solid line) is almost textbook perfect. At 1.6 kHz (broken line), the performance departs from the ideal.*

Add components for a bandstop version

Suppose now that you wish to convert **Fig 1**'s filter to a bandstop arrangement. In that design (**Fig 6**), each inductor requires a parallel capacitor and each capacitor a series inductor. Each new capacitor or inductor has a value equal to the reciprocal of the original inductor or capacitor (the impedance's magnitude remains the same). You can choose all capacitor and inductor values to provide resonance at a desired frequency; for the special case of the octave filter, the values are the same as for the bandpass design although the components are rearranged.

Fig 7 reveals the performance of the **Fig 6** design. The broken lines represent the first attempt to produce the filter; the undesirable narrow spike results from the circuit's shunt parallel resonator's permitting transmission at the center frequency. In theory, the filter's two series resonators, functioning at the same frequency, cancel the effect; in practice, the frequencies don't match perfectly. Padding the capacitor in the shunt resonator to move the spike down into the center notch produces the solid curve, which meets the filter's theoretical specifications.

Take care in debugging

Apply some relatively simple rules when debugging filters of the foregoing type. Each synthetic inductor

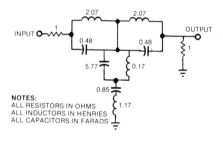

Fig 6—Converting Fig 1's design to a bandstop version *involves adding a parallel capacitor to each inductor and a series inductor to each capacitor. The values of the added components are the reciprocals of those of the original parts.*

matches up with a capacitor, and each pair resonates at its center frequency. The first step in isolating bad components is to isolate each resonator by grounding one end and lifting the other end from the circuit. Then insert a sine wave into the resonator through a resistance equal to the filter's impedance; one source of a suitable resistance value is the end section's terminating resistors. The resonator should show a peak or null at the center frequency.

Once you have verified that all resonators are working, make certain that they are interconnected

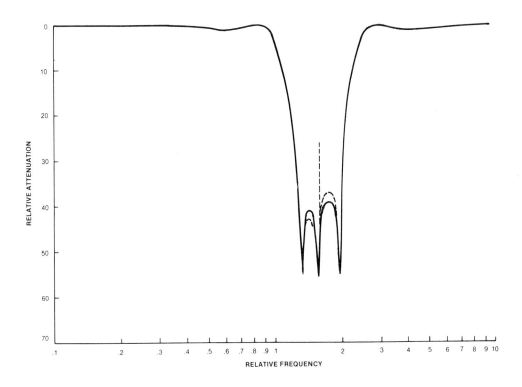

Fig 7—The initial bandstop performance of *Fig 6*'s design (broken line) reflects undesirable spikes, arising from nonideal performance of the shunt parallel resonators. Capacitor padding corrects this problem (solid line).

properly. Discontinuities in the frequency-response curve probably result from overloading. Check the amplitudes at all op-amp outputs for all frequencies; some of these might be considerably higher than the input level. Indeed, even placing a scope probe on the op-amp inputs can unbalance the circuits sufficiently to cause oscillation. Thus, view the filter output on another scope trace to verify that it's not changing as you test various portions of the filter with another probe.

Treat leftover op amps with caution

As noted, it's easiest to use a quad op amp for each synthetic inductor, leaving one of its sections uncommitted. Use two uncommitted op amps as input and output buffers because passive-filter-based designs are sensitive to driving and loading impedances; never leave any other inputs unconnected. For high-impedance op amps, a small residue on the circuit board might prove sufficient to bias the input ON, and the op amp might oscillate or amplify the actual signal to clipping; either situation can cause noise on the output. Furthermore, because some types of op amps draw excessive power in saturation, connecting an extra section as a follower proves wise. Other alternatives include grounding the input or connecting it to some point in the circuit for use as a high-impedance scope

buffer to aid in debugging.

A final note: You can use the floating-inductor circuit in passive low-pass designs to avoid the conversion to D elements that conversion of those designs to active form requires. Because the D-element approach uses fewer op amps, though, the floating-inductor approach is generally not optimal in such cases.

References

1. Delagrange, Arthur D, "Design active elliptic filters with a 4-function calculator," *EDN*, March 3, 1982, pgs 135-138.
2. Bidwell, David C, letter to *EDN*, June 9, 1982, pg 36.
3. Zverev, A I, *Handbook of Filter Synthesis*, John Wiley & Sons, New York, 1967.
4. Guillemin, E A, *Synthesis of Passive Networks*, John Wiley & Sons, New York, 1957.

39 Op amp provides linear current source

Linearizing the large signal performance of a long-tailed pair

Emitter resistors can improve the large-signal linearity of a long-tailed pair only up to a point, and then only at the cost of reduced transconductance. This handy circuit solves the problem very neatly, though the op amp restricts its use to audio frequencies. More modern op amps will of course substantially extend the frequency range over which the circuit can be used.

Donald E Hall
Tektronix Inc, Beaverton, OR

A common 2-transistor differential amplifier provides a simple voltage-controlled method for driving circuits requiring such inputs. This approach, however, suffers from irregularities over much of the source's dynamic range, producing the familiar characteristic shown in **Fig 1**. Notice in this example that for operation with less than 1% nonlinearity, differential base voltage must remain within a ±26-mV range—leaving a large portion of the dynamic range unused.

An improved circuit (**Fig 2**) uses a 741 op amp to overcome nonlinearity. With ideal op-amp response, the transfer function is described by

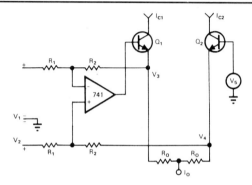

Fig 2—**Adding an op amp** *linearizes the output of the current source.*

This relationship indicates that even though transconductance of individual transistors can change, the op amp maintains a linear relationship in the current source. Linear opera-

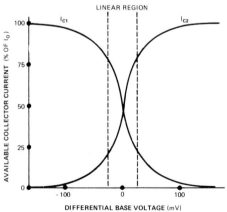

Fig 1—**A typical 2-transistor differential amplifier** *proves linear only within a narrow range of base voltages.*

$$(V_3 - V_4)/(V_2 - V_1) = R_2/R_1.$$

Because

$$I_{C1} - I_{C2} = (V_3 - V_4)/R_0,$$

then

$$(I_{C1} - I_{C2})/(V_2 - V_1) = R_2/R_0 R_1.$$

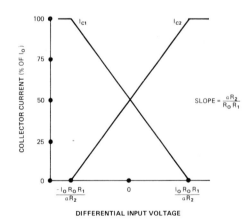

Fig 3—**The improvement in linearity** *effects a significant increase in the circuit's dynamic range.*

tion continues until I_{C1} or I_{C2} equals I_0, as shown in **Fig 3**.

40 Design method yields low-noise, wide-range crystal oscillators

Crystal oscillator design

It is easy to knock up a crystal oscillator with one of the commonly used circuit arrangements, and the result may well be adequate for an undemanding application. But if low noise and/or wide tuning range is a requirement, a slightly more scientific approach is called for. Next time you have to design a crystal oscillator, the following article will provide food for thought.

Tim L Hillstrom, *Hewlett-Packard Co*

Traditionally, designing crystal oscillators that have wide tuning range and acceptable noise performance requires time-consuming trial-and-error methods. However, you can use a straightforward design procedure to achieve a tuning range of hundreds of ppm without compromising noise performance. By characterizing the tuning range of the frequency-determining network of a crystal oscillator, you can accurately quantify all the effects that determine oscillator performance and fully include them in your design.

This design technique extends the traditional approach that uses a crystal's equivalent-circuit model—a model that fails to adequately characterize the crystal in difficult designs. The equivalent-circuit approach simply does not accommodate such relevant effects as off-resonance lossiness, crystal-model element variation with frequency, and spurious modes. Traditionally, these effects are lumped into a vague term called "crystal pullability."

The material given here will concentrate on feedback-type oscillators using crystals configured in the series-resonant mode (**Fig 1a**). Note, however, that the design techniques presented here are applicable to other topologies as well. In this block diagram, H(f) is a low-Q bandpass filter that selects the desired harmonic. G_2 is a buffer that provides a low-impedance termination for the frequency-determining network, and G_1 is a nonlinear gain block that provides the variable gain or amplitude limiting necessary for stable oscillation. The gain of G_1 decreases monotonically as a function of signal level. When the circuit turns on (and signal levels are low), G_1 varies to provide an open-loop gain greater than three to ensure that the circuit oscillates. Once the circuit is oscillating and signal levels attain a steady-state condition, G_1's gain is approximately unity.

The frequency-determining network contains the crystal and associated tuning elements. This circuit block is a 1-port network ideally described as $Z_f(f)$. For optimum performance, you must minimize undesirable admittances, such as those attributable to stray capacitance and varactor-isolating resistors. The dotted ground connection (which carries negligible current) from the frequency-determining network is an example of a low-admittance stray network path.

In order for the circuit to oscillate, open-loop phase shift must equal 0°. Because the circuit in **Fig 1** contains two frequency-dependent blocks, a number of harmonic-selecting filter and frequency-determining-network phase combinations will provide an overall loop phase shift of 0°. For two reasons (maximum loop gain and minimum phase noise), it's best to have 0° phase shift in each network. The design method shown here uses 0° phase shift as a condition.

Now it's time to concentrate on the crystal loop—the closed path around R_{t1}, the frequency-determining network, and R_{t2}. The crystal loop partially determines the oscillator's phase noise and totally determines the frequency tuning. The frequency-determining aspect of the loop is true because everything outside the crystal loop is independent of frequency over the narrow frequency range of interest. In the model, G_1's input impedance is infinite, and G_2's output impedance equals zero. If I_{STRAY} is negligible, you can consider the frequency-determining network to be a 1-port impedance $Z_f(f)$. Therefore, the relevant equations for oscillation and noise become

$$I_m [Z_f(f)] = 0 \tag{1}$$

$$Q_L(f) = \frac{f_o}{2(R_{t1} + R_{t2} + Re[Zf(f)])} \cdot \frac{dIm[Zf(f)]}{df}, \tag{2}$$

where $Q_L(f)$ is the Q of the frequency-determining network. This parameter is also known as the "loaded

Q" of the crystal. The dominant parameter under designer control, $Q_L(f)$, determines the oscillator's noise level. According to Leason's equation, the single-sided phase noise equals

$$L(f_m) = \frac{FkT}{2P_0} \left[1 + \left(\frac{f_0}{f_m 2Q_L} \right)^2 \right] \left[1 + \frac{f_1}{f_m} \right] \qquad (3)$$

$$\cong \frac{FkT}{2P_0} \left[\frac{f_0}{f_m 2Q_L} \right]^2 \text{ for } f_1 < f_m < \frac{f_0}{2Q_L}$$

$$\cong \frac{FkT}{2P_0} \left[\frac{f_0}{2Q_L} \right]^2 \left[\frac{f_1}{f_m^3} \right] \text{ for } f_m < f_1 < \frac{f_0}{2Q_L},$$

where
f_0 = oscillation frequency
$f_m \approx f - f_0$ = offset frequency
$f_1 = [1/f]$ noise corner ($< f_0/2Q_L$) = resonator half bandwidth
k_T = thermal noise floor = -174 dBm/Hz
F = noise figure of the circuit
P_0 = output power
Q_L = loaded Q

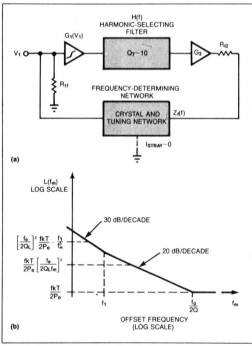

(a)

(b)

Fig 1—Because this circuit includes two frequency-dependent blocks, a number of harmonic-selecting filter and frequency-determining-network phase combinations will provide an overall loop phase shift of 0°—a necessary condition for oscillation.

Fig 1b illustrates this phase-noise characteristic. It's worth noting that the crystal itself can contribute noise that exceeds that predicted by Leason's equation. This noise is generally attributable to contaminants in the crystal. Proper crystal-manufacturing techniques (in a clean room) and cold- or resistive-weld sealing techniques minimize the problem.

Inspection of **Eq 2** and **Eq 3** suggests that for minimum phase noise over the entire tuning range, $Z_f(f)$ must have an imaginary part having a large slope and a real part that remains small. Ideally, oscillator loop gain remains constant over the tuning range. This condition ensures oscillator start-up and minimal AM noise over the tuning range. You can realize constant loop gain by selecting $Z_f(f)$ such that it has a small and fairly constant real part over the tuning range. A constant Q_L is also desirable because it provides consistent noise performance over the tuning range and also simplifies the design of the tuning network. For constant loop gain and optimal noise performance over the tuning range, therefore, you'll need a $Z_f(f)$ that has a large slope, an imaginary part that's fairly linear, and a real part that's small and fairly constant.

You must observe one final requirement for stable oscillation—the imaginary part of $Z_f(f)$ must equal zero at only one frequency over the entire frequency range in which sufficient loop gain exists for oscillation. To meet this requirement, you'll need a crystal that has a monotonic reactance-vs-frequency characteristic.

Frequency-determining network

To attack the design problem, first consider an ideal ($C_0 = 0$) crystal connected in series with a variable tuning capacitor (**Fig 2**). As **Fig 2** illustrates, this network meets all the requirements stated above. The variable tuning capacitance C_S shifts the crystal reactance down by a variable amount that's essentially independent of frequency over a small fractional frequency range. Oscillation occurs at the point where the shifted reactance curve crosses zero. A straightforward analysis yields the equation

$$\frac{\Delta f}{f_0} = \frac{C_m}{2C_{smin}} \left[1 - \frac{1}{C_R} \right], \qquad (4)$$

where Δf is the tuning range and C_R is the tuning-capacitance ratio (C_{smax}/C_{smin}).

Clearly, a series tuning capacitor can only shift the oscillation frequency to a value above the series-resonant frequency of the crystal. Therefore, most VCXOs (voltage-controlled crystal oscillators) using this configuration are tuneable to a frequency above the series-resonant frequency of their crystals. You can lower the tuning frequency by adding an inductor in series with the tuning capacitor. Although adding inductance helps avoid the spurious modes that typically occur at frequencies above the crystal's series-resonant frequency, the addition introduces susceptibility to magnetic-pickup problems.

Now consider a network (**Fig 3**) in which the ideal crystal's C_0 is greater than 0 pF. Clearly, this circuit fails to meet two of the previously cited requirements—the real part of Z_X is not constantly low, and the imaginary part is not linear. You can remove the effects of C_0 by adding an appropriate inductor L_0 to form a parallel-resonant circuit. Unfortunately, you cannot select L_0's value based on measured or specified values of C_0, because the crystal model is not adequate for difficult applications.

The best design approach is to measure $\text{Re}[Z_X(f)]$ and $\text{Im}[Z_X(f)]$ over the entire tuning range. You then mathematically (or physically) add enough parallel inductance to satisfy the design requirements. Although in theory it's possible to precisely meet the crystal's requirements, the crystal could deviate substantially from any modeled performance in practice. However, the approach does allow you to quickly evaluate crystal prototypes in environments that mirror the actual application. This advantage can be a real time saver.

To get down to specifics, let's design an 80-MHz

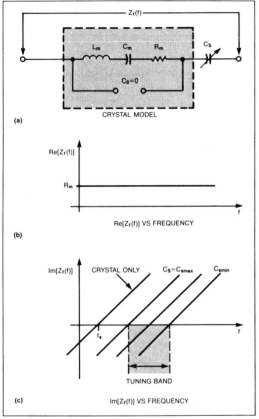

Fig 2—*Because a series tuning capacitor can only raise the oscillation frequency* above the series-resonant frequency of the crystal, oscillators using this configuration are tunable to frequencies above their crystal's series-resonant frequency.

VCXO for use in a phase-locked loop that must accommodate a ±15-ppm absolute error in its reference frequency. Typically, low-cost crystals specify a ±5-ppm absolute frequency error, a ±15-ppm aging error over 10 years, and a ±10-ppm variation as a function of temperature (over an industrial operating range). To accommodate all these error sources, the oscillator must have a ±45-ppm tuning-range capability —that is, $\Delta f=90$ ppm. This is considered a very wide tuning range for a low-noise, 80-MHz VCXO.

In some cases, you could use two devices to develop the required overall tuning capacitance—a mechanical trimmer capacitor for crystal-frequency error and

aging, and a varactor to satisfy the remaining tuning requirement. In this example, however, the design will

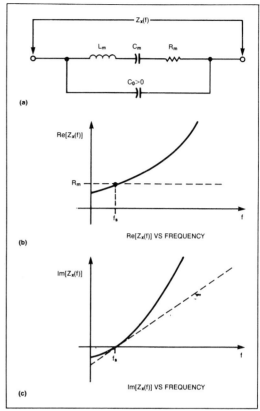

Fig 3—*Tuning range is limited* (and oscillator noise is inconsistent) when the ideal crystal's C_0 is greater than 0 pF, because the real part of Z_X is not constantly low and the imaginary part is not linear.

use a varactor for the entire 90-ppm tuning range. **Eq 4** shows that a wide tuning range requires a large varactor capacitance ratio (C_R), a small C_{smin}, and an appropriately large crystal motional capacitance C_M. Increasing C_M may decrease the unloaded-crystal Q, so you must make some tradeoffs to realize the optimum combination.

To obtain a large varactor C_R, you must use a hyper-abrupt diode. For a hyper-abrupt VHF varactor like the BB105, $C_R \approx 5.5$ and $C_{smin}=2.2$ pF. From **Eq 4**, therefore, C_M must be at least 0.5 fF to ensure $\Delta=90$ ppm. The mean frequency (80 MHz by design in this case) over the tuning range is

$$\bar{f} = f_o \left[1 + \frac{C_m}{4C_{smin}} \left(1 + \frac{1}{C_r} \right) \right]. \qquad (5)$$

From **Eq 5**, the crystal's series-resonant frequency comes out to 79.99462 MHz, or 67 ppm below 80 MHz. The crystal must have no spurious modes or aberrant characteristics over the tuning range—between 22 and 112 ppm above the series resonant frequency.

137

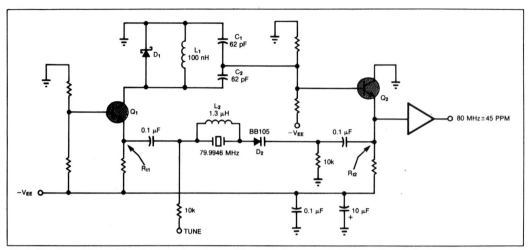

Fig 4—C₁, C₂, and L₁ combine to set the desired crystal harmonic frequency *in this 2-transistor feedback oscillator. The network comprising the crystal, L₂, and D₂ determines the oscillator frequency.*

This design is based on the properties of an ideal crystal. In a real-world situation, you'll have to measure a real crystal to determine the tuning-band measurements of the frequency-determining network. You then use this data to select the correct varactor and a crystal with the proper frequency.

To add detail to the theory, **Fig 4** illustrates a 2-transistor feedback oscillator that effectively implements the block diagram of **Fig 1**. L_1, C_1, and C_2 combine to set the desired crystal harmonic frequency. D_1, which is isolated from the crystal, provides amplitude limiting. D_1's impedance decreases with signal level. This impedance drop reduces Q_1's voltage gain and thereby implements the G_1 variable-gain block of **Fig 1**. The network comprising the crystal, L_2, and D_2 determines the oscillator's frequency. Q_2 isolates the tank from the crystal and provides a low-impedance termination for the crystal's closed loop, composed of R_{t1}, the crystal, D_2, and R_{t2}. Q_1 supplies the voltage gain necessary for oscillation and also provides a low-impedance termination for the crystal loop.

To start, you must adjust the oscillator's frequency-determining network to run at 0° phase. To do this, you can substitute an ac-coupled resistor whose value is equal to the typical value of Re[Z_f(f)] over the tuning range. You then select C_1 and/or C_2 to establish the oscillator's desired operating frequency—80 MHz in this case. You then replace the resistor by the frequency-determining network to complete the design.

When you physically add the frequency-determining network, you should minimize stray admittances. You can do this by removing the ground plane from beneath the frequency-determining network and using large impedance values for the varactor's bias resistors. Note that some nodal impedances in the frequency-determining network are very high—900Ω in this case. To maintain this high impedance at high frequencies, pay strict attention to the physical layout. At this point, the oscillator's tuning range should be very close to the design goal. In addition, noise performance will be fairly constant over the tuning range.

Several mechanisms will act to limit your attempts to achieve greater and greater oscillator tuning ranges. Spurious operating modes are inevitable as you attempt to tune further away from the crystal's series-resonant frequency. Other crystal characteristics can also cause problems.

Crystal reactance, for example, may become non-monotonic with frequency and thus cause unstable tuning. Maintaining high impedance at high frequencies is another problem area. The crystal's high-impedance node has a design impedance of

$$Z(f) \cong R_{t1} + R_m + j\frac{f - f_5}{\pi f_o{}^2 C_m}.$$

Stray capacitance and the varactor-bias ports will eventually limit your attempts to increase the design impedance. In addition, the accuracy of measurements of the frequency-determining network decreases as you attempt to develop very high impedance levels. For example, if you use an HP3577A vector network analyzer and an HP35677A s-parameter test set, the measurements will have adequate accuracy for impedances between 0.5 and 1000Ω.

41 Nonlinear load extends PLL frequency range

Wide range PLL

The widely second sourced 4046 PLL chip has a limited frequency range when used, as is usual, with a fixed timing resistor. This useful circuit removes that limitation.

Basel F Azzam and Christopher R Paul
Coherent Communications, Hauppauge, NY

A PLL chip such as the 74HC4046 in **Fig 1** uses an external capacitor and resistor to set the frequency range for an internal voltage-controlled oscillator (VCO). By replacing the fixed resistor R_4 with a nonlinear one, you can extend the VCO's frequency range by a factor of 50 or more. For the component values shown, when pin 11 connects to R_4, the range is 17 to 300 kHz; in contrast, when the pin connects to the nonlinear load, the range is 2 kHz to 2 MHz.

Capacitor C_1 and the current through pin 11 control the PLL's output frequency. Higher current produces a higher frequency. When V_{11} equals 0.5V, for example, the high-β transistor Q_1 is off and the resistance from pin 11 to ground is $R_2 + R_3$. As V_{11} increases, Q_1 turns on and draws more current from pin 11. Thus, the effective impedance, Z, is

$$Z = \frac{\dfrac{R_2 R_3}{\beta(R_2 + R_3)} + R_c}{\dfrac{R_3}{R_2 + R_3} - \dfrac{V_{BE}}{V_{11}}},$$

where β is the transistor's beta and V_{BE} equals 0.75V.

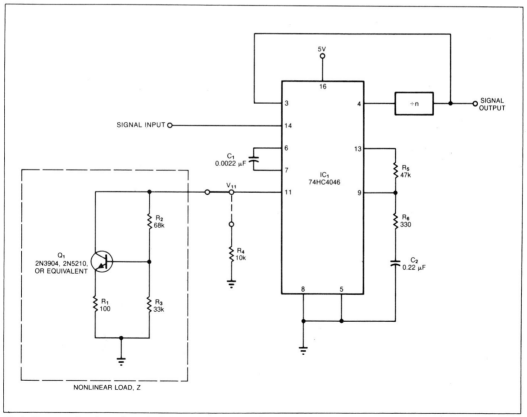

Fig 1—By connecting the nonlinear load Z to pin 11 of the PLL chip IC_1, you can extend the PLL's frequency range by a factor of 50, as compared with that possible by using a fixed resistor (R_4).

42 Squarewave oscillator spans DC to 20 MHz

Digitally controlled clock source

This circuit makes a useful digitally controlled clock for switched capacitor filters. Its spectral purity (close-in phase noise) will not be exceptionally good, but for this application that is not too important, though in other applications it could be a disadvantage.

Michael Jachowski
Precision Monolithics Inc, Santa Clara, CA

The digitally controlled oscillator of **Fig 1** is useful as a clock source for switched-capacitor filters, and it costs less than $1 (OEM qty). During operation, the voltage at node A oscillates between the hysteresis thresholds at the input of IC_{2A}, a Schmitt-trigger inverter. The D/A converter, IC_1, sets the oscillation frequency by controlling the current into pin 4 (I_0), which sets the charge rate for capacitor C_1.

To understand how the circuit oscillates, first assume that C_1 is discharged (the node A voltage is 5V). Node B is at 0V, so diode D_1 is reverse biased. The current into pin 4 of IC_1 determines the linear charge rate of C_1; this current ranges from 4 μA to 4 mA, depending on the D/A converter's input code D and reference current I_{REF}. C_1 charges until node A's voltage ramps below the lower switching threshold (V_{TL}) of IC_{2A}.

The output of inverter IC_{2A} then switches high, although it clamps briefly at the voltage level of node A

plus the diode's forward-voltage drop. The inverter can deliver more than 50 mA in this state, overdriving the D/A converter's output current and rapidly discharging C_1. When node A rises to the inverter's upper threshold V_{TH}, node B returns to 0V and the cycle repeats.

Inverter IC_{2B} buffers the capacitor-discharge current and provides a negative-strobe output; IC_{2C} provides a positive strobe. Flip-flop IC_3 provides a square-wave output at one-half the strobe frequency (**Fig 2**). The strobe period T equals $T_1 + T_2$ (within the converter's 8-bit accuracy) for frequencies below 200 kHz and for values of C_1 greater than 1000 pF:

$$T \approx \frac{C_1(V_{TH} - V_{TL})}{I_{REF}D} + 60C_1\ln\left(\frac{5 - V_{TL}}{5 - V_{TH}}\right),$$

where D = (digital input)/256.

For C_1 values below 1000 pF, you must account for stray capacitance. The following will add stray capacitance directly to C_1: converter output, 12 pF; inverter input, 5 to 10 pF; diode, 2 pF. An IC socket will

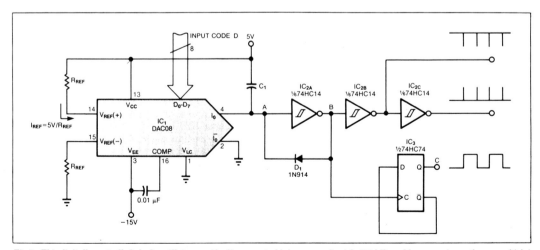

Fig 1—This digitally controlled clock oscillator provides linear control below approximately 200 kHz and has a maximum frequency higher than 20 MHz.

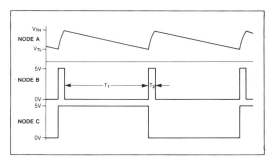

Fig 2—These idealized waveforms from Fig 1 illustrate the oscillator's operation for frequencies of 200 kHz and below.

contribute additional capacitance. For strobe frequencies greater than 200 kHz, you must also include the effects of the inverter output's rise and fall times and its propagation delay T_{PD}:

$$T \approx (C_1 + C_{DAC} + C_{2A} + C_D) \left[\frac{V_{TH} - V_{TL}}{I_{REF}D} + 60\ln\left(\frac{5 - V_{TL}}{5 - V_{TH}}\right) \right] + T_{RISE} + T_{FALL} + T_{PD},$$

where C_{DAC} is the converter's output capacitance, C_{2A} is IC_{2A}'s input capacitance, and C_D is the diode's capacitance.

Fig 3 shows the oscillator operating at a strobe frequency of 20 MHz. Capacitance at node A is 30 pF (including 10 pF from the oscilloscope probe). Notice that the fast-moving node A waveform overshoots both switching thresholds, producing an amplitude of 3.5V. Frequency vs input D becomes nonlinear at higher frequencies because of propagation delays, rise times, and fall times in the inverter. At 20 MHz, for example,

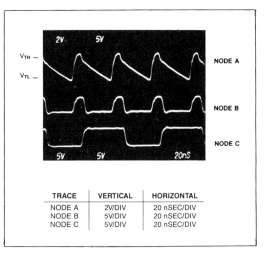

TRACE	VERTICAL	HORIZONTAL
NODE A	2V/DIV	20 nSEC/DIV
NODE B	5V/DIV	20 nSEC/DIV
NODE C	5V/DIV	20 nSEC/DIV

Fig 3—These waveforms are of Fig 1's circuit operating at 20 MHz. The strobe pulse width (node B) equals the sum of the rise time, fall time, and propagation delay for inverter IC_{2A}.

the converter controls less than half of the waveform period at node A.

Although the oscillator is capable of high speed, its operation is more stable below 200 kHz. You can set the converter's I_{REF} as low as 100 μA and set C_1 as high as you like—resulting in an operating frequency with no significant lower limit. For higher accuracy and greater dynamic range, you can replace the DAC-08 with a 10- or 12-bit D/A converter.

43 Design active elliptic filters with a 4-function calculator

Simple low- and high-pass filter design

Another very useful filter article by A.D.D., this chooses the best approach for each filter type. Thus, for high-pass filters, a passive design prototype is used, with the inductors replaced by synthetic inductors based upon the impedance converter circuit. On the other hand, for low-pass filters, an FDNR (frequency-dependent negative resistance) approach is used. In both cases, this not only minimizes the number of devices (active inductors or FDNRs respectively) which are required, but means that they can have one end grounded – the more complicated floating circuits are not required.

Arthur D Delagrange, Department of the Navy

Although they achieve high performance, active elliptic filters are unfortunately difficult to design—a task simplified by the methods described in this article. It explains how to calculate a passive elliptic filter's elements and convert those values into an active-filter design using only a 4-function calculator.

An elliptic filter's advantages—staying within spec'd passband-ripple limits, staying below spec'd stopband response limits and very steep cutoff slope—make it preferable to more common realizations such as the Butterworth, Chebyshev or Constant K for many applications. Its sharp cutoff, for example, proves advantageous in digital-communications systems, where you want to operate as close to the Nyquist frequency as possible (to achieve the greatest bandwidth) yet still attain the highest possible stopband rejection (to preclude signal aliasing).

Solve complex forms with simple transforms

If you'd like to design such a filter in a low-pass application, start with the prototype shown in **Fig 1a**. The element designators for this passive prototype elliptic filter appear in the **table**'s first column. (The prototype's elements are normalized in the standard

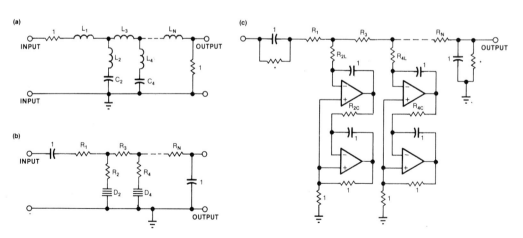

Fig 1—Elliptic low-pass filters *evolve from the classical passive LC realization* **(a)**, *through a transformed RC equivalent* **(b)**—*where the inductors become "super capacitors"* $D_{2.4}$—*to an active version* **(c)**. *Employing an op amp's differential inputs in composite feedback loops makes the super capacitors into split RC networks.*

NOTES:
RESISTORS NORMALIZED TO OHMS
CAPACITORS NORMALIZED TO FARADS
D_2, D_4 = SUPER CAPACITORS (SEE TEXT)
 • = REQUIRED FOR DC CONTINUITY, TYPICALLY 100Ω NORMALIZED

ELEMENT DESIGNATORS AND NORMALIZED VALUES FOR ELLIPTIC FILTERS

PASSIVE LOW-PASS	ACTIVE LOW-PASS	PASSIVE HIGH-PASS	ACTIVE HIGH-PASS	9-POLE 8-ZERO	7-POLE 6-ZERO	5-POLE 4-ZERO	3-POLE 2-ZERO
STOPBAND ATTENUATION				139.176	104.268	69.360	34.454
L_1	R_1	$\frac{1}{C_1}$	$\frac{1}{C_1}$	2.15275	2.12329	2.05594	1.85199
C_2	R_{2C}	$\frac{1}{L_2}$	$\frac{1}{C_{2L}}$	1.09942	1.07993	1.03392	0.85903
L_2	R_{2L}	$\frac{1}{C_2}$	$\frac{1}{C_{2C}}$	0.03012	0.04884	0.09152	0.22590
L_3	R_3	$\frac{1}{C_3}$	$\frac{1}{C_3}$	2.92871	2.84446	2.73567	1.85199
C_4	R_{4C}	$\frac{1}{L_4}$	$\frac{1}{C_{4L}}$	1.06415	1.01638	0.93561	
L_4	R_{4L}	$\frac{1}{C_4}$	$\frac{1}{C_{4C}}$	0.18236	0.23538	0.24486	
L_5	R_5	$\frac{1}{C_5}$	$\frac{1}{C_5}$	2.79680	2.75306	1.91939	
C_6	R_{6C}	$\frac{1}{L_6}$	$\frac{1}{C_{6L}}$	1.02979	1.00567		
L_6	R_{6L}	$\frac{1}{C_6}$	$\frac{1}{C_{6C}}$	0.23642	0.16034		
L_7	R_7	$\frac{1}{C_7}$	$\frac{1}{C_7}$	2.81748	2.01924		
C_8	R_{8C}	$\frac{1}{L_8}$	$\frac{1}{C_{8L}}$	1.04688			
L_8	R_{8L}	$\frac{1}{C_8}$	$\frac{1}{C_{8C}}$	0.10706			
L_9	R_9	$\frac{1}{C_9}$	$\frac{1}{C_9}$	2.07916			

1-rad/sec, 1Ω-impedance form; the **table**'s values (**Refs 1 and 2**) are spec'd for 1-dB p-p passband ripple.) **Ref 3**'s transformations exchange component types in the prototype design to eliminate its inductors. Thus, in the resulting equivalent filter (**Fig 1b**), inductors become resistors, resistors become capacitors and capacitors become "super capacitors." (These last-named elements are also designated D elements or frequency-dependent negative resistors.)

There are many circuit topologies for realizing the super-capacitor function; the final filter design in **Fig 1c** uses one that's both practical and easily attained. Furthermore, all its capacitors have equal values, so resistors become the only variables. (The resistors marked with an asterisk function only to re-establish the dc continuity lost during transformation.) The **table**'s second column refers to these resistors; the subscripts indicate when a resistor represents an inductor or a capacitor (note especially the two R_2s). Because the circuit is derived from an equal-termination passive version and therefore has a 6-dB passband insertion loss, you might want to add a gain stage to the filter's output. Additionally, the circuit's load impedance must be high compared with filter impedance.

Fig 2 demonstrates how these elliptic-filter techniques apply to active high-pass configurations. The high-pass prototype's elements (**Fig 2a**) get interchanged with those of the original low-pass filter, and this exchange holds true for **Fig 2b**'s active realization. For the actual filter design, you still need the **table**, but note that impedance and admittance are now inverted because the low-pass filter's resistive equivalent of an inductor now represents a capacitance, and what was capacitive is now inductive.

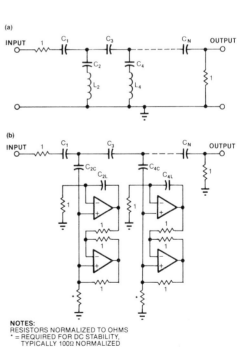

NOTES:
RESISTORS NORMALIZED TO OHMS
* = REQUIRED FOR DC STABILITY,
  TYPICALLY 100Ω NORMALIZED

Fig 2—Active elliptic high-pass filters *resemble their low-pass counterparts (**Fig 1c**) in that split RC networks replace the passive versions' LC circuits (**a**). Unlike **Fig 1**'s low-pass equivalent, this high-pass realization (**b**) achieves the impedance transforms by splitting the capacitors.*

143

An active example shows the way

To appreciate how easily these transformations lend themselves to real-world applications, consider **Fig 3**'s 5-pole active high-pass filter. The requirements' constraints include a 10-kΩ impedance level and a cutoff frequency of 10,000 rad/sec (ie, 1.6 kHz). For this 5-pole design, use the **table**'s second-to-last column to find the appropriate element values, but remember to invert them because you're solving for capacitance values in this high-pass design.

Next, because the filter's spec'd impedance level equals 10 kΩ, multiply the resistor values by 10k and divide the capacitors' by 10k. Then divide the capacitor values by 10k once again to scale up the normalized 1 rad/sec to the 10,000-rad/sec requirement. This procedure derives **Fig 3**'s values, which are 1% resistors and capacitors with the nearest 20% value. When the circuit uses an HA-4605 quad op amp, it performs as in **Fig 4**.

This example represents the worst case: The expected stopband notches characteristic of elliptic filters don't appear because the test oscillator's harmonics aren't attenuated. Additionally, these op amps' limited high-frequency response causes the passband droop.

Fig 5, on the other hand, better depicts this technique's superiority. Response for this 7-pole active

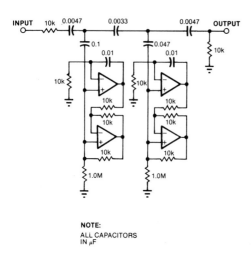

NOTE:
ALL CAPACITORS
IN μF

Fig 3—A design example *demonstrates how to apply* **Fig 2**'s *generalized circuit topology. Find this 5-pole elliptic high-pass filter's element values by dividing the table's parameters by the design's 10-kΩ/10-kHz requirements.* **Fig 4** *depicts the circuit's performance.*

low-pass filter drops within an octave to the measuring system's 70-dB resolution limit—and stays there.

Tradeoffs spec the practical limits

Although you can transform the elliptic filter's passive versions into bandpass or bandstop configurations, the techniques presented here prove impractical for active realizations—there's no practical way to rearrange the equivalent inductors and capacitors so

that they're all grounded within the same circuit. (You can, however, cascade the appropriate low- and high-pass blocks to meet your needs.)

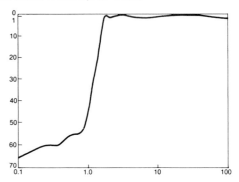

Fig 4—Nearly ideal elliptic high-pass performance *results from* **Fig 3**'s *5-pole design. It doesn't achieve an elliptic's characteristic stopband notches because the test oscillator's harmonics aren't inhibited. The indicated stopband droop results from the op amp's limited high-frequency response.*

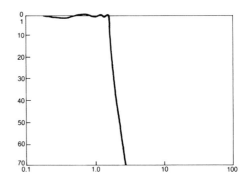

Fig 5—Optimum low-pass characteristics *result when this article's techniques are applied to a 7-pole active elliptic design. In contrast to the performance depicted in* **Fig 4**, *this low-pass realization doesn't suffer from harmonic feedthrough or amplifier-response problems. The design reaches the measurement system's 70-dB resolution limit within an octave of cutoff.*

These active designs reflect the good element sensitivities characteristic of their passive prototypes. Element sensitivities for the higher order designs are more critical because the poles are closer together; resistors, at least, should have 1% tolerances. The lower order realizations work well even if you use 5% resistors and 10% capacitors. The op amps selected must not only be unity-gain compensated, they must also provide sufficiently high gain at the pole and zero frequencies, including those well above the cutoff frequency. Additionally, don't overdrive the filter; the circuit's internal swings at the high-Q nodes can be much greater than the input level. (With **Fig 3**'s circuit and ±15V supplies, you can safely input 2V.)

Although the parameters listed in the **table** can meet many requirements, other arrangements are possible.

But most of the tradeoffs are seldom advantageous: There's no need to use an even number of poles when adding another requires only one more resistor or capacitor. And making the numbers of poles and zeros equal only means that the stopband eventually flattens out instead of continuously falling at 6 dB/octave.

Perhaps the only parameter you might want to vary is passband ripple. Here you can achieve lower in-band ripple at the expense of the transition band's rate or stopband attenuation, or vice versa.

References

1. Baezlopez, David Jose, ''Sensitivity and Synthesis of Elliptic Function,'' PhD dissertation, University of Arizona, Tucson, 1978.

2. Huelsman and Allen, *Introduction to the Theory and Design of Active Filters*, McGraw-Hill, New York, 1980.

3. Bruton, L T and Trelaeven, David, ''Active-filter design using generalized impedance converters,'' *EDN*, February 5, 1973, pgs 68-75.

44 Transistor powers low-dropout regulator

Low headroom regulator

In battery-powered instruments, a regulator needing very little headroom can substantially extend the useful life of primary batteries, or allow less frequent recharging of secondary (rechargeable) batteries. This circuit can provide 100 mA at 5 V from an input as low as 5.1 V.

James E Dekis
Maxim Integrated Products, Sunnyvale, CA
and Terry Blake
Motorola, Schaumberg, IL

The monolithic regulator chip in **Fig 1**, combined with an external pnp transistor, forms a very-low-dropout regulator. The composite regulator can supply several hundred milliamps at 5V from an input as low as 5.3V. Such low-dropout performance suits battery-powered applications, because it extends the useful life of batteries having sloping discharge curves, such as sealed lead-acid and lithium batteries.

The monolithic regulator derives its supply current from the base circuit of the external pnp transistor. The feedback-resistor ratio sets the output voltage:

$$V_{OUT} = 1.3V \times (R_1 + R_2)/R_1.$$

If the output-voltage feedback to the chip's V_{SET} input is below the bandgap-reference voltage (1.3V), the supply current into V_{IN} (the pnp transistor's base current) increases. The transistor multiplies this base current by β and delivers it to the load. The circuit's quiescent current is a function of the transistor's β and load current.

When there's no load, the quiescent current is typically 10 μA. For larger load currents, the quiescent current is simply the load current divided by the transistor's β. The regulator chip can sink 40 mA max. When you enable the chip's shut-down input, the circuit consumes 6 μA typ. R_4 supplies current to the chip under no-load conditions.

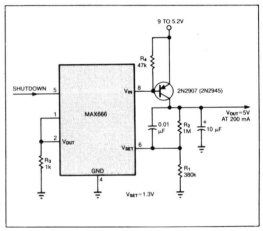

Fig 1—A monolithic regulator chip driving a dummy load sets the base current of an external, series-pass pnp transistor; the result is a very-low-dropout regulator for batteries whose output voltage droops under load.

R_3 can limit the transistor's base current. The chip's V_{OUT} pin will try to raise its voltage level to that of the V_{IN} pin when the output voltage of the chip is low. Reducing R_3 has the effect of supplying larger base currents to the external transistor.

You can substitute a 2N2945 for the 2N2907 shown in **Fig 1**. With this substitution, the circuit will supply a 5V, 100-mA max output from a 5.1V input.

45 Simplify FIR-filter design with a cookbook approach

> ## Filtering in DSP reviewed
>
> I guess any budding digital engineer would find this article useful. Even if you are an analog engineer, it is handy to know what goes on on the digital side of the stream. I certainly found it useful.

Bill Windsor, Harvard Business School
and **Paul Toldalagi,** Analog Devices Inc

Because hardware-implemented digital signal processors promise real-time capability that's difficult to achieve in software, an increasing number of hardware engineers now face the unfamiliar task of designing such systems. The task is easier than you might think, though, and following a tried-and-true procedure can make it relatively painless. This article describes such a procedure for finite-impulse-response (FIR) filters—one of the most commonly used digital filters—and subsequent articles will describe the design of infinite-impulse-response (IIR) filters and other signal-processing hardware.

New devices implement filters in hardware

VLSI technology advances—resulting in new devices such as less expensive and more practical high-speed multiplier/accumulators—are behind the push toward hardware-implemented filters; the devices' speed accommodates real-time filtering not previously feasible. To make good use of the devices, though, you must understand their capabilities and limitations. A device with too small a word size, for example, is inadequate for some filtering applications.

You must also be familiar with the characteristics of different types of filters (see **box,** "Comparison of FIR, IIR and lattice filters"), plus digital-filter design parameters and different design techniques. It's also helpful to know how digital filters compare with their analog counterparts.

Digital filters have advantages

First compare digital and analog filters. Both types perform the same basic function: Passing signals in a specified frequency range and attenuating signals outside that range. But digital filters have certain advantages—sharper rolloffs and better stability over time, power-supply fluctuations and temperature, for example. As a result, they often find use in modems, digital oscilloscopes, spectrum analyzers and speech- and image-processing equipment. Digital filters also allow real-time changes in their characteristics (adaptive filtering), whereas many analog filters require component changes to modify their frequency response.

Digital-filter terminology

Attenuation—A decrease in output signal magnitude relative to the input signal.

Passband—The frequency range of no signal attenuation. Signals in this range pass through the filter unaltered, except possibly for some gain in the passband.

Stopband—The frequency range of signal attenuation.

Stopband attenuation—The minimum amount of attenuation in the stopband.

Passband ripple—The maximum amount of excursion in the passband from the desired output magnitude.

Sampling rate—The rate at which an A/D converter samples the input signal value.

Filter coefficients—Numbers that define a filter's characteristics. These numbers represent the Fourier transform of the desired filter transfer function.

Taps—Delays in a digital filter. The number of taps equals the number of filter coefficients and also the number of sampled input values processed by the filter for each output point.

For low-performance filtering (8- to 24-dB/octave rolloff), analog filters are less expensive than digital filters, but as rolloff requirements reach 24 to 36 dB/octave, digital filters demand less complex implementations than do analog filters, especially when passband ripple must be small. Moreover, prototype changes with digital filters often involve only software changes, and software simulation of a digital filter can reflect the filter's exact performance.

Comparison of FIR, IIR and lattice filters

FIR filters **(figure)** are nonrecursive filters; they have no feedback terms. Their outputs are a function only of a finite number of previous input signals. Compared with IIR and lattice designs, FIR filters have several advantages:

- Stability. FIR filters have no poles in their transfer function, so their output is always finite and stable. And because they have no poles, they have no analog equivalent. IIR filters, on the other hand, require careful design to ensure stability.
- Linear phase response. With linear phase, the phase delay of the output signal increases linearly with the frequency of the input signal; equivalently, the output has a constant time delay with respect to the input signal. Linear phase is useful in applications such as speech processing, sonar and radar, where knowledge of the phase delay is necessary. IIR filters, unlike the FIR type, have nonlinear phase response.
- Ease of design. The FIR filter is the easiest of the three types to understand, design and implement.
- Low sensitivity to coefficient accuracy. This feature allows FIR-filter implementation with small word sizes. A typical range of FIR-coefficient accuracy is 12 to 16 bits, whereas typical IIR filters need 16 to 24 bits per coefficient.
- Simple implementation of adaptive FIR filters. Adaptive filters change their coef-

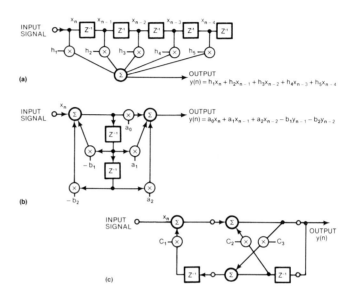

Block diagrams *illustrate the differences among FIR* **(a)**, *IIR* **(b)** *and lattice* **(c)** *filters.*

ficients in real time to accommodate changes in external conditions. Modems' equalization filters, for example, change their characteristics in response to transmission-line degradations.

Unlike FIR filters, IIR filters are recursive. Their outputs derive both from previous input values and previous output values fed back into the circuit. As in all feedback circuits, positive feedback with gain greater than one results in instability. IIRs need large coefficient word sizes to ensure stability, and their phase shift is nonlinear with frequency. IIR filters, however, have several advantages compared with FIR units and lattice designs:

- Highest efficiency. IIR filters have the fewest coefficients,

resulting in the smallest number of multiplications and the highest throughput.
- Smallest storage requirements. Because an IIR filter has the fewest coefficients, it requires the least amount of ROM storage. For example, an IIR high-pass filter typically requires only one-third the coefficients of an equivalent FIR filter.

Lattice filters are the newest form of digital filter; they promise greater stability than IIR filters and use less hardware than FIR designs. Because they're new, however, the theory describing them isn't well developed, and they're difficult to design. In addition, like IIR filters, they show high sensitivity to coefficient accuracy.

Filter design requires calculating coefficients

Designing a digital filter necessitates calculating the filter's coefficients. These coefficients define the filter's performance characteristics (see **box**, "Digital-filtering theory"), and they filter an input signal's sample values through convolution—a process of multiplications and additions.

Digital filters have performance aspects similar to those of analog filters—a certain ripple in the passband and a certain attenuation in the stopband, for example (see **box**, "Digital-filter terminology"). To generate an FIR filter's coefficients, you must specify the following design parameters (**Fig 1**):

- N, the number of taps in the filter, which equals the number of filter coefficients.
- f_P, the normalized passband cutoff frequency
- f_S, the normalized stopband cutoff frequency
- $K=(\delta_1/\delta_2)$, the ratio of the ripple in the passband to the ripple in the stopband.

For example, a filter with a 100-kHz sampling frequency, 10-kHz actual passband cutoff frequency and 20-kHz actual stopband cutoff frequency has a normalized passband cutoff frequency f_P equaling 10 kHz/100 kHz=0.1 and a normalized f_S equaling 20 kHz/100 kHz=0.2.

In addition, passband and stopband ripple are often expressed in decibels:

$$\text{passband ripple (dB)}=20\log_{10}(1+\delta_1)$$
$$\text{stopband ripple (dB)}=-20\log_{10}(\delta_2).$$

By convention, f_P and f_S are expressed in units of normalized frequency—the actual signal frequency divided by the sampling frequency. Typical values for passband ripple range from 1 to 0.001 dB, and values for stopband ripple are typically between 10 and 90 dB.

Note that the normalized frequency axis extends from 0.0 to 0.5, because the Nyquist sampling theorem requires sampling a signal at more than twice its highest frequency component for accurate signal reconstruction. Thus, the ratio of any signal frequency to its sampling frequency must always be less than 0.5 to avoid aliasing errors; keeping the values below 0.33, as in this example, merely is conservative design.

Several tradeoffs exist among these design parameters. With a fixed number of filter taps, for example, steeper rolloff means more ripple. Obtaining both small ripple and a steep rolloff requires increasing the number of taps (and hardware) in the digital filter.

Two design techniques predominate

The two most commonly used FIR-filter design techniques are the traditional windowing method and the Remez Exchange algorithm. The latter is preferable because it always results in a more efficient filter; it's also available in FORTRAN (**Refs 2** and **4**) to assist in the design process. (A free program listing is available from Analog Devices's DSP Marketing Dept.)

A knowledge of windowing aids your understanding of filtering theory, though, so that technique merits discussion here. Windowing is simple to use, and it generates filter coefficients with minimal computation.

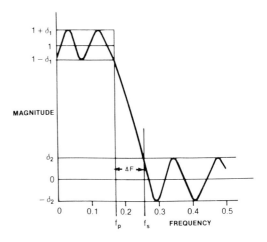

Fig 1—Passband and stopband cutoff frequencies *(f_P and f_S, respectively) and ripple (δ_1 and δ_2) help specify the performance of a low-pass filter. Similar specifications define high-pass and bandpass filters.*

Unfortunately, it satisfies no known optimality criterion (**Ref 5**).

A design example serves to illustrate the windowing technique. Consider a low-pass filter with a desired stopband attenuation of 50 dB or more, a normalized passband cutoff frequency of 0.2 and a normalized stopband cutoff frequency of 0.3. The actual cutoff frequencies depend on the filter's sampling frequency.

The ideal transfer function for the filter, H(f), appears in **Fig 2**. To obtain the Fourier series coefficients, solve the inverse Fourier transform:

$$h(n) = \int_{-0.5}^{0.5} H(e^{j2\pi f})e^{j2\pi fn}df$$

$$h(n) = \int_{-f_1}^{+f_1} e^{j2\pi fn}df$$

$$h(n) = \frac{\sin(\pi f_1 n)}{\pi n}$$

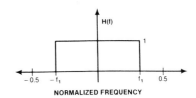

Fig 2—A low-pass filter's ideal transfer function *furnishes unity gain from dc to the cutoff frequency, f_1, and zero gain at higher frequencies.*

149

Digital-filter theory

Consider the frequency domain and assume a signal H(f) with a magnitude graph in the frequency domain as shown in part **(a)** of the **figure.** This graph merely shows the signal's frequency components—cosine waves at particular frequencies. For example, a signal expressed as cos(2π3t) has one frequency component—at 3 Hz. The signal H(f) contains frequency components from 0 to f_1 Hz, which means that in H(f) you can find cosine waves which have frequencies from 0 to f_1 Hz. Note that the highest frequency component of H(f) is f_1; any cosine signal with frequency higher than f_1 is not part of H(f).

Now consider a second signal, X(f), whose frequency-domain graph appears in **(b)**. This graph shows that X(f) has only two frequency components—f_2 and f_3. X(f) is the sum of cos(2πf_2n) and cos(2πf_3n).

Now suppose you want to separate the X(f) signal to obtain only the cosine wave at frequency f_2 **(c)**. It would be ideal if you could just multiply the signal H(f) by the signal X(f), because H(f)=1 at frequency f_2 and H(f)=0 at frequency f_3. The result would be cos(2πf_2n)—what you want.

Fortunately, you can perform the desired multiplication by using a trick from Fourier's theorem. Fourier showed that multiplication in the frequency domain is analo-gous to convolution in the time domain.

So what's convolution? It's just a series of multiplications and additions performed in a particular order. The convolution equation states that:

$$y(n)=h(n)*x(n)$$

$$= \sum_{m=1}^{N} h(m)x(n-m),$$

where * indicates a special convolution operator. This equation assumes that h(n) is zero for m<1 and for m>N—always true for FIR filters. What the equation states is that if you just perform the specified series of multiplications and additions, you'll automatically low-pass-filter the input signal x(n). Fourier's theorem takes care of the why and how, so all you have to know is what to do (the multiplications and additions) to implement the filter.

Now consider a practical example of the equation. For a 27th-order FIR filter, N=27; the 28th output value you compute will be

$$y(28)=h(1)x(27)+h(2)x(26)+h(3)x(25)+ \\ ...+h(26)x(2)+h(27)x(1).$$

These multiplications and additions perform the convolution.

Now, what are the h(n) and x(n) signals? They're the Fourier transforms of the signal H(f) and X(f). Don't worry about having to solve the Fourier integral, though. It turns out that the Fourier transform of X(f) is a simple cosine wave,

$$x(t)=cos(2\pi f_2 t)+cos(2\pi f_3 t).$$

You can use a pocket calculator to calculate the sample values of x(t) and x(n) if you know f_2, f_3 and the sample rate. The values of h(n) are slightly more complicated; their computation requires a computer program. Note that the h(n) values are filter coefficients, and when you multiply them by the x(n) values they implement a low-pass filter.

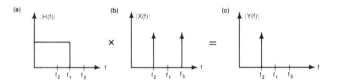

(a) |H(f)| (b) |X(f)| (c) |Y(f)|

× = f f_2 f_1 f_3

Multiplication of signals in the frequency domain is equivalent to convolution in the time domain.

Now select a window with an applied weighting function that truncates the infinite Fourier series above and below specified limits (**Fig 3**). This window weights the Fourier series coefficients by different amounts to generate the filter's coefficients; the window's width determines the required number of coefficients. The result is a finite-impulse-response approximation (hence the filter's name) to the desired transfer function H(f). This design example uses one of the more widely used windows, the Hamming window; other commonly used windows include the Kaiser, Blackman, and Hanning windows (**Ref 1**).

After choosing a weighted window, the next step is to determine the number of filter coefficients, N. This number comes from the designed rolloff band,

$\Delta F = f_S - f_P$. For the Hamming window, $\Delta F \approx 4/N$. For this design example, $\Delta F = f_S - f_P = (0.3 - 0.2) = 0.1$, so
$$N \approx 4/\Delta F = 4/0.1 = 40.$$
This approximation usually yields a slightly larger number of taps (N) than the filter actually needs, though, so a downward adjustment (by two to five taps in this case) is a practical measure for meeting design specs without producing an excessive number of multiplications in the filter's implementation. For this example, a value of 36 for N is reasonable.

The actual filter coefficients, h'(n), result from multiplying each Fourier coefficient, h(n), by its corresponding weight, w(n). Because the coefficients are symmetrical, however, only half of them require computing. (The coefficients are symmetrical because

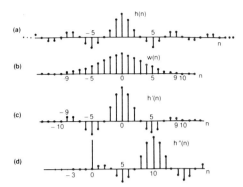

Fig 3—Fourier coefficients h(n) *(a) result from performing the inverse Fourier transform of the filter's desired transfer function (Fig 2). Multiplication of the coefficients by samples w(n) from a weighted window (b) yields filter coefficients h'(n) (c), which require shifting (d).*

they describe the function (sin x)/x shown in **Fig 3a**, which implements a low-pass filter and which is the Fourier transform of the H(f) shown in **Fig 2**.)

Remez Exchange algorithm aids design

The Remez Exchange algorithm is another—and very powerful—method for designing FIR filters. It uses linear programming techniques to estimate filter order with approximate relationships between filter parameters (**Ref 6** and **7**). You don't need to understand how it works, though—just how to use its **Ref 2** or **4** FORTRAN implementations.

The Remez Exchange algorithm yields optimal filters that satisfy the so-called minimax error criterion (**Ref 5**): For a given number of coefficients, the filter minimizes the maximum ripple in the passband.

This criterion has two major implications. First, the Remez Exchange yields an FIR filter with the smallest number of filter coefficients, so the filter uses less memory and operates more rapidly than filters produced from window designs. Second, the passband ripple components all have equal amplitude (assuming no quantization errors). The passband ripple needn't equal the stopband ripple, but you must specify their ratio.

Consider now an example design procedure with the Remez Exchange program. Assume a fixed 50-kHz sampling rate, a 10-kHz passband frequency and a 14-kHz stopband frequency; the normalized passband and stopband frequencies are thus $f_P = 0.20$ and $f_S = 0.28$. Assume also that the desired minimum stopband attenuation is 40 dB, the desired maximum passband ripple is 0.20 dB and that passband and stopband ripple are equal ($\delta_1/\delta_2 = 1$).

Inputs to the Remez Exchange program include these design parameters and a few control parameters. The program's output contains an estimate for the required number of filter taps, N, plus computed values for the filter coefficients. It also contains first-pass computed values for design parameters such as passband ripple and stopband attenuation; if the computed

values fall short of design goals, you must increase N slightly and run the program again.

For the design example previously outlined, the Remez Exchange program recommends a 24-tap filter, and it estimates a passband ripple of 0.18 dB for such a filter. It also predicts a 39.08-dB stopband attenuation —slightly short of the design goal. By instructing the program to consider more taps, though, you can tune the design. Experimentation finally yields a 27-tap filter that satisfies the design specifications (41.07-dB stopband attenuation and 0.15-dB passband ripple).

Implement the filter in hardware

Having designed your FIR filter on paper, you're now ready to put it in hardware. As an illustration of this procedure, consider the foregoing 27-tap filter and assume its implementation in hardware having 16-bit words. A block diagram for a hardware FIR filter appears in **Fig 4**.

The input block is an antialiasing filter—an analog filter that prevents the sampling of high-frequency noise components. It isn't a high-performance filter, but it does need good attenuation at the noise frequencies. Typical rolloff characteristics for antialiasing filters are 6 to 24 dB/octave.

The antialiasing filter's output goes to an A/D converter, which samples the incoming analog signal at a given frequency and converts it to digital form. The sampling frequency should be approximately three times the input signal's highest frequency component. From the ADC, the samples go to a RAM (with size N taps×16 bits/word) for storage. The 27-tap filter, for example, needs 27 16-bit locations.

A PROM typically stores the filter coefficients, although a RAM can replace the PROM. The number of required memory locations equals the number of different filter coefficients; because an FIR filter's coefficients are symmetrical, the number of different coefficients is N/2 when N is even and $1 + N/2$ when N is odd. In the example 27th-order filter, 14 locations are necessary. A clock and counter circuit steps through the RAM and the PROM, presenting the coefficients and input values to a multiplier.

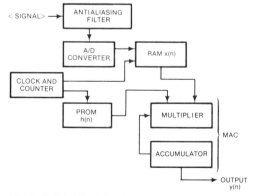

Fig 4—A digital filter's block diagram *illustrates the filter's operation. The sampled input signal goes to RAM and gets operated on by filter coefficients stored in PROM.*

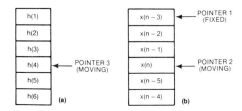

Fig 5—Stacks with fixed and moving pointers *assist a convolution process. The stacks hold filter coefficients* (a) *and data samples* (b).

Actually, the multiplier is part of a multiplier/accumulator (MAC), which multiplies the filter's coefficients by the signal's input values. Analog Devices's ADSP-1010 is one such device; it features 16×16-bit multiplication and has a 35-bit accumulator, thus providing three bits of extended precision to handle overflows from the addition of multiple 32-bit products.

Examine each design component

Using this hardware block diagram as a structural base, consider the design details of each block element. First, store the filter coefficients in the PROM after obtaining their 16-bit fixed-point (or floating-point) representation. For a fixed-point arithmetic system, multiply each coefficient by 2^{15}; for a floating-point system, convert the coefficients to the system's required format.

Next, round off—don't truncate—the coefficient values to the nearest least significant bit. Rounding preserves the accuracy of the filter-coefficient values, and it results in filter performance close to the theoretical limit for a system's number of bits. Store the rounded 16-bit coefficients in the PROM.

You also must decide whether an external multiplier chip is necessary to handle the filter's speed requirements, or whether you can perform the multiplications with a μP. To decide, calculate the multiplication rate that the filter requires: The number of multiplications per second equals the sampling rate times the number of coefficients. In the example 27-tap filter, the sampling rate is 50 kHz, and the number of multiply/accumulates is thus $50,000 \times 27 = 1,350,000$. The processing time per multiply/accumulate is therefore $1/(1,350,000) = 740$ nsec. This multiply/accumulate time is too short for μPs, so the filter implementation requires a separate multiplier chip.

To coordinate the filter multiplications, you must ensure that the memory-control circuitry (RAM, PROM, counter) retrieves the correct words from RAM and PROM; data pointers can assist in this process, as **Fig 5** shows. Pointer 2 directs the storage of each new data point on a stack (actually a circular buffer), and a multiplication procedure uses pointers 1 and 3 for determining which filter coordinates and data samples require multiplying at any particular time.

The procedure for choosing coefficients and samples to multiply is fairly simple. For the pointer positions of

Fig 5, the filter output sample is
$$h(4)x(n-3)+h(3)x(n-2)+h(2)x(n-1)$$
$$+h(1)x(n)+h(5)x(n-4)+h(6)x(n-5).$$
After computing each sample, increment pointers 2 and 3, resetting the pointers when they reach the stack boundary.

Next, decide how to handle accumulator overflow.

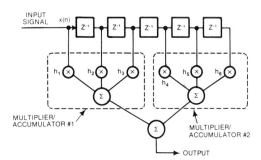

Fig 6—Parallel multiplier/accumulators *speed digital filtering in high-throughput applications.*

When a filter performs its multiplications and accumulates the sum of products, the required number of bits usually exceeds the 32-bit result of a 16×16 multiply. To handle this, first calculate a reasonable upper bound for the amount of overflow your filter can experience. If this upper bound exceeds your accumulator's capacity, you'll have to take additional steps.

Three different procedures can handle overflow. An easy method uses the multiplier/accumulator's extended precision bits. An alternative method scales the coefficients down by one to five bits. This latter approach sacrifices some accuracy in the filter for the considerable advantage of overflow prevention. A third method allows the accumulator to saturate at its maximum value; for some applications you might not want to accommodate the full dynamic range of the input signal, purposely allowing overflow to occur.

Finally, you must determine whether you need a parallel architecture to meet speed requirements. Some filters require a multiply/accumulate speed faster than one MAC can handle. A parallel architecture (**Fig 6**) uses two or more multipliers or processors to increase throughput. The 27-tap example filter requires only one multiplier, however.

Software simulation detects resolution problems

After designing a filter, simulating it in software can help detect potential problems with hardware resolution. One significant advantage of digital filters is that you can model their performance exactly with software. Before examining the simulation procedure, though, consider the potential hardware problems, which often result from limited processor precision (**Ref 3**). One contributing factor is the rounding of filter coefficients computed on a high-precision mainframe computer to the 16 bits of the filter hardware's memory width. Rounding the coefficients before storage in PROM

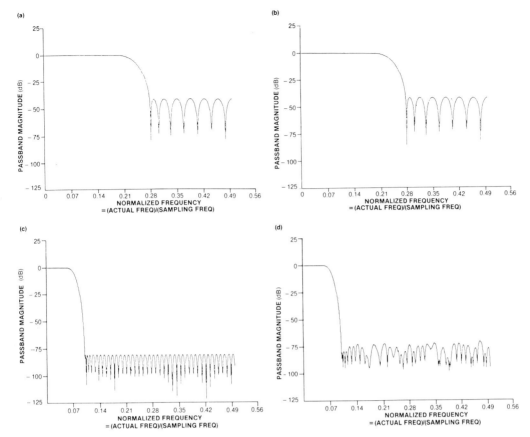

Fig 7—Rounding errors *can result from employing small word sizes in digital-filter implementations. A 27-tap 32-bit filter's performance (a) is essentially duplicated by that of a 16-bit version (b), but response degrades when a 90-tap 32-bit filter (c) is implemented in 16-bit hardware (d).*

produces less error than truncating the coefficients, but it produces error nonetheless. Furthermore, roundoff errors result from the many sequential finite-precision multiplications and accumulations; arithmetic results must frequently be truncated to fit into finite-width registers. These cumulative errors are more significant than coefficient-rounding errors for high-order filters, and they cause a deterioration of filter performance compared with the performance originally calculated on a mainframe.

How do you know if the word size you're using will cause problems for your filter? Here's a guideline for 16-bit systems, based on simulations of many FIR filters: If you're shooting for more than 67 dB of stopband attenuation or less than 0.05 dB of passband ripple, you should definitely do software simulation because you can reasonably expect hardware resolution problems. The software simulation determines whether 16-bit resolution is adequate or whether you need to go to higher resolution, such as 24 or 32 bits.

How serious are errors arising from limited processor precision? **Fig 7** shows simulated performance results for the example 27-tap filter and for a 90-tap

filter with low-passband cutoff frequency. The errors generated for the 90-tap filter are much more significant than those for the 27-tap filter, even though both use 16-bit arithmetic. More important, the 90-tap filter doesn't yield the 80-dB stopband attenuation calculated on a mainframe with 32-bit arithmetic. The simulation shows that 80-dB stopband attenuation requires more than 16 bits of resolution.

Simulate the filter with a FORTRAN program

A FORTRAN program available from Analog Devices's DSP Marketing Dept performs the actual filter simulation. It simulates FIR filters using the ADSP-1010 16×16 multiplier/accumulator.

The steps of the simulation appear in the flowchart shown in **Fig 8**. First, obtain an accurate representation of the filter coefficients as they will appear in the hardware. To do this, the program repeats the steps in the hardware design. It obtains the filter coefficients h(n) from the Remez Exchange computer program, performs overflow checking and any necessary scaling of the coefficients and obtains the 16-bit fixed-point or floating-point coefficient representation. This array of coefficients simulates the hardware filter's PROM, which stores the coefficients in the same format.

Next, the program simulates a digitized input signal by generating an input signal array x(n); the number of values in the array is the same as the number of filter taps. The first input signal array is a cosine wave of frequency 0 Hz, sampled at the sampling rate of the simulated system. This input signal array simulates the A/D converter and the RAM that stores the input signal values. The program later generates input signals with higher frequencies. Next, the program performs all arithmetic operations with 16-bit precision. It also includes an accumulator-overflow check that verifies the coefficient scaling performed before storing the coefficients in PROM. If the software flags an accumulator overflow, you must scale down the coefficients further and run the simulation again.

Finally, the program computes the filter output values, y(n), by setting up a loop to perform filter convolution. It computes an output value for each cosine frequency value; each computation involves N multiplications and additions, where N is the number of filter taps.

To find the magnitude of the filter's output, the program chooses the largest absolute value from the output y(n) array. This value is usually very close to the actual magnitude of y(n): finding a more exact magnitude requires interpolation. Having computed the output magnitude for a particular cosine input frequency (0 Hz), the program computes the frequency response for a range of frequencies. It typically sweeps from 0 Hz to just below the Nyquist frequency of 0.500. The result is a filter transfer function (**Fig 7**). If the simulation results match your filter requirements, you can then build your hardware with confidence.

References

1. Harris, Frederick J, "On the Use of Windows for Harmonic Analysis with the Discrete Fourier Transform," *Proceedings of the IEEE,* Vol 66, No 1, January 1978.

2. McClellan, J H, Parks, T W, and Rabiner, L R, "A Computer Program for Designing Optimum FIR Linear Phase Digital Filters," *IEEE Transactions on Audio and Electroacoustics,* Vol AU-21, No 8, December 1973.

3. Oppenheim, A V, and Schafer, R W, *Digital Signal Processing,* Prentice-Hall Inc, Englewood Cliffs, NJ, 1975, Chapter 9.

4. Peled, A, and Liu, B, *Digital Signal Processing,* John Wiley and Sons Inc, New York, NY, 1976, Chapter 2.

5. Rabiner, L R, and Gold, B, *Theory and Application of Digital Signal Processing,* Prentice-Hall Inc, Englewood Cliffs, NJ, 1975, Chapter 3.

6. Rabiner, L R, "Practical Design Rules for Optimum Finite Impulse Response Low-Pass Digital Filters," *Bell System Technical Journal,* Vol 52, No 6, July-August, 1973.

7. Rabiner, L R, "Approximate Design Relationships for Low-Pass FIR Digital Filters," *IEEE Transactions on Audio and Electroacoustics,* Vol AU-21, No 5, October 1973.

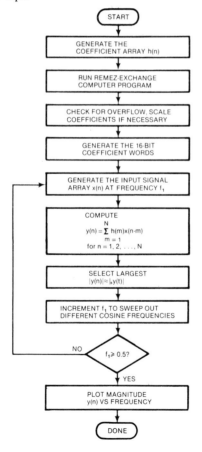

Fig 8—Software simulation *of digital filters follows the steps of this flowchart. Simulation helps detect potential problems before hardware implementation.*

46 Single cell lights LED

Battery 'on' indicator

A neat circuit providing an 'on' indicator for battery instruments powered from a single 1.5 V cell.

Lacz Gyula and Bunsits József
Hiradástechnika Szövetkezet, Budapest, Hungary

You can light LEDs from a low-voltage source with the 150-kHz shunt switch-mode driver in **Fig 1**. Without this circuit, for example, a 1.2V battery has insufficient voltage to bias an LED on via a series resistor.

In the circuit, comparator Q_1 turns electronic switch Q_2 on and off. When Q_2 turns on, current flow ramps up in L_1, and LED D_2 is back-biased. Eventually, the voltage this current flow develops across R_6 turns off

Q_1. Q_1's turning off, in turn, turns off Q_2. When Q_2 turns off, LED D_2 acts as a freewheel diode for L_1 and lights up.

Diode D_1 compensates for the temperature dependence of Q_1's base-emitter voltage and reduces the sensitivity of the R_1/R_2 divider to changes in supply voltage. R_4 limits the base current of Q_2, and R_5 adds hysteresis to the Q_1 comparator.

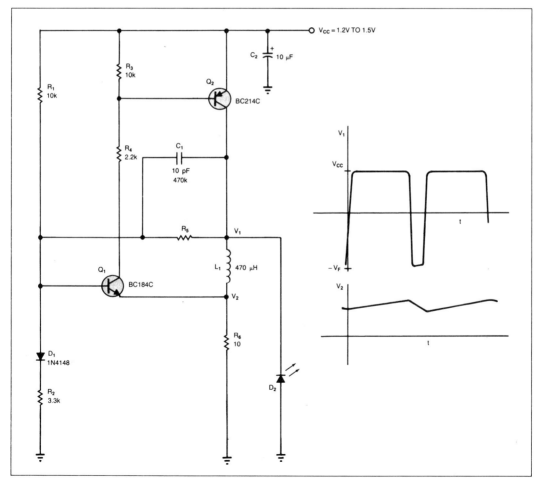

Fig 1—*This free-running switch-mode driver* *can light an LED from a low-voltage source.*

47 Circuit deletes power-line cycles

Poor mains simulator

Or rather, a good simulator of poor mains supplies. Such simulators are available from a number of manufacturers, but tend to be expensive. Anyone contemplating exporting electronic kits to third world countries, though, had better be sure his or her kit can survive the vagaries of the local electricity supply. This circuit will look after one aspect, though further tests will be necessary to demonstrate the kit's ability to survive surges and spikes.

Steve Ross
Kentrox Industries, Portland, OR

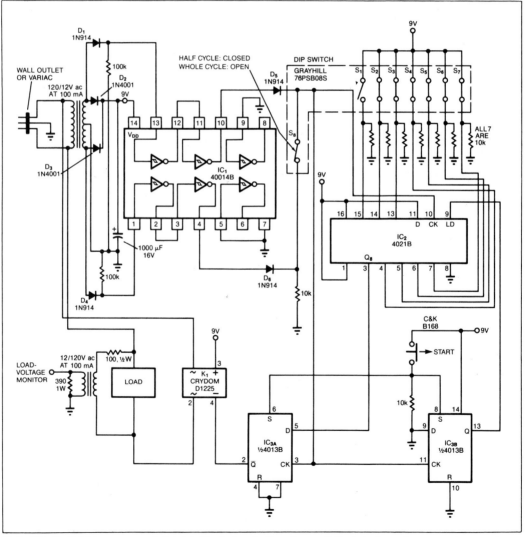

Fig 1—This circuit deletes a sequence of whole or half cycles from the line voltage applied to the load according to a 7-cycle pattern that you program using the DIP switch's sections S_1 through S_8.

The circuit of **Fig 1** is useful in testing the response of equipment to a momentary loss of power. Each time you depress the normally on start switch, the circuit deletes zero to seven full or half cycles from the line voltage applied to the load. You can create various load-voltage waveforms by appropriate settings of the 8-pole DIP switch.

The simple full-wave rectifier (diodes D_2 and D_3) supplies about 9V to the logic ICs. Diodes D_1 and D_4 also rectify the stepped-down line voltage and apply alternate half cycles to the Schmitt-trigger inverters in IC_1. The inverters square these half-sinusoidal waveforms, and diodes D_5 and D_6 constitute an OR gate that combines the inverter outputs for use as a clock signal to IC_2 and IC_3.

Section S_8 of the DIP switch determines whether the circuit deletes half or full cycles. The remaining sections (S_1 through S_7) determine the number and serial position of the cycles deleted. Shift register IC_2 converts the information in these sections to a serial bit stream, which controls the solid-state relay K_1 via flip-flop IC_{3A}. (An open switch deletes a full or half cycle by opening the relay, removing line voltage from the load during that period.)

In each scope photo of **Fig 2**, the top traces show the load voltage (which you measure at the monitor terminal,) and the bottom traces show the corresponding control voltage for the solid-state relay K_1 (which you measure at IC_{3A}, pin 2). You trigger the scope on the falling voltage (IC_3, pins 6 and 8), which you create by activating the start button.

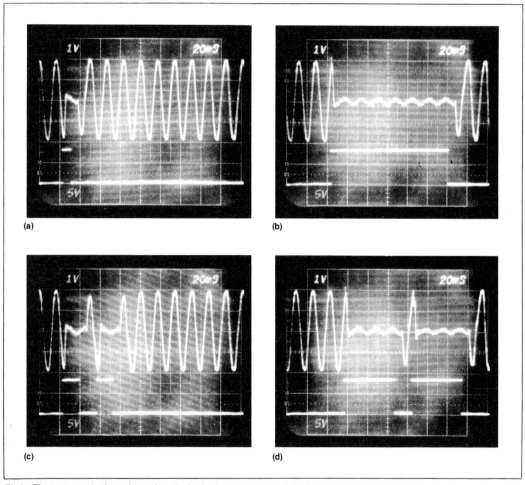

(a) (b) (c) (d)

Fig 2—The top traces in these photos show the load-voltage waveforms, following activation of the start switch, for various settings of the DIP switch: With S_1 open and all others closed, one half cycle is deleted **(a)**; with all switches open, seven full cycles are deleted **(b)**; with either S_1, S_2, S_3, and S_6 open or S_1, S_4, and S_8 open, two alternate full cycles are deleted **(c)**; and with all switches open except S_4, three full cycles on either side of a single full cycle are deleted **(d)**.

48 Understand capacitor soakage to optimize analog systems

Dark secrets of capacitors

An item of essential reading from Bob Pease for anyone designing low level analog circuits where low frequency/DC performance is important. The big surprise for me was how poorly silver mica capacitors – considered by many to be one of the most stable and reliable types – made out in the soakage tests.

Robert A Pease, National Semiconductor Corp

Veteran circuit designers often got a shocking introduction to dielectric absorption when supposedly discharged high-voltage oil-filled paper capacitors reached out and bit them. Indeed, the old oil-filled paper capacitors were notorious for what was once called soakage—a capacitor's propensity to regain some charge after removal of a momentary short. Today, you won't find very many of these capacitors in use, but you will still encounter soakage. Do you know how to deal with it?

Nowadays, you're more likely to notice the effects of dielectric absorption in some more subtle way, perhaps in the performance of an integrator that can't be reset to zero or a sample/hold that refuses to work correctly. But whether you literally feel its effects or merely observe them in a circuit's behavior, dielectric absorption is an undesirable characteristic that every capacitor possesses to some degree. This characteristic is inherent in the dielectric material itself, although a poor manufacturing procedure or inferior foil electrodes can contribute to the problem.

Indeed, soakage seems an apt term for dielectric absorption when you note what the capacitor seems to be doing. Consider a typical example: A capacitor charges to 10V for a long time T and then discharges through a small-value resistor for a short time t. If you remove the short circuit and monitor the capacitor terminals with a high-impedance voltmeter, you see the capacitor charge back to 0.1%, 1% or as much as 10% of the original voltage. For example, a 1-μF Mylar capacitor charged to 10V for 60 sec (T_{CHARGE}) and discharged for 6 sec ($t_{DISCHARGE}$) charges to 20 or 30 mV after 1 min (T_{HOLD}). **Fig 1** shows a simple evaluation circuit for measuring this characteristic.

A capacitor exhibiting dielectric absorption acts as if during its long precharge time the dielectric material has soaked up some charge that remains in the

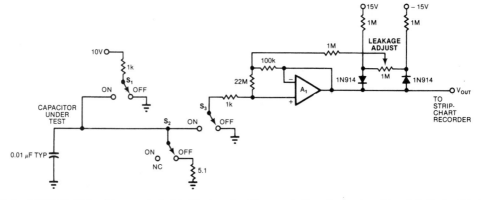

Fig 1—A simple test fixture *lets you evaluate dielectric absorption at low speeds. To use the one shown here, start with all switches off and throw S_1 and S_2 on for 1 min; then throw S_1 and S_2 off and wait 6 sec, throwing S_3 on during the wait period. Next, turn S_2 on and watch V_{OUT} for 1 min. To compensate for leakage, leave all switches off for 1 min and then throw S_2 and S_3 on. Monitor V_{OUT} for 1 min and subtract this value from the V_{OUT} value obtained earlier.*

dielectric during the brief discharge period. This charge then bleeds back out of the dielectric during the relaxation period and causes a voltage to appear at the capacitor terminals. **Fig 2** depicts a simple model of this capacitor: When 10V is applied for 1 min, the 0.006-μF capacitor gets almost completely charged, but during a 6-sec discharge period it only partially discharges. Then, over the next minute, the charge flows back out of the 0.006 μF and charges the 1-μF capacitor to a couple of dozen millivolts. This example indicates that a longer discharging time reduces soakage error but that discharging for only a small fraction of that time results in a larger error. Illustrating this point, **Fig 3** shows the results of conducting **Fig 1**'s basic test sequence for 1-, 6- and 12-sec discharge times. Note that the capacitor tries to remember its old voltage, but the longer you hold it at its new voltage, the better it forgets—in the **Fig 3** case, soakage errors equal 31 mV at $t_{DISCHARGE}=1$ sec, 20 mV at $t_{DISCHARGE}=6$ sec and 14 mV at $t_{DISCHARGE}=12$ sec.

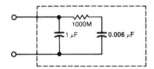

Fig 2—To model the soakage *characteristic of a 1-μF Mylar capacitor, consider a circuit that incorporates a 0.006-μF capacitor to represent the dielectric's charge-storage characteristic.*

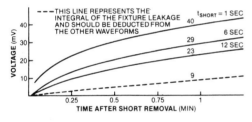

Fig 3—Obtained using Fig 1's test circuit, *these dielectric-absorption-measurement results for a 1-μF capacitor show that longer $t_{DISCHARGE}$ times reduce soakage-caused errors.*

High-speed tests predict S/H performance

You might now ask whether these low-speed tests have any bearing on a capacitor's suitability in fast millisecond or microsecond sample/hold applications. If you repeat the **Fig 1** experiment for $T_{CHARGE}=T_{HOLD}=1000$ μsec and $t_{DISCHARGE}=100$ μsec, you see very similar capacitor-voltage waveforms but with about 10-times-smaller amplitudes. In fact, for a constant T:t ratio, the resulting soakage error decreases only slightly in tests ranging in length from minutes to microseconds.

Fig 4's circuit approximates this capacitor characteristic, which you can observe on actual capacitors by using **Fig 5**'s test setup. Here, a sample/hold IC exercises the capacitor under test at various speeds and duty cycles, and a limiter amplifier facilitates close

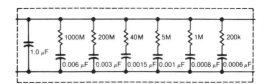

Fig 4—More precise than Fig 2's equivalent circuit, *a capacitor model employing several time constants proves valid for a wide range of charge and discharge times. This model approximates a Mylar capacitor.*

study of the small residual waveforms, without overdriving the oscilloscope when the capacitor is charged to full voltage.

Such experiments illustrate that if you put a certain amount of charge into a less-than-ideal capacitor, you will get out a different amount of charge, depending on how long you wait. Thus, using low-soakage capacitors proves important in applications such as those involving high-resolution dual-slope integrating ADCs. And sure enough, many top-of-the-line digital voltmeters do use polypropylene (a low-soakage dielectric) devices for their main integrating capacitors.

But dielectric-absorption characteristics are most obviously detrimental in applications involving sample/holds. Manufacturers guarantee how fast these devices can charge a capacitor in their Sample mode and how much their circuits' leakage causes capacitor-voltage droop during the Hold mode, but they don't give any warning about how much the capacitor voltage changes because of soakage. This factor is especially important in a data-acquisition system, where some channels might handle small voltages while others operate near full scale. Even with a good dielectric, a sample/hold can hurt your accuracy, especially if the sample time is a small fraction of T_{HOLD}. For example, although a good polypropylene device can have only 1-mV hysteresis per 10V step if T/t=100 msec/10 msec, this figure increases to 6 mV if the T/t ratio equals 100 msec/0.5 msec. Because most sample/hold data sheets don't warn you of such factors, you should evaluate capacitors in a circuit such as **Fig 5**'s, using time scaling suited to your application.

Other applications in which soakage can degrade performance are those involving fast-settling ac active filters or ac-coupled amplifiers. In **Fig 6**'s circuit, C_1 can be a Mylar or tantalum unit because it always has 0V dc on it, but making C_2 polypropylene instead of Mylar noticeably improves settling. For example, settling to within ±0.2 mV for a 10V step improves from 10 to 1.6 sec with the elimination of Mylar's dielectric absorption. Similarly, voltage-to-frequency converters benefit from low-soakage timing capacitors, which improve V/F linearity.

Some dielectrics are excellent at all speeds

Fortunately, good capacitors such as those employing polystyrene, polypropylene, NP0 ceramic and Teflon dielectrics perform well at all speeds. **Fig 7** shows the characteristics of capacitors using these dielectrics and others such as silver mica and Mylar. In general, polystyrene, polypropylene or NP0-ceramic capacitors

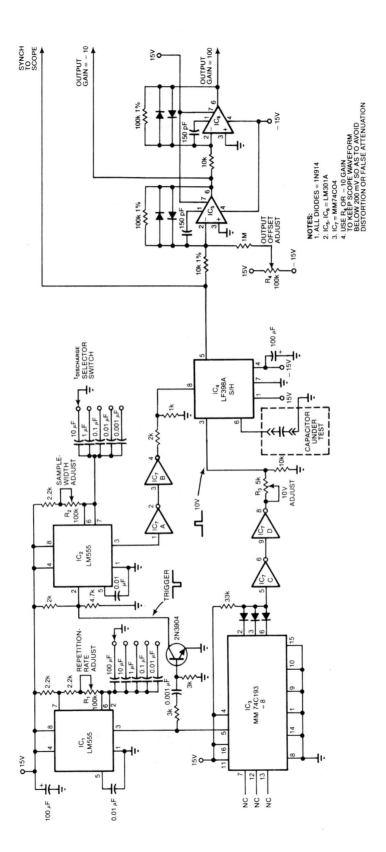

Fig 5—Capable of automatically sequencing the dielectric-absorption tests, a circuit employing timers, a sample/hold and limiting stages allows you to make measurements for a wide range of t_{CHARGE}, T_{HOLD} and $t_{DISCHARGE}$ values. **Fig 7 shows results** obtained using the circuit shown here.

160

furnish good performance, although polystyrene can't be used at temperatures greater than 80°C. And although NP0 ceramic capacitors are expensive and hard to find in values much larger than 0.01 μF, they do achieve a low temperature coefficient (a spec not usually significant for a S/H but one that might prove advantageous for precision integrators or voltage-to-frequency converters). Teflon is rather expensive but definitely the best material to use when high performance is important. Furthermore, only Teflon and NP0 ceramic capacitors suit use at 125°C.

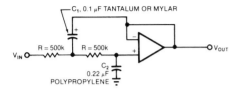

Fig 6—**Soakage can present problems** when you're designing a fast-settling amplifier or filter. In the circuit shown here, for example, C_1 can be a Mylar or tantalum unit, but making C_2 a polypropylene device improves performance.

If you look at **Fig 7**'s dielectric-absorption values, you can see wide differences in performance for a given dielectric material. For example, polypropylene sample A is about as good as B at t=6 sec, but B is four times better at high speeds. Similarly, NP0-ceramic sample A is slightly worse than NP0-ceramic sample B at low speeds, but A is definitely better at high speeds. And

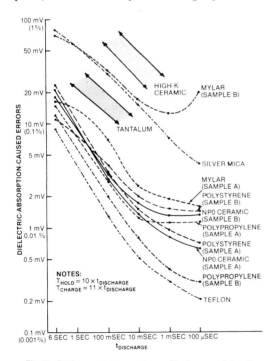

Fig 7—**Soakage-measurement results** for a variety of capacitors illustrate the effects of $t_{DISCHARGE}$ values on dielectric-absorption-caused errors. Note that the curves for two different samples of NP0 ceramic capacitors intersect.

some Mylar capacitors (sample A) get better as speed increases from 1000 to 100 μsec, but others (sample B) get worse. So if you want consistently good performance from your capacitors, evaluate and specify them for the speed at which they'll be used in your application. Keep in mind that because most sample/holds are used at much faster speeds than those corresponding to the 1- or 5-min ratings usually given in data sheets, a published specification for dielectric absorption has limited value.

In addition, other dielectrics furnish various levels of performance:

- Because any long word that starts with poly seems to have good dielectric properties, how about polycarbonate or polysulfone? No—they are about as bad as Mylar.
- Does an air or vacuum capacitor have low soakage? Well, it might, but many standard capacitors of this type are old designs with ceramic spacers, and they might give poor results because of the ceramic's hysteresis.
- If a ceramic capacitor is not an NP0 device, is it any good? Most of the conventional high-K ceramics are just terrible—20 to 1000 times worse than NP0 and even worse than tantalum.
- Is silicon dioxide suitable for small capacitances? Although **Fig 5**'s test setup, used in preparing **Fig 7**'s chart, only measures moderate capacitances (500 to 200,000 pF), silicon dioxide appears suitable for the small capacitors needed for fast S/Hs or deglitchers.

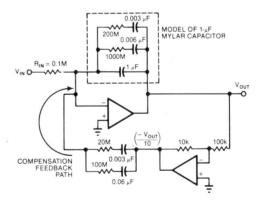

Fig 8—**You can compensate an integrator for dielectric absorption** by feeding its inverted output back to the input through one or more experimentally chosen RC networks, which cancel the equivalent network inherent in the capacitor's dielectric material.

Cancellation circuit improves accuracy

A practical method of getting good performance with less-than-perfect capacitors is to use a soakage-cancellation circuit such as one of the form shown in **Fig 8**, in which a capacitor of the type modeled in **Fig 4** serves as an integrator. (Only the first two soakage elements are shown.) The integrator's output is invert-

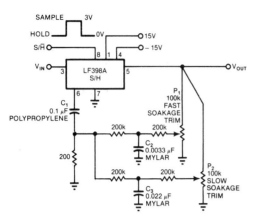

Fig 9—Adding compensation circuitry to a sample/hold yields better-than-Teflon performance with a polypropylene capacitor. Using Teflon capacitors in such circuits can yield a 15- to 17-bit dynamic range.

ed with a scale factor of -0.1, and this voltage is then fed through one or more experimentally chosen RC networks to cancel the equivalent network inherent in the capacitor's dielectric material.

Fig 9 shows a practical sample/hold circuit with an easily trimmed compensator. This network provides about a 10-fold improvement for sample times in the 50- to 2000-μsec range **(Fig 10)**. Although this compensation is subject to limitations at very fast or slow speeds, the number of RC sections and trimming pots employed can be extended.

Simple circuits similar to **Fig 9**'s or **Fig 8**'s have been used in production to let inexpensive polypropylene capacitors provide better-than-Teflon performance. In turn, using these compensator circuits with a good Teflon capacitor furnishes a dynamic range of 15 to 17 bits.

BEFORE COMPENSATION

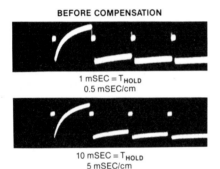

1 mSEC = T$_{HOLD}$
0.5 mSEC/cm

10 mSEC = T$_{HOLD}$
5 mSEC/cm

AFTER COMPENSATION WITH FIG 9 CIRCUIT

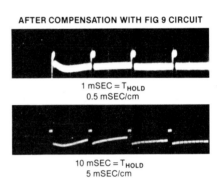

1 mSEC = T$_{HOLD}$
0.5 mSEC/cm

10 mSEC = T$_{HOLD}$
5 mSEC/cm

NOTES: 1. DIELECTRIC ABSORPTION ERRORS WITH GOOD POLYPROPYLENE CAPACITOR
2. ALL WAVEFORMS AT 1 mV/cm; $\dfrac{T_{SAMPLE}}{T_{HOLD}} = \dfrac{1}{10}$

Fig 10—Adding Fig 9's compensation network to a sample/hold circuit yields a 10-fold performance improvement for sample times of 50 to 2000 μsec; additional RC networks and trimming pots can extend the time range. The short pulses represent normal S/H jumps and occur during the sample time. The exponentially rising waveform during the hold time results from soakage. Note that soakage effects are still visible during the second hold period.

49 Analog delay line uses digital techniques

Digital analog delay line

This circuit will produce a delayed exact replica of a sampled input signal, without any of the approximations involved in schemes designed to handle speech, such as delta modulation and its derivatives, which cannot handle large signal energies in the upper part of the passband. By using a counter providing more address bits, in conjunction with an 8K × 8 SRAM or larger, the time delay product can be extended as required.

T G Barnett and J Millar
*The London Hospital Medical College,
London, UK*

The analog delay line of **Fig 1** uses a digital technique to delay an analog signal for as long as two seconds, reconstructing the signal with 8-bit resolution. The product of the delay time and the bandwidth is a constant: For a 1.024-kHz clock frequency (2-sec delay), the analog bandwidth is 100 Hz; for the maximum 40.96-kHz clock frequency (50-msec delay), the analog bandwidth is 4 kHz. There is no lower limit for the clock frequency.

The clock signal drives a binary counter (IC_2), which then scans the address inputs of a 2048-byte×8-bit RAM (IC_3). The RAM writes the contents of each memory location to the D/A converter (IC_4) and then reads out the results of a just-completed conversion by the 8-bit A/D converter IC_1. The RAM reads out each data sample 2048 cycles after it is read in, so the delay is 2048 times the clock period, or 2048 divided by the clock

frequency.

The clock signal also drives two monostable multivibrators in parallel (IC_{5A} and IC_{5B}). IC_{5A} triggers on the clock's rising edge; IC_{5B} triggers on the clock's falling edge. You choose the timing components R and C so that each device produces a pulse of approximately 1 μsec. These pulses have the proper polarity and phase to control the A/D converter, D/A converter, and RAM as shown.

You should scale the analog input for a range of 0 to 2.5V. The 100-pF capacitor sets the A/D converter's internal clock to its maximum rate of 900 kHz; you should monitor the $\overline{BUSY}$ signal (pin 1) and adjust the capacitor value as required to achieve 900 kHz. Both converters include a 2.5V voltage reference, but to improve accuracy use the A/D converter's reference for both. Power consumption is 120 mA from the 5V supply and 50 μA from the −5V supply. You can greatly reduce current drain from the positive supply by adding logic to control the RAM's chip-enable input (pin 18).

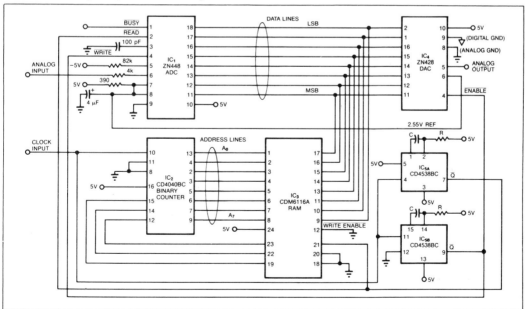

Fig 1—This analog delay line digitizes a signal once per clock cycle, stores the result in a 2048-word RAM, and converts one sample per clock cycle with a D/A converter. The resulting delay equals 2048 divided by the clock frequency.

50 Nonlinear components lower settling time of noise-reduction filters

Fast settling filters

Filters are often incorporated at the input of an instrument to reduce noise, for example in a DVM to clean up the DC input ahead of the measuring circuit. However, they frequently increase the settling time by an embarrassing amount: this can be substantially reduced by incorporating nonlinear techniques, as the following article shows.

Rod Burt and R Mark Stitt, *Burr-Brown Corp*

The most common method of improving S/N ratio is noise reduction by filtering. The attendant increase in settling time, however, can be a serious disadvantage in certain applications, such as high-speed data acquisition. A nonlinear filter is a simple way to achieve a 4-to-1 improvement in settling time over conventional filters.

First, consider the dynamics of a single-pole RC filter (**Fig 1a**). Filtering reduces broadband or white noise by the square root of the bandwidth reduction, according to the following equations, where e_n is the total noise in V_{rms}, e_B is the broadband noise in $V/\sqrt{Hz}$, and f_1 to f_2 is the filter's frequency range in hertz:

$$e_n^2 = \int_{f_1}^{f_2} e_B^2 \, df = e_B^2 \cdot f \Big|_{f_1}^{f_2},$$

and thus,

$$e_n = e_B \sqrt{f_2 - f_1}.$$

These equations show that if you reduce the frequency range, $f_2 - f_1$, by a factor of 100, the total noise decreases by a factor of 10.

Unfortunately, the settling time increases as the bandwidth decreases. For a single-pole filter, you can calculate the time needed for the signal to settle to any given accuracy using the following equations, where t_S is the settling time in seconds, % is the percent of accuracy at time t_S, and R_1C_1 is the RC time constant in ΩF. At time t_S,

$$\frac{V_{OUT}}{V_{IN}} = 1 - e^{-(t_S/R_1C_1)},$$

and

$$-\left(\frac{V_{OUT}}{V_{IN}} - 1\right)100 = \%.$$

Therefore,

$$t_s = -\ln(\%/100) \, R_1C_1.$$

To determine the number of time constants required for the signal to settle within 0.01%, simply calculate $\ln(0.01/100)$, which equals -9.2. Thus, it takes 9.2 RC time constants for an input step to settle to within 0.01% of its final value.

A simple, diode-clamped nonlinear filter (**Fig 1b**) can improve the settling time of a simple RC filter. When you initially apply a large input step to V_{in}, the filter capacitor, C_1, charges faster through the forward-biased diode's low impedance than it can through R_1. When the difference between the input and output voltages becomes less than the forward-biased diode's drop (about 0.6V), the diode stops conducting, and C_1 and R_1 are the only active components. At this point, the circuit behaves like a normal, single-pole RC filter.

Assuming that the diode's R_{on} is very small and thus negligible, this filter's improvement in settling time depends on the ratio of the input step and the forward-biased diode's voltage. For a 20V step—-10 to $+10V$, for example—the filter improves settling time by $\ln(0.6/20)$, or 3.5 time constants. In other words, for a 20V step, the simple, diode-clamped nonlinear filter shortens the normal RC filter's 0.01% settling time from 9.2 time constants to $9.2 - 3.5 = 5.7$ time constants. However, as the ratio between the input voltage and the diode's forward voltage decreases, so does this circuit's advantages. The settling-time improvement decreases for smaller input steps. When the input step equals the forward-biased diode's voltage drop, the circuit provides no improvement in settling time.

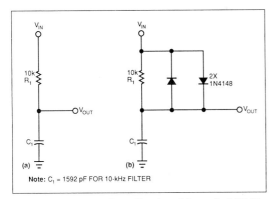

Note: C_1 = 1592 pF FOR 10-kHz FILTER

Fig 1—You can improve the settling time of the standard RC filter (a) by adding two diodes (b). C_1 charges and discharges much faster through the diode's low on-resistance than it can through R_1, thus improving settling time.

Lower the threshold

By reducing the threshold to below 0.6V, you can improve the settling time for even smaller inputs. The improved nonlinear filter shown in **Fig 2** lets you adjust the clamp threshold by choosing the values of R_1 and R_2.

Fig 2's op amp forces the voltage at its inverting input to be the same as the signal at the noninverting input. Small voltage differences between the input and the output voltages appear across R_1, because the diodes don't have adequate forward bias and are therefore off. Under these conditions, the filter behaves like a single-pole filter with a time constant determined by the values of R_1 and C_1.

The voltage divider formed by R_1 and R_2 forces the voltage V_A to equal

$$V_A = V_B[1 + (R_2/R_1)].$$

When the input voltage increases (when you apply a step voltage, for example), V_A increases. When the voltage difference between the input and output approaches $0.6V/(1 + R_2/R_1)$, the diode that corresponds to the input's signal polarity will begin to conduct, and the capacitor will rapidly charge through that diode.

To determine **Fig 2**'s component values, you'll have to consider the noise-reduction requirements of your filter. For example, if you want to filter the noise of a 20V step to 0.01% resolution, you'll also filter the signal's peak noise to less than 0.01% of 20V, or 2-mV peak. A clamp threshold of ten times this peak, or 20 mV, is an arbitrary but ample nonlinear threshold. The component values shown in **Fig 2** set the filter's threshold to 20 mV. The time constant of the filter is very small, regardless of which diode is on, and the settling time is limited only by the op amp's slew rate

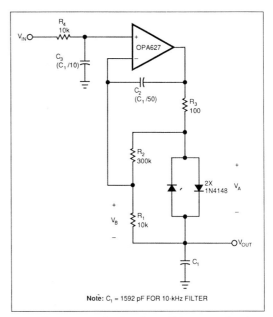

Note: C_1 = 1592 pF FOR 10-kHz FILTER

Fig 2—To improve settling time for small inputs as well as large inputs, this circuit allows you to set the noise threshold by choosing the values of R_1 and R_2.

or current limit. For a 20V step, **Fig 2**'s improvement in settling time is $\ln(0.02/20) = 6.9$ time constants. In other words, the improved nonlinear filter can improve the 0.01% settling time of a 20V step from 9.2 time constants to $9.2 - 6.9$, or 2.3, time constants—a 4-to-1 improvement. Further reducing the 20-mV threshold provides little additional settling-time improvement.

To use this filter successfully, you need to know the noise content of your input signal. If the noise of your signal is greater than the threshold—20 mV in this case—the filter will mistake the noise as a step input and fail to filter it out. Thus, **Fig 2** only behaves like the desired filter for noise signals below the threshold that you set. If the noise exceeds 20 mV, **Fig 2**'s circuit won't behave as an RC filter with the desired 10-kHz cutoff. To prevent this situation, you can ensure that the noise signal at the op amp's input doesn't exceed 20 mV by using C_3 and R_4 to prefilter the input.

To reduce the prefilter's effect on settling time, the values of R_4 and C_3 set the prefilter's bandwidth ten times higher than the bandwidth of the noise filter. At this higher bandwidth, the prefilter's effect on settling time is negligible, and the noise at the prefilter's output is $\sqrt{10}$ times greater than 2 mV, or a little over 6-mV peak. (Recall that noise is proportional to the square root of the bandwidth.) A noise level of 6 mV provides a comfortable margin for a 20-mV threshold.

Choose the right filter ingredients

Op amps tend to become unstable and to oscillate when driving large capacitive loads. The network comprising C_2 and R_3 in **Fig 2** ensures circuit stability when the op amp is driving large values of C_1 through the low impedance of the forward-biased diode network. You may not need this network if C_1 is a small value.

When choosing the op amp for the improved filter, make sure it has enough output-drive capability to charge C_1. Also, the op amp's bandwidth, slew rate, settling time, and dc precision must be adequate for the necessary filter response. Choose an op amp such as the OPA627, which combines dc precision, high slew rate, fast settling time and high output-drive capability. Also, notice that any unity-gain op amp's noise adds noise to the signal. If you choose a low-noise op amp, the op amp's noise contribution is usually negligible. For example, the OPA627 adds only 6% of the 10-kΩ resistor's theoretical minimum noise to the total system noise. Remember that noise adds as the square root of the sum of the squares. Therefore, to determine

how much the 4.5 $nV/\sqrt{Hz}$ noise of the op amp adds to the 12.8 $nV/\sqrt{Hz}$ noise of the resistor, calculate the square root of the sum of the squares of the combination and compare that to the noise of the resistor alone. In this case, $\sqrt{(4.5)^2 + (12.8)^2}/12.8 = 1.06$, or a 6% increase.

Fig 3a shows the responses of the standard RC, diode-clamped, and improved nonlinear filters to a −10-to-+10V input step. The bandwidth of each filter is 10 kHz. The measurement circuit adds a gain of 100 between the scope and the circuit, so each horizontal division for traces B, C, and D represents 2 mV, or 0.01% of a 20V step. Thus, the filters settle to within 0.01% when their corresponding traces lie within one division below the center line of the scope.

For a 10-kHz filter, one RC time constant is 15.9 μsec. **Table 1** displays the theoretical settling times of each filter. These tabulated settling times ignore the input slew rate and the diode forward resistance,

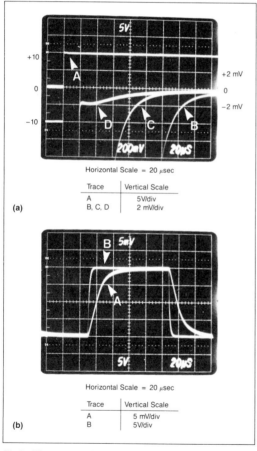

Horizontal Scale = 20 μsec

Trace	Vertical Scale
A	5V/div
B, C, D	2 mV/div

(a)

Horizontal Scale = 20 μsec

Trace	Vertical Scale
A	5 mV/div
B	5V/div

(b)

Table 1 — Theoretical time constants and settling times

Filter type	Theoretical settling time (time constants)	Theoretical settling time (μsec)*
Single-pole RC	9.2	147
Diode-clamped nonlinear	5.7	91
Improved nonlinear	2.3	37

*Time required to settle within 0.01% of final value for a 10-kHz filter

which are good approximations for the OPA627-based, 10-kHz filter. The actual measurements closely match the theoretical calculations.

Fig 3b is a double-exposure scope photo of the improved nonlinear filter operating with a low (trace A) and high (trace B) input signal level. The filter's response to a ±10-mV step looks like the response of a standard, 10-kHz, single-pole RC filter. You'd expect this response, because the input is equal to the threshold voltage. When the circuit operates with a high input level (a ±10V input step), the settling time greatly improves.

Fig 3—The response of each filter (a) to an input step (trace A) shows the graduated settling-time improvement from the simple RC filter (trace B) to the improved nonlinear filter (trace D). The double-exposure scope photo in (b) contrasts the small-signal (trace A) and large-signal (trace B) settling times of the improved nonlinear filter.

51 Intermittent converter saves power

Better battery economy

This brilliantly simple idea avoids the chronic low efficiency of converters running under light-load conditions. It features a novel application of the popular and widely second sourced 555 timer chip.

Paul D Gracie
The Microdocters Inc, Palo Alto, CA

The circuit in **Fig 1** switches its dc/dc converter, IC_1, off whenever the large filter capacitor, C_6, has sufficient charge to power the load. This scheme, which proves especially useful for battery-powered systems, saves power because virtually all dc/dc converters have poor efficiency at low and zero output-power levels.

This particular circuit uses a dc/dc converter that produces 115V dc from a 9V-dc input; you can tailor the circuit to suit other converters. The heart of the circuit is a 555 timer configured as a dual-limit comparator. An input of less than $\frac{1}{3} V_{CC}$ to pin 2 of the 555 turns the output, pin 3, on; an input of more than $\frac{2}{3} V_{CC}$ to pin 6 turns the output off. Thus, the 555 turns the converter on or off, depending on the voltage across C_6. The 555's complementary output lights the charge LED when the FET is on.

Initially, the voltage on C_6 is zero, and the 555's output turns on the FET, Q_1. Q_1, in turn, enables the converter to run, which charges up C_6. When the voltage on the capacitor reaches the value set by R_3, the 555 turns off the converter. Then C_6 slowly discharges into the combined load of the voltage divider (R_2, R_3, and R_4) and the reverse-biased blocking diode, D_1.

When the voltage falls below $\frac{1}{3} V_{CC}$, the 555 restarts the dc/dc converter. If this circuit powers a load that periodically goes into a zero-power, shut-down mode, the 555 switches the dc/dc converter on full time whenever the load kicks in.

The 78L05 voltage regulator stablizes the 555's internal resistive divider in the face of varying battery voltages. The regulator also enables the circuit to detect low battery voltage. When the supply voltage falls below 7.5V, the output of the converter is no longer high enough to charge the capacitor to the upper set point; hence, the charge LED no longer lights.

The circuit uses 205 mA when the converter is on and 10 mA when the converter is off. The duty cycle comprises a 5-sec on period and a 150-sec off period and represents a 92% power reduction. You can further reduce power consumption by removing the charge LED and using a CMOS 555 and a CMOS 78L05 regulator.

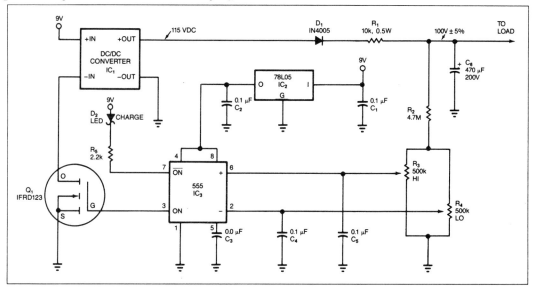

Fig 1—*Employing a 555 timer acting as a dual-limit* comparator, this circuit reduces low- and no-load power consumption by switching off the dc/dc converter when the filter capacitor is charged up.

52 Amp provides 100 V common-mode range

Amplifier with large common mode range

By operating an op-amp at a gain of less than unity, both common-mode and the desired differential mode inputs are attenuated by the same amount. At the same time , the permissible input common-mode voltage is increased, as shown in this article.

Mark Stitt

Burr-Brown Corp, Tucson, AZ

The unity-gain amplifier of **Fig 1** can reject common-mode voltages as high as 100V. For an application that does not require galvanic isolation, this circuit is an inexpensive alternative to the conventional isolation-amplifier solution.

IC_1 is a monolithic gain-of-10 difference amplifier. By reversing normal connections to the on-chip resistor network, you place 100-kΩ resistors (instead of the 10-kΩ ones) at the amplifier's input, which attenuates the normal- and common-mode signals by a factor of 10. Then, resistors R_1, R_5, and R_6 form a T network in the feedback path that boosts the normal-mode gain to unity.

Because the addition of R_5 and R_6 degrades common-mode rejection by unbalancing the internal resistor ratios, you should restore the balance by adding about 158Ω (R_7) in series with R_3. A fixed-value R_7 that differs by 2% from the T network's equivalent value degrades CMR by only a few dB, but note that IC_1's CMR is already 20 dB below its specified value (100 dB min) because the amplifier is operating at a gain of 0.1 instead of 10. You can improve the CMR by using a 500Ω potentiometer for R_7, as shown.

The differential-gain accuracy is within 2% if you use 1% resistors for R_5 and R_6. Adjusting the R_6/R_5 ratio can improve the gain accuracy, but calibration is diffi-

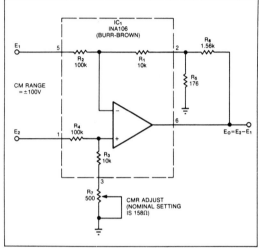

Fig 1—This amplifier offers unity gain to E_2-E_1 signals while rejecting common-mode voltages as high as ±100V.

cult because the gain and CMR adjustments interact. You can eliminate this interaction and improve the gain accuracy by using the **Fig 2** circuit.

In **Fig 2**, IC_2 preserves IC_1's CMR by buffering the R_5/R_6 network. Again, IC_1's gain-of-0.1 connection reduces the guaranteed CMR by 20 dB—to 80 dB min. (This CMR estimate is reliable because the IC_1 amplifi-

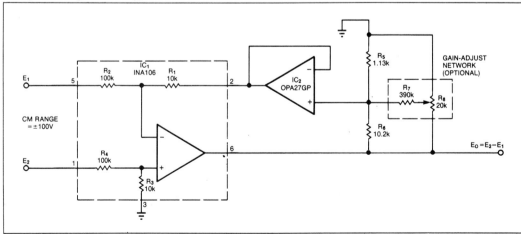

Fig 2—Adding an op amp to the Fig 1 circuit eliminates interaction between the gain-adjust potentiometer and the CMR-adjustment pot (not shown).

er (distinct from its thin-film resistor network) contributes only -120 dB of CMR error. Therefore, the resistor network is responsible for most of the residual CMR error that remains after laser trimming. This trim error affects CMR by about the same amount whether operating with a gain of 10 or a gain of 0.1.)

You can improve this circuit's CMR by adding 10Ω in series with R_1 (pin 2) and adding a 20Ω potentiometer in series with R_3 (pin 3). To adjust CMR, connect the inputs and drive them with a 1-kHz square wave whose amplitude is in the range from ±10V to ±100V. (A sine wave will introduce unwelcome CMR-vs-frequency effects.) Adjust the 20Ω pot for a minimum-amplitude signal at E_O.

As before, $1+R_6/R_5$ sets the gain. The tolerance on this expression plus $\pm0.01\%$ (contributed by IC_1) determines the overall gain accuracy. You can improve gain accuracy by using higher-precision resistors or by adding the optional gain-adjust network shown (R_7 and R_8). Gain and CMR adjustments don't interact in the **Fig 2** circuit.

One application for the circuit of **Fig 1** or **Fig 2** is in monitoring high-side load current in a regulator or power supply. By connecting the difference amplifier across a 1Ω resistor in series with the supply's output, you can interpret the difference amplifier's output as one ampere of load current per volt for supply voltages in the range from -100V to 100V.

53 Improve circuit performance with a 1-op-amp current pump

High compliance bipolar current source

This article, which appeared in *EDN* in 1983, introduced me to a constant current generator circuit which was first described in the late 1950s. I subsequently realized that I had seen it used before in a design, published in 1970, for a sawtooth generator based on an op amp integrator with one end of the capacitor grounded. However, in that article there was no mention of the original inventor. I have since used the Howland current pump in a number of applications, including a published design for a very economical triangle/squarewave generator. Altogether a most useful circuit and well worth knowing about.

Robert A Pease, National Semiconductor Corp

If you can lower an op amp's output impedance and use negative feedback to make the amp a voltage source, can you use positive feedback to raise the device's output impedance and thereby create a current source? You can, indeed: An ingenious single-op-amp circuit, invented more than 20 yrs ago by Brad Howland at MIT, uses a combination of positive and negative feedback to implement an excellent current pump (see **box**, "A flexible current source"). This circuit suits many applications, and if you require even better

and the circuit exhibits a high output impedance. The value of R_2 is not very important so long as you maintain this relationship:

$$R_1/nR_1 = R_2/nR_2.$$

Note, however, that if you choose resistors with values of $50\ k\Omega \pm 1\%$, worst-case output impedance is no better than 2 to 3 MΩ. And although such a circuit can

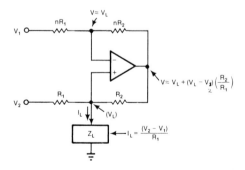

Fig 1—The basic Howland current pump *provides a current of magnitude* $(V_2 - V_1)/R_1$ *into its load.*

performance, you can increase its output impedance by adding a trim.

Maintain a key relationship

Fig 1 shows the basic configuration of Howland's current pump. The current forced in the load is
$$I_L = (V_2 - V_1)/R_1,$$

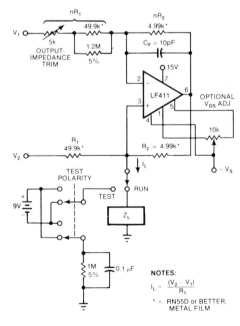

Fig 2—You can null the basic circuit's current offset *and increase output impedance to more than 200 MΩ by using the trims shown.*

A flexible current source

Because Howland's current source doesn't usually lend itself to intuitive analysis, to understand its operation ask yourself this question: If the circuit has as much feedback to its positive input as to its negative input, why won't it go out of control and hang up with the amplifier's output at

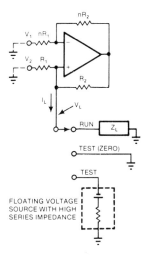

Measure the output impedance of Howland's circuit by determining the change in current that occurs with a floating voltage source in series with the load.

the rail? Well, it could and it would if there were no load on the output. But this current pump, just like any other, is only characterized for a finite load impedance. It can put its current into a resistor, a capacitor, an inductor or a zener diode, but if you try to run it with no load connected, it goes off to the rail. (It comes back promptly when you attach a load.)

Once you see how the circuit works, though, how can you get a feel for its operational characteristics? Consider the circuit **(figure)** from two viewpoints:

• The current delivered into the load is

$$\frac{V_2 - V_1}{R_1}.$$

Consider that the transfer characteristic from V_2 to Z_L with $V_1=0$ and Z_L a short to ground is

$$I_L = \frac{V_2}{R_1}.$$

In addition, the transfer characteristic from V_1 to Z_L with V_2 at 0V and Z_L shorted is:

$$I_L = \left(-\frac{V_1}{nR_1}\right)\left(\frac{nR_2}{R_2}\right)$$

$$= \frac{-V_1}{R_1}.$$

Using superposition,

$$I_L = \frac{V_2 - V_1}{R_1}$$

if $Z_L=0\Omega$, and I_L remains at the value

$$\frac{V_2 - V_1}{R_1}$$

so long as the output impedance is high—if the circuit is linear.

• The circuit's output impedance is high. Consider the case of V_1 and V_2 grounded. If you try to drive V_L above ground by using a signal source as Z_L, does it have to drive a heavy load? Every time V_L rises 1V, the op amp's output rises $(R_2/R_1) \times 1V$, and the current fed through R_2 back to V_L is just equal to the current needed to lift R_1 1V above ground. If these two currents are well matched, the output impedance is very high. (Another way to view the situation is to say that Z_L would have to drive R_1 to ground, but the rest of the circuit acts as a negative resistance with value $-R_1$, so the conductances cancel out.) If you assume the circuit is linear (the output does not limit), the high output impedance implies

$$I_L = \frac{V_2 - V_1}{R_1}$$

even if V_{LOAD} is not zero.

---

force 0.2 mA into a grounded load, it can only drive the load to ±5V. That performance is only mediocre—but a start toward some far better circuits.

Fig 2 shows a few refinements. Here, you choose R_2 to be $R_1/10$, so the load voltage can range to ±11.5 or ±12V for a ±15V supply. A small feedback capacitor is added to improve loop stability, and a trimming pot allows you to compensate for resistor tolerances. For example, when $V_1=V_2=0$, connect the test load and trim R_1 so that the current is the same with and without the 9V test offset voltage in series with the load (within 2 or 3 nA). Now Z_{OUT} is 200 to 1000 MΩ—not bad.

You can set I_L to zero by adjusting the V_{OS} trimming pot. If you choose $nR_1=1$ kΩ and $R_2=100\Omega$, for example, you can force as much as 10 mA into low-voltage loads: zeners, diodes, resistors or nonlinear or active circuits. And if you choose R_1 in the megohm range, you can design precision nanoampere circuit sources.

Modified current pump provides higher compliance

Now suppose you want to force ±1 mA into a ±10V load, using a ±1V input signal. The basic equation shows that R_1 would have to be 1 kΩ in this case, and even with R_2 of 100Ω, when V_1 is −1V and the V_2 input is grounded, the op amp has to force 10 mA into R_1 as well as 1 mA into the load—an inefficient use of power.

The improved Howland circuit shown in **Fig 3** avoids this wastefulness. For this circuit,

$$I_L=((V_2-V_1)/R_5)\times(R_2/R_1),$$

but you should trim R_3 to obtain the best Z_{OUT}. So

$$R_3=((R_4+R_5)/R_2)R_1.$$

Although the action of this circuit is not entirely obvious, it becomes more so after you read the box's analysis. You can see that Z_{OUT} is large, because if $V_1=V_2=0$ and you lift the output terminal V_L, no current is required so long as

$$R_3/R_1=(R_4+R_5)/R_2.$$

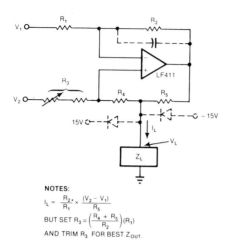

NOTES:

$$I_L = \frac{R_2}{R_1} \times \frac{(V_2 - V_1)}{R_5}$$

$$\text{BUT SET } R_3 = \left(\frac{R_4 + R_5}{R_2}\right)(R_1)$$

AND TRIM R_3 FOR BEST Z_{OUT}.

Fig 3—Further modifying the basic Howland circuit *increases voltage compliance and the amount of current deliverable into the load.*

In **Fig 3**'s circuit, each resistor can have a high value (100 kΩ or 1 MΩ), but using a small value for R_5 sets the gain (I_L/V_{IN}) high, and very little current is then wasted. For the example of driving ±1 mA into a ±10V load with R_5=1 kΩ, you'd waste only a few microamperes in R_3 and R_4.

A further refinement uses two op amps and four equal-valued resistors, plus a group of two or more switched gain-setting resistors (**Fig 4**). The buffer amplifier (A_2) ensures that the bridge is balanced with a high output impedance, no matter what value you choose for R_3 or R_4. Circuits such as this find wide use in automatic test equipment that must force a current and then read a voltage, or vice versa.

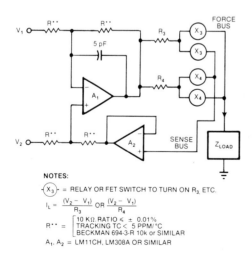

NOTES:

(X_3) = RELAY OR FET SWITCH TO TURN ON R_3, ETC.

$$I_L = \frac{(V_2 - V_1)}{R_3} \text{ OR } \frac{(V_2 - V_1)}{R_4}$$

$R^{\cdot\cdot} = \begin{bmatrix} 10 \text{ K}\Omega. \text{ RATIO} \leqslant \pm 0.01\% \\ \text{TRACKING TC} < 5 \text{ PPM/°C} \\ \text{BECKMAN 694-3-R 10k or SIMILAR} \end{bmatrix}$

A_1, A_2 = LM11CH, LM308A OR SIMILAR

Fig 4—A practical application of Howland's pump *finds wide use in automatic test equipment. Buffer amplifier A_2 ensures that the bridge is balanced with a high output impedance regardless of the values of R_3 and R_4.*

Where might you use the Howland current pump? In many instances, one op amp does the work of two or more when used in this configuration. And even though the days are long gone when op amps were so expensive that designers gladly struggled to get one to do the work of two, the circuit can indeed prove quite useful.

Early analog-computer applications often called for integration—a function implemented with an inverter (**Fig 5**). But because op amps were expensive, designers instead sometimes used a differential integrator (**Fig 6**). This circuit saves the cost of an op amp but requires two integrating capacitors. And to obtain accurate results, you must trim both resistors or both capacitors. Consequently, the circuit never saw wide use.

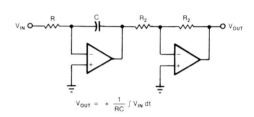

$$V_{OUT} = +\frac{1}{RC}\int V_{IN}\, dt$$

Fig 5—A conventional noninverting integrator *calls for two op amps—once an expensive requirement.*

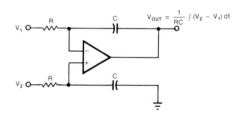

$$V_{OUT} = \frac{1}{RC}\int (V_2 - V_1)\, dt$$

Fig 6—A differential integrator, *now rarely used, was once a less expensive alternative to Fig 5's design. It achieves positive integration with a single op amp. However, it requires two capacitors.*

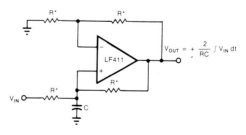

$$V_{OUT} = +\frac{2}{RC}\int V_{IN}\, dt$$

Fig 7—A Howland integrator *achieves positive integration with just one capacitor, overcoming the limitations of Fig 6's circuit.*

A Howland integrator (**Fig 7**), on the other hand, uses only one op amp and one capacitor. And although it requires four resistors, they can be part of an inexpensive thin-film network, thus achieving good matching accuracy. You can combine this integrator with a conventional one (**Fig 8**) to make a sinusoidal oscillator with both sine and cosine outputs.

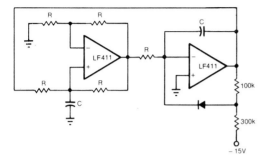

Fig 8—Build a sine-wave oscillator *with sine and cosine outputs by combining Howland's integrator* **(Fig 7)** *with some additional circuitry.*

Circuit improves multiplying DAC

The Howland current pump has also been used in an ultrafast multiplying DAC (**Fig 9a**). In this circuit, an analog input change from 10 mV to 10V requires the op amp's output to change by only 360 mV, so the amplifier's slew rate is not a limiting factor in the DAC's response. The response speed is further enhanced by the use of grounded-base transistors: When the bit input goes LOW, the emitter of Q_2 falls 1.5V in a few nanoseconds, but the emitter of Q_1 shifts only a millivolt. Thus, the op amp corrects only a minor error.

Although this configuration appears to be a profligate use of op amps (one per bit), you can show that each op amp would have approximately the same output voltage at all levels of signal and temperature. Therefore, the **Fig 9b** circuit can serve in practice.

Howland's pump thus imparts precision to a very-fast-settling DAC. Note, however, that **Fig 9a**'s pump can only put out a current in one polarity, via Q_1. All other uses of the design have full bipolar capability, unlike most transistorized current pumps.

Current pump linearizes RTD

The circuit of **Fig 10** shows a Howland current pump used as part of a precision platinum-RTD thermometer. This configuration performs the same function as the bare-bones circuit shown in **Fig 11**, but it provides some definite advantages. The current pump (A_1 and R_1 to

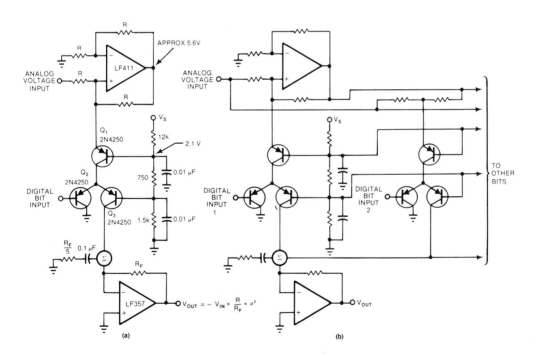

Fig 9—A fast multiplying DAC (a) *works well because the switching transistors are connected in the grounded-base configuration. In addition, you can configure the circuit so that all bits require only one current source between them* **(b).**

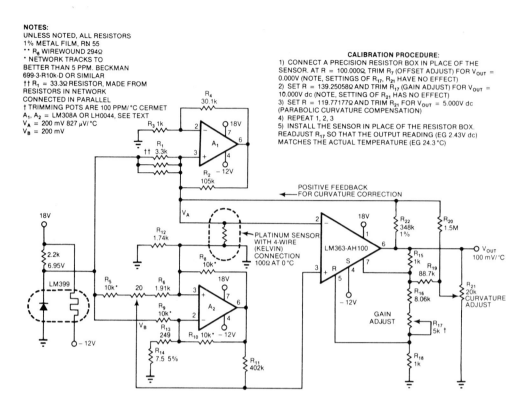

NOTES:
UNLESS NOTED, ALL RESISTORS
1% METAL FILM, RN 55
** R_6 WIREWOUND 294Ω
* NETWORK TRACKS TO
BETTER THAN 5 PPM. BECKMAN
699-3-R10k-D OR SIMILAR
†† R_1 = 33.3Ω RESISTOR, MADE FROM
RESISTORS IN NETWORK
CONNECTED IN PARALLEL
† TRIMMING POTS ARE 100 PPM/°C CERMET
A_1, A_2 = LM308A OR LH0044, SEE TEXT
V_A = 200 mV 827 µV/°C
V_B = 200 mV

CALIBRATION PROCEDURE:
1) CONNECT A PRECISION RESISTOR BOX IN PLACE OF THE
SENSOR. AT R = 100.000Ω, TRIM R_7 (OFFSET ADJUST) FOR V_{OUT} =
0.000V (NOTE, SETTINGS OF R_{17}, R_{21} HAVE NO EFFECT)
2) SET R = 139.25058Ω AND TRIM R_{17} (GAIN ADJUST) FOR V_{OUT} =
10.000V dc (NOTE, SETTING OF R_{21} HAS NO EFFECT)
3) SET R = 119.7717Ω AND TRIM R_{21} FOR V_{OUT} = 5.000V dc
(PARABOLIC CURVATURE COMPENSATION)
4) REPEAT 1, 2, 3
5) INSTALL THE SENSOR IN PLACE OF THE RESISTOR BOX.
READJUST R_{17} SO THAT THE OUTPUT READING (EG 2.43V dc)
MATCHES THE ACTUAL TEMPERATURE (EG 24.3 °C)

Fig 10—Feedback from the Howland current source *linearizes this platinum RTD thermometer. Performance is further improved by buffering the platinum sensor's ground-sense voltage.*

R_4) forces a current through the 100Ω platinum resistance sensor, despite any Kelvin or wiring resistance. A second amplifier, A_2, serves to buffer the sensor's ground-sense voltage and adds an offset from the stable reference via R_5 and R_6. You can also consider A_2 to be a current pump, because it has equal feedback to its inverting and noninverting inputs; it can thus amplify the bridge output without loading or drawing any current from the bridge.

So although **Fig 10**'s circuit is more complex than **Fig 11**'s, it's much less sensitive to amplifier offset and

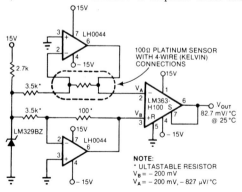

Fig 11—A bare-bones circuit *for RTD-based temperature measurement illustrates the basic operation of **Fig 10**'s more complex design.*

drift. It can provide high precision with ordinary amplifiers (LM308s) or ultrahigh precision if you use LH0044s—about 30 times greater accuracy than **Fig 11**'s circuit.

Feeding back a fraction of **Fig 10**'s bridge amplifier's output proves useful in correcting for the platinum sensor's inherent square-law error via R_{20} and R_{22}. This feedback improves the bridge's accuracy and linearity from ±0.6 to ±0.01°C over −50 to +150°C.

Final notes on Howland sources

In an all-resistive system, the stray capacitance from the op amp's noninverting input to ground could be sufficient to ensure stability. But a few picofarads from the positive input to ground provide a safety factor when used in addition to the usual stabilizing capacitor from the op amp's output to inverting input.

Any current pump requires an infinite voltage to drive a step of current into an inductive load. Because the op amp's output-voltage capability (voltage compliance) is finite, you'll note a definite current rise time in practice: di/dt=V/L. For a larger di/dt, you need a larger V. However, after you get the current flowing, don't just turn off the power; the flowing current will generate a large inductive spike that will probably damage the op amp's input. Instead, for any significantly large inductive load, clamp the load with diodes to the supplies, as in **Fig 3**'s dashed-line portion.

Finally, if a load can suddenly change in impedance (eg, if it's a switched resistance), a fast FET-input amplifier such as an LF351 can maintain a more precise constant flow than the slower bipolar amplifiers. To tolerate a fast jump of load voltage with submicro-second settling, use a grounded-base transistor in a configuration similar to **Fig 9a**'s Q_1. If a 1% loss of gain arising from the transistor's alpha is not acceptable, use an FET or Darlington transistor to improve dc accuracy to 0.01%.

54 Two-way amplifier uses few parts

Two-way amplifier for two-wire line

A conventional amplifier for a two-wire line uses 2 wire to 4 wire conversions using hybrids, with a separate amplifier for each path direction. In applications where the return loss of the ends is large, a simpler arrangement is possible, shown here implemented for unbalanced two wire lines. It can be extended to balanced lines if required, by duplicating the whole circuit for the other wire.

Rudy Stefenel
Luma Telecom, Santa Clara, CA

Fig 1 depicts a conventional 2-way amplifier used with 2-wire telephone lines. This approach requires separate amplifiers for each direction, hybrid 2- to 4-line transformers, and carefully designed complex-impedance terminations to match the capacitive reactance normally associated with telephone lines.

For 2-wire signal lines whose impedance is mostly resistive (telecommunications test equipment, for example), you can use the simpler, resistively terminated circuit of **Fig 2**. The boxes labeled "termination" are two telecomm devices (such as modems, modem test equipment, short-haul 2-wire communication lines, or minimum-loss impedance-matching pads) that are communicating with each other.

Like all 2-way amplifiers, both of these circuits may oscillate unless terminated with the proper impedance. Moreover, higher audio gain imposes greater accuracy constraints on the terminating impedance values. Because resistors R_A, R_B, R_C, and R_D have a fixed relationship with one another, you can set the circuit's "resistance level" by choosing a value for one of them—R_D, for example. Given the desired termination resistance R_L and amplifier gain A, you can then calculate values for the remaining resistors R_A, R_B, and R_C.

First, note that R_A contributes the only significant resistance between each amplifier and its load. Source impedance should equal the load impedance, so

$$R_A = R_L \tag{1}$$

is the first of three design equations. Because IC_2 mustn't contribute a signal while IC_1 is operating (and vice versa), IC_2's output must remain at virtual ground during that time. Therefore, R_A is also the input impedance for each amplifier.

Next, the gain from IC_1's noninverting input to its output is

$$\frac{R_D + \dfrac{R_C R_B}{R_C + R_B}}{\dfrac{R_C R_B}{R_C + R_B}},$$

and the gain from IC_1's output to R_L is ½ because $R_A = R_L$ (**Eq 1**). The product of these gains must equal the given gain A:

$$A = \frac{1}{2} \left[\frac{R_D + \dfrac{R_C R_B}{R_C + R_B}}{\dfrac{R_C R_B}{R_C + R_B}} \right]. \tag{2}$$

To ensure that no signal is emitted from IC_2 when only the lefthand signal source is active, IC_2's differential input must be zero. This is so if IC_2's inputs are equal, which implies equal voltage dividers:

$$\frac{\dfrac{R_C R_D}{R_C + R_D}}{R_B + \dfrac{R_C R_D}{R_C + R_D}} = \frac{R_L}{R_A + R_L} = \frac{1}{2}.$$

Simplifying this equation yields

$$\frac{R_C R_D}{R_B R_C + R_B R_D + R_C R_D} = \frac{1}{2}. \tag{3}$$

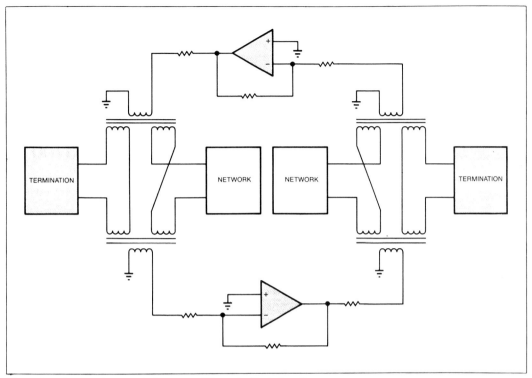

Fig 1—This schematic shows a typical 2-way amplifier used with telephone lines.

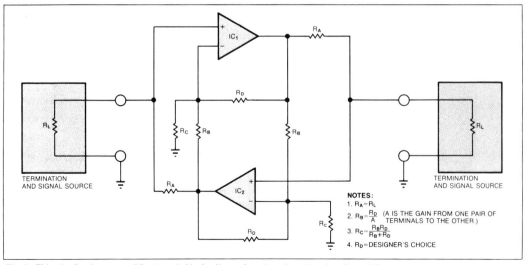

Fig 2—This simpler 2-way amplifier is suitable for lines whose impedance is primarily resistive.

You can solve **Eqs 2** and **3** simultaneously for the remaining unknowns R_B and R_C. First, simplify **Eq 2**:

$$A = \frac{1}{2}\left(\frac{R_D R_C + R_D R_B + R_C R_B}{R_C R_B}\right) \qquad (4)$$

Next, rearrange **Eq 3** as

$$R_B R_C + R_B R_D = R_C R_D, \qquad (5)$$

and substitute into **Eq 4**:

$$A = \frac{1}{2}\left(\frac{R_D R_C + R_C R_D}{R_C R_B}\right) = \frac{R_D}{R_B}.$$

Therefore,

$$R_B = \frac{R_D}{A}$$

is the second design equation.

For the last design equation, solve **Eq 5** for R_C:

$$R_C = \frac{R_B R_D}{R_D - R_B}.$$

Fig 3 shows an example of a circuit using 600Ω resistive loads and a gain of 2. The signal at IC_{1B}'s output measures only 2 to 3% of the signal-generator output.

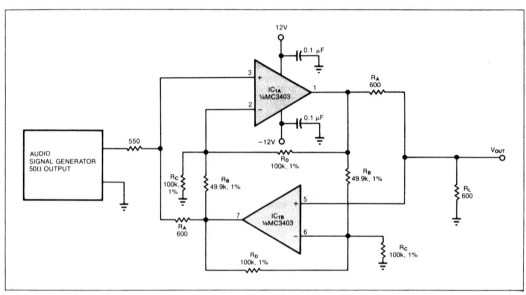

Fig 3—Based on the circuit of Fig 2, *this 2-way amplifier provides a gain of 2 between 600Ω terminations.*

55 Amplifier handles duplex line

Another amplifier for a two-wire line

Another approach to amplification in a two-wire line is simply to bridge a negative resistance across the line. As in the previous example, if the return loss of the terminations is too low at some frequency, the circuit will sing around at that frequency.

Mansour Ahmadian
*Technical and Engineering University,
Tehran, Iran*

The circuit in **Fig 1** is a bidirectional amplifier that can amplify both signals of a duplex telephone conversation. It uses the principle of negative resistance. Obviously, such an amplifier could easily be unstable; how-

ever, you can adjust R_1 in **Fig 1** for maximum amplification and the circuit will remain stable. You might also consider replacing the LM324 op amps with op amps that would distort less, such as the LM1558, LF412, LF353, or LF442.

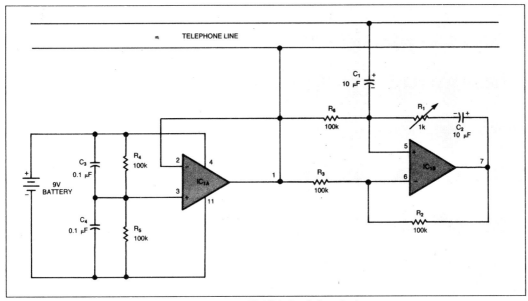

Fig 1—This amplifier uses the **negative-resistance** principle to amplify full-duplex telephone signals.

56 Active feedback improves amplifier phase accuracy

> ## Improved op-amp phase response
>
> Here is an interesting technique which is implemented at little cost, in these days of dual-
> and quad-op-amps. I have not had occasion to use it yet, but the secret of the successful
> analog engineer is knowing how to do something when the need arises.

James Wong, *Precision Monolithics Inc*

In applications such as sonar and image-processing systems, the phase relationship between two or more signals reveals essential information. These systems require accurate phase response in their amplifier circuitry to minimize measurement errors. In such cases, active feedback can often serve much better than other approaches. A typical op amp is insufficient in this situation because it introduces significant phase shift long before it reaches its -3-dB frequency. The consequent phase error reduces the effective bandwidth of an op amp to something significantly less than the -3-dB point.

You can use a wideband amplifier to overcome this phase-error problem. If the wideband amplifier operates with a -3-dB bandwidth that is much higher than that of the signal that you intend to amplify, then the phase error at your signal's frequency decreases proportionately. The wideband amplifier's greater expense is the main drawback to this approach.

If you cascade two or three amplifiers, each of which has its gain reduced to share the overall gain of the composite amplifier, the gain reduction at each stage of the amplifier increases the -3-dB bandwidth of each stage of the amplifier. Consequently, the overall bandwidth for a given phase accuracy is increased, but you pay for this improvement with increasingly higher costs and noise levels.

Another, less expensive way to solve the phase-error problem is to introduce extra circuitry in the amplifier's feedback loop, which provides frequency compensation. You can use an RC circuit to create a zero in the feedback loop that cancels the amplifier's pole. This cancellation improves the phase response markedly by lessening the amplifier's phase-response roll-off. The chief disadvantage of the RC technique is that it requires extensive tuning to match the zero with the pole. Furthermore, the different temperature coefficients of the RC components cause the zero to drift. And when the zero drifts, it no longer cancels the pole, and phase error becomes a problem once again.

Placing an op-amp circuit in the feedback stage of the amplifier creates the active feedback that can overcome the temperature drift of the RC networks. It is also a thriftier approach than using a wideband amplifier. You must make sure, however, that the op amps are very closely matched. Monolithically matched dual or quad op amps can provide the frequency-matching characteristics (to within 1 to 2%) necessary for the success of the active-feedback approach. This close matching is necessary across the full temperature range of your application. It's easier to achieve in an integrated dual or quad op amp than it is in discrete resistors and capacitors.

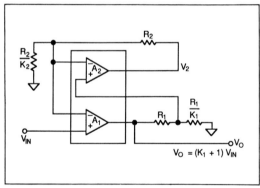

Fig 1—Second-order compensation, *as provided by the op amp in the feedback path of this circuit, extends the effective bandwith of an amplifier substantially.*

Fig 1 shows a basic active-feedback circuit. It requires an op amp and two external resistors to achieve phase-error cancellation. In the circuit, op amp A_1 provides the forward gain of the composite amplifier. Resistors R_1 and R_1/K_1 determine the closed loop gain $A_V \gg 1 + K_1$. Amplifier A_2 provides active feedback to op amp A_1. The ratio of resistors R_2 and R_2/K_2 determines the amount of phase-error compensation and has no effect on the forward gain of the composite amplifier. You obtain optimum error cancellation when $K_1 = K_2$.

In terms of the complex frequency response, the error terms for the circuit are given by

$$\text{magnitude error} \cong \left(\frac{\omega}{B\,\omega_{\mathrm{T}}}\right)^2$$

$$\text{phase error} \cong -\left(\frac{\omega}{B\,\omega_{\mathrm{T}}}\right)^3.$$

These equations let you compare the phase error associated with a single amplifier with that associated with the 2-op-amp, active-feedback approach. They arise from a complete analysis of the basic circuit and its derivatives (see **box**, "Analyzing compensation techniques").

Dominant poles occur at 500 kHz

Table 1 tabulates the phase error and magnitude error for an amplifier with a gain of 10. The comparison assumes that the op amp's unity-gain bandwidth is 5 MHz. As you can see in the **table**, the dominant poles of all three amplifiers occur at 500 kHz, where the phase shift for each technique is $-45°$. Clearly, the compensation techniques do not extend the bandwidth of the op amp itself. Rather, these second-order compensation techniques reduce the phase error at lower frequencies by adding an equal but opposite phase shift in the amplifier feedback loop.

If you must limit phase error to less than half a degree, the second-order compensation technique increases the effective bandwidth of your amplifier from about 5 kHz to more than 100 kHz. If you need to limit

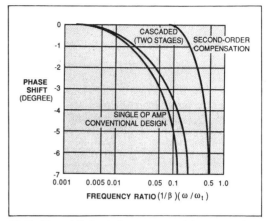

Fig 2—Phase shift for single-op-amp, cascaded-op-amp, and second-order-compensation designs is charted here. Note the significant improvement brought about by second-order compensation.

peaks at about 3 dB at the $-45°$ phase frequency, well outside the useful range. Within the frequency range where phase shift is negligible, the gain error is also insignificant. In **Fig 3**, for example, at 1⁄10 of the corner frequency, gain error is only 0.1 dB, about 1.2%.

In executing the second-order compensation design, it's extremely important to use op amps with frequency responses matched to within 1 to 2%. Op amps packaged separately can have mismatches as high as 10 to 20%, and high levels of mismatching cause either over- or undercompensation. Overcompensation creates excessive phase peaking, and undercompensation causes early phase roll-off.

TABLE 1—AC-ERROR COMPARISON

FREQUENCY	SINGLE-STAGE CONVENTIONAL PHASE (DEGREE)	CASCADED (TWO-STAGE) PHASE (DEGREE)	SECOND-ORDER COMPENSATION PHASE (DEGREE)
5 kHZ	−0.57	−0.36	0
10 kHZ	−1.15	−0.72	−0.0005
50 kHZ	−5.7	−3.62	−0.06
100 kHZ	−11.3	−7.21	−0.46
500 kHZ	−45.0	−45.0	−45.0

phase entirely, the second-order compensation limits phase error virtually to zero at frequencies to 50 kHz; a single-stage amplifier would be limited to well below 500 Hz.

The magnitude and phase responses are plotted in **Figs 2** and **3**, respectively. The single op-amp response serves as a basis for comparison. The maximum scale of 1.0 represents the $-45°$ phase-shift frequency. **Fig 2** shows that the cascaded 2-stage amplifier offers only a slight improvement in bandwidth, and that the second-order compensation method offers a significant improvement in effective bandwidth.

The tradeoffs are minor

The tradeoffs associated with the second-order feedback technique are minimal. **Fig 3** illustrates the appreciable gain peaking incurred, but the circuit typically

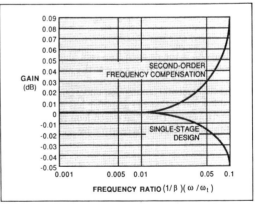

Fig 3—Second-order compensation does carry the penalty of gain peaking, but this doesn't become significant until close to the corner frequency.

Theoretically, second-order compensation works for any closed-loop gain. In practice though, at low gains, within the 1-to-5 range, the circuit may become unstable due to phase-margin degradation introduced by the active feedback. As a rule of thumb, you should work with a gain of 10 or greater. The match between theoretical and actual performance improves as the gain of the circuit is increased.

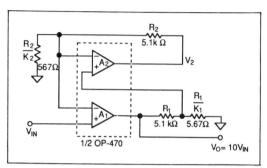

Fig 4—*This amplifier uses* the second-order compensation technique and has a gain of 10.

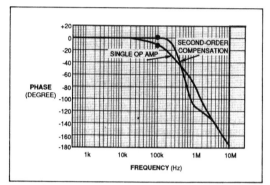

Fig 5—*The phase response of Fig 4's circuit* illustrates the improved flatness of response that can be attributed to second-order compensation.

A circuit using the second-order compensation is illustrated in **Fig 4**. The op amp used in this example is an OP-470, which is unity-gain stable and provides a 6-MHz unity-gain bandwidth. It's a quad op amp that offers a 1% match in ac characteristics between the four op amps on the chip. The circuit provides a gain of 10 for the amplifier.

The actual phase response of the circuit was measured using a network analyzer and is compared with a single-stage amplifier in **Fig 5**. The measurement confirms that the phase shifts of the second-order-compensated design and the single-stage design converge at

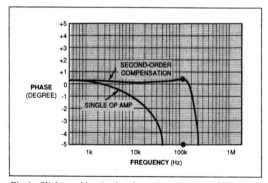

Fig 6—*Slight peaking in the phase response at 100 kHz for the* second-order-compensated circuit is illustrated in this closeup view of **Fig 5**.

$-45°$ and $135°$, respectively. The second-order response runs virtually flat with negligible phase shift to a much higher frequency before bandwidth limitation sets in. The roll-off is much steeper for the the second-order system than for the single-stage system. **Fig 6** illustrates more clearly that the second-order circuit's phase error remains nearly zero out to 100 kHz, while the single-stage amplifier's low phase-shift bandwidth is limited to 2 kHz.

Fig 6 also reveals a slight amount of phase peaking at about 100 kHz, just before the response rolls off. The peaking stems from the op amps' second poles near the unity-gain frequency. With a closed-loop gain of 10, the dominant pole and the second pole are separated by only one decade in frequency. This proximity causes secondary effects on the phase response of the amplifier. However, if you increase the closed-loop gain of the circuit, you further separate the two poles, reducing the second-pole effect.

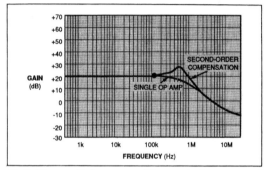

Fig 7—*The magnitude response* of the second-order-compensated circuit exhibits peaking at a frequency that is well beyond the useful range of the circuit.

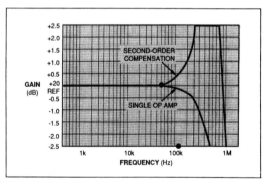

Fig 8—*Taking a closer look at the magnitude response,* you see that below 100 kHz, the frequency range where phase error is negligible, only a small degradation in gain accuracy occurs.

Fortunately, the second-order compensation's improvement in phase error does not exact much of a penalty in magnitude error. **Fig 7** charts the magnitude response versus frequency. Some gain peaking is apparent, but as predicted, the peaking occurs well beyond the amplifier's useful bandwidth. (**Fig 8** shows a close up of the gain peaking for the second-order-compensated circuit.) In the frequency range below 100 kHz, gain error is held to less than 0.25 dB or 3%. In comparison to the single-stage approach, a second-order compensation offers both low phase error and low magnitude error over a significantly expanded bandwidth.

Either resistor tolerances or op-amp mismatches can degrade the compensation circuit's performance but to no great extent. What does make a big difference is variations in K_2 (**Fig 9**). If you assume that the op amps

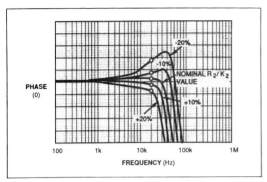

Fig 9—Phase-response sensitivity to variations in the compensation resistor ratio results in slight over- and undercompensation.

in **Fig 1** match perfectly, the resistor ratio, K_2, is the only variable that affects the amount of phase compensation that the feedback circuit provides. If you decrease K_2, the gain of op amp A_2 is also decreased; in turn, the dominant pole of A_2 shifts to a higher frequency, thereby decreasing the compensation. In the extreme case, where op amp A_2's gain is reduced to unity, the circuit behaves as if it had no compensation at all. It then responds as a single-stage amplifier. On the other hand, if you increase K_2, the gain of A_2 is likewise increased, and A_2's bandwidth decreases; overcompensation results. The end effect is that phase and gain peak more.

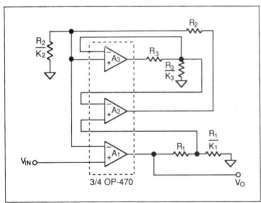

Fig 10—Third-order compensation takes the concept of active feedback one step further, adding another level of compensation to the feedback path.

Third-order compensation, which requires another op amp and two resistors in the feedback path, provides even greater phase compensation than afforded by second-order compensation. The schematic for the

third-order compensation circuit is given in **Fig 10**. The additional compensation comes from op amp A_3 in the feedback path of op amp A_2. The basic circuit is the same as that of the second-order compensation circuit.

The sinusoidal transfer function when the phase difference is minimized may be written:

$$\frac{V_O}{V_{IN}} =$$
$$(1 + K_1)\left[\frac{1 - j(T\omega)^5}{1 - 0.618034(T\omega)^2 - 0.618034(T\omega)^4 - (T\omega)^6}\right]$$

where: $T = \dfrac{1}{B\omega_T}$.

The numerator contains the phase information and the denominator contains the magnitude information. **Table 2** contrasts the magnitude and phase errors for the second-order response with that of the third-order response. Magnitude error is 38% lower for third-order compensation. Phase error is reduced from a third-order to a fifth-order term.

TABLE 2—ERROR COMPARISON OF SECOND-ORDER VS THIRD-ORDER COMPENSATION

	SECOND-ORDER	THIRD-ORDER
CLOSED-LOOP GAIN	$\dfrac{1}{\beta}$	$\dfrac{1}{\beta}$
MAGNITUDE ERROR	$\left(\dfrac{\omega}{\beta\omega_T}\right)^2$	$0.618\left(\dfrac{\omega}{\beta\omega_T}\right)^2$
PHASE ERROR	$-\left(\dfrac{\omega}{\beta\omega_T}\right)^3$	$-\left(\dfrac{\omega}{\beta\omega_T}\right)^5$

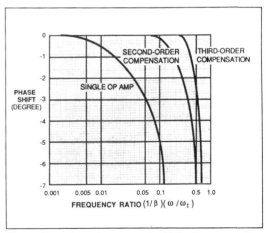

Fig 11—For a given phase error, the third-order compensation technique offers twice the bandwidth that the second-order technique does.

The third-order frequency response is plotted in **Fig 11** in comparison to that of the second-order compensation and of the single op-amp design. Given a prescribed error band—for example, one degree of phase error—

third-order compensation doubles the effective band width of an amplifier design over the second-orde compensation technique.

As you might imagine, the extra op amp in the feedback loop causes the gain to peak more at the −45° corner frequency. However, in the frequency range where phase error is minimal, gain accuracy is also improved. At a frequency ratio below 0.1, magnitude errors do not exceed 0.1 dB.

Fig 12 shows a test circuit that implements the third-order compensation. The phase response, measured by a network analyzer, is compared to that of the second-order compensation and of a single-op-amp design in **Fig 13**. The phase response of the third-order design remains flat beyond 400 kHz, double the 200 kHz provided by the second-order design. The magnitude

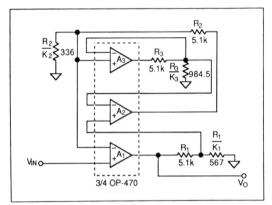

Fig 12—A third-order compensation circuit with component values that set a gain of 10 for the amplifier is illustrated here.

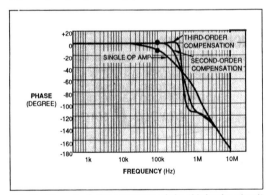

Fig 13—The actual phase response of the third-order circuit remains flat to a higher frequency than the second-order circuit or the single-op-amp design.

response, on the other hand, has considerably higher peaking than the second-order design, but below 350 kHz, the third-order design actually provides lower magnitude error than does the second-order design.

Analyzing compensation techniques

A single-stage amplifier without any band-limiting circuit, as shown in **Fig A**, rolls off according to the closed-loop gain of the circuit and the amplifier's own natural frequency response. You can approximate the amplifier's open-loop frequency response in this way:

$$\text{open-loop gain } A(s) \cong \frac{A_0}{1 + \frac{A_0}{\omega_T}s},$$

where A_0 is the dc open-loop gain and, ω_T is the unity-gain radian frequency of the amplifier.

The fundamental assumption underlying this approximation is that the amplifier has a single-pole response. Thus, the closed-loop response as a function of frequency is given by

$$\text{closed-loop gain } A_{CL}(s) = \frac{1}{B}\left(\frac{1}{1 + \frac{1}{A_0 B} + \frac{1}{B\,\omega_T}s}\right).$$

As long as the loop gain is much greater than unity—which is usually the case—you can rewrite the expression as

$$\text{closed-loop gain } A_{CL}(s) \cong \frac{1}{B}\left(\frac{1}{1 + \frac{1}{B\,\omega_T}s}\right).$$

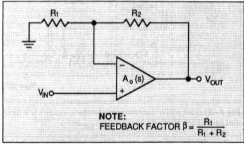

NOTE:
FEEDBACK FACTOR $\beta = \dfrac{R_1}{R_1 + R_2}$

Fig A—A basic single-stage amplifier without any band-limiting circuit rolls off according to the closed-loop gain of the circuit and the amplifier's own natural frequency response.

Fig B illustrates the magnitude and phase response of the closed-loop amplifier. Notice tha,t at the −3-dB corner frequency ω_c, the phase shift is −45°. Even at ¹⁄₁₀ of the corner frequency, the amplifier still has a 5.7° phase lag. The maximum frequency must be nearly two decades below the corner frequency to limit phase error to less than one degree.

Fig 1 (pg 180) illustrates the second-order, active-feedback compensation circuit that you can model by writing the transfer equation for

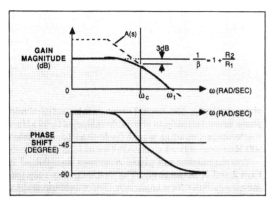

Fig B—Magnitude and phase response are shown for the basic single-stage amplifier. Notice that, at the −3-dB corner frequency ω_c, the phase shift is −45°.

the two amplifier loops. In solving this equation, assume that each amplifier has a single-pole roll-off response and that the two amplifier responses match perfectly.

At the junction of R_1 and R_1/K_1, the resistor divider expression becomes

$$V_0\left(\frac{1}{1 + K_2}\right).$$

Similarly, the resistor divider expression for R_2 and R_2/K_2 is

$$V_2\left(\frac{1}{1 + K_2}\right).$$

For ac response, the loop equations can now be written:

A_1 loop: $V_0 = \left[V_{IN} - \left(\frac{1}{1 + K_2}\right)V_2\right]\frac{\omega_T}{s}$

A_2 loop: $V_2 = \left[\left(\frac{1}{1 + K_1}\right)V_0 - \left(\frac{1}{1 + K_2}\right)V_2\right]\frac{\omega_T}{s}.$

Solving the simultaneous equations in terms of V_0 and V_{IN}, the transfer function is,

$$\frac{V_0}{V_{IN}} = (1 + K_1)\left[\frac{1 + \frac{(1 + K_2)}{\omega_T}s}{1 + \frac{(1 + K_1)s}{\omega_T} + \frac{(1 + K_1)(1 + K_2)s^2}{\omega_T^2}}\right].$$

Defining the time constants

$$T_1 = \frac{1 + K_1}{\omega_T} \text{ and } T_2 = \frac{1 + K_2}{\omega_T},$$

and substituting those time constants into the previous equations yields

$$\frac{V_0}{V_{IN}} = (1 + K_1)\left[\frac{1 + T_2s}{1 + T_1s + T_1T_2s^2}\right].$$

For optimum compensation, the time constants T_1 and T_2 are made equal:

$$\frac{V_0}{V_{IN}} = (1 + K_1)\left[\frac{1 + Ts}{1 + Ts + T^2s^2}\right].$$

For sinusoidal input, where phase information is important, the complex frequency domain is used.

$$\frac{V_0}{V_{IN}}(j\omega) = (1 + K_1)\left[\frac{1 + jT\omega}{1 + jT\omega - T^2\omega^2}\right].$$

Now we calculate the complex conjugates to simplify:

$$\frac{V_0}{V_{IN}} = (1 + K_1)\left[\frac{(1 + jT\omega)(1 + T^2\omega^2 - jT\omega)}{(1 - T^2\omega^2)^2 + T^2\omega^2}\right]$$

$$= (1 + K_1)\left[\frac{1 - jT^3\omega^3}{1 - T^2\omega^2 + T^4\omega^4}\right].$$

From this equation, the magnitude error expression can be derived.

$$\text{magnitude error} = \left|\frac{1 - jT^3\omega^3}{1 - T^2\omega^2 + T^4\omega^4}\right| - 1$$

$$\text{for } T\omega << 1, \cong \left|\frac{1}{1 - T^2\omega^2}\right| - 1$$

$$\cong 1 + T^2\omega^2 - 1$$

$$\cong T^2\omega^2.$$

Similarly, the phase error expression can be derived.

$$\text{Phase error} = \text{ARC}(1 - jT^3\omega^3)$$

$$\cong -T^3\omega^3.$$

$T\omega$ relates to closed-loop gain as

$$\frac{1}{B} = 1 + K_1 = 1 + K_2,$$

therefore,

$$T\omega = \frac{\omega}{B\omega_T}.$$

The transfer function can then be rewritten as

$$\frac{V_0}{V_{IN}} = \frac{1}{B}\left[\frac{1 - j\left(\frac{\omega}{B\omega_T}\right)^3}{1 - \left(\frac{\omega}{B\omega_T}\right)^2 + \left(\frac{\omega}{B\omega_T}\right)^4}\right].$$

Using this equation, the phase and magnitude behaviors as functions of frequency are tabulated in **Table A**. Note that, at $1/10$ of the corner frequency, the compensated circuit produces a

$-0.057°$ phase shift, far superior to the $-5.7°$ produced by the uncompensated circuit.

TABLE A—SECOND-ORDER COMPENSATION PHASE AND MAGNITUDE BEHAVIOR

$\frac{\omega}{\beta\omega_T}$	PHASE (DEGREE)	MAGNITUDE	20 LOG (MAG) IN dB
0.01	-5.7×10^{-5}	1.00000	0.0000
0.02	-0.0005	1.0004	0.0035
0.04	-0.00367	1.0016	0.0139
0.05	-0.00716	1.0025	0.0217
0.06	-0.01238	1.0036	0.0312
0.07	-0.01965	1.0049	0.0425
0.08	-0.0293	1.0064	0.0554
0.1	-0.0573	1.01	0.0864
0.2	-0.458	1.04	0.3404
0.3	-1.547	1.0896	0.745
0.4	-3.662	1.1576	1.271
0.5	-7.162	1.25	1.938
0.7	-14.428	1.37657	2.776
0.8	-27.1125	1.45979	3.2858
1.0	-45.0	1.4125	3.0

You can model the third-order compensation circuit of **Fig 10** (pg 186) in a similar way. Assume that all three op amps in the circuit have a single-pole roll-off in the frequency response represented by

$$A_0(s) \simeq \left(\frac{\omega_T}{s}\right)$$

where ω_T is the amplifier unity-gain crossover frequency.

For ac sinusoidal response, the loop equations can be written:

$$A_1 \text{ loop: } V_0 = \frac{\omega_T}{s}\left[V_{IN} - \frac{1}{(1+K_2)}V_2\right]$$

$$A_2 \text{ loop: } V_2 = \frac{\omega_T}{s}\left[\frac{1}{(1+K_1)}V_0 - \frac{1}{(1+K_3)}V_3\right]$$

$$A_3 \text{ loop: } V_3 = \frac{\omega_T}{s}\left[\frac{1}{(1+K_2)}V_2 - \frac{1}{(1+K_3)}V_3\right].$$

Solving the three simultaneous equations in terms of V_0 and V_{IN}, the transfer function is

$$\frac{V_0}{V_{IN}} = \frac{ax^2 + bx + 1}{ax^3 + bx^2 + \left(1 + \frac{1+K_3}{1+K_1}\right)X + \left(\frac{1}{1+K_1}\right)},$$

where $a = (1 + K_2)(1 + K_3)$,

$b = 1 + K_2$

$X = \dfrac{S}{\omega_T}$

Define the time constants

$$T_1 = \frac{1+K_1}{\omega_T}, \quad T_2 = \frac{1+K_2}{\omega_T},$$

and $T_3 = \dfrac{1+K_3}{\omega_T}$, then substitute,

$$\frac{V_0}{V_{IN}} =$$
$$(1+K_1)\left[\frac{1 + T_2s + T_2T_3s^2}{1 + (T_1+T_3)s + T_1T_2s^2 + T_1T_2T_3s^3}\right].$$

The dc gain of the amplifier is $(1 + K_1)$. And the ac response has the general form:

$$\frac{V_0}{V_{IN}} = (1+K_1)\,\epsilon_p(s),$$

where

$$\epsilon_p(s) = \frac{1 + T_2s + T_2T_3s^2}{1 + (T_1+T_3)s + T_1T_2s^2 + T_1T_2T_3s^3}.$$

Solve for ac response in terms of T_1, T_2, and T_3.

$$\epsilon_p(j\omega) =$$
$$\frac{1 - T_2T_3\omega^2 + jT_2\omega}{1 - T_1T_2\omega^2 + j[(T_1+T_3)\omega - T_1T_2T_3\omega^3]}.$$

Defining:
$a = 1 - T_2T_3\omega^2$, $b = T_2\omega$
$c = 1 - T_1T_2\omega^2$, $d = (T_1+T_3)\omega - T_1T_2T_3\omega^3$

$$\epsilon_p(j\omega) = \frac{a+jb}{c+jd} = \frac{ac+bd+j(bc-ad)}{c^2+d^2}.$$

The numerator determines the phase shift of the amplifier. Solve the numerator of $\epsilon_p(j\omega)$:

$$\epsilon_p(j\omega) = 1 + j\,[(T_2 - T_1 - T_3)\omega - (T_1T_2^2 - T_2T_3^2 - 2T_1T_2T_3)\omega^3 - T_1T_2^2T_3^2\omega^5.$$

To minimize phase shift, make $T_2 - T_1 - T_3 = 0$, and

numerator $\epsilon_p(j\omega) =$
$1 + j[(-T_2)(T_1T_2 - 2T_1T_3 - T_3^2)\omega^3 - T_1T_2^2T_3^2\omega^5].$

The objective is to eliminate the ω^3 term:
$-T_2\,[T_1(T_2 - 2T_3) - T_3^2] \to 0.$

First substitute $T_1 + T_3$ for T_2, then let $T_3 = \alpha T_1$. Set the equation equal to zero and solve for α.

$$-(T_1 + \alpha T_1)[T_1(T_1 - \alpha T_1) - (\alpha T_1)^2] = 0$$
$$\alpha^2 + \alpha - 1 = 0$$

Solving α for the two roots, you obtain

$\alpha = 0.618034$
$\alpha = -1.618034$

For minimum phase shift, the relationships $T_1 + T_3 = T_2$ and $T_3 = 0.618T_1$, are used.

$T_1 = T$
$T_2 = 1.618034T$
$T_3 = 0.618034T$,

recalling that $T_1 = \dfrac{1 + K_1}{\omega_T}$, $T_2 = \dfrac{1 + K_2}{\omega_T}$, and $T_3 = \dfrac{1 + K_3}{\omega_T}$.

Since K_1 relates to the dc gain $1/B$ of the amplifier as $(1 + K_1) = 1/B$, the design equations are:

$K_1 = \dfrac{1}{B} - 1.$

Substituting and solving for K_2 and K_3 in terms of K_1,

$K_2 = 1.618034\ K_1 + 0.618034$
$K_3 = 0.618034\ K_1 - 0.382.$

These three last design equations produce optimum phase cancellation for an amplifier with any gain. For example, for an amplifier gain of 10, $K_1 = 9$, $K_2 = 15.18$, and $K_3 = 5.18$.

In order to derive the complete transfer function, the denominator is similarly solved. Therefore, with

denominator $\epsilon_p(j\omega) = 1 - 0.618T^2\omega^2 - 0.618T^4\omega^4 + T^6\omega^6$,

the complete ac response is:

$\epsilon_p(j\omega) =$

$$\frac{1 - j(T\omega)^5}{1 - 0.618034\,(T\omega)^2 - 0.618034\,(T\omega)^4 - (T\omega)^6}$$

Finally, the complete amplifier transfer function is,

$$\frac{V_O}{V_{IN}} = (1 + K_1)\left[\frac{1 - j(T\omega)^5}{1 - 0.618034\,(T\omega)^2 - 0.618034\,(T\omega)^4 - (T\omega)^6}\right].$$

References

1. Soliman, Ahmed M, "Design of High-Frequency Amplifiers," *IEEE Circuits and Systems*, June 1983.
2. Soliman, A M and Ismail, M, "Active Compensation of Op Amps," *IEEE Transactions on Circuits and Systems*, February 1979.

57 Decode overlapped EPROM, RAM and I/O

Flexible addressing for microcontrollers

This useful memory mapping arrangement enables you to devote as much or as little memory as you need to EPROM (to the nearest 256 bit boundary) with the rest available for RAM, except for a few locations at the top of memory which it reserves for I/O.

W H Payne
Sandia Labs, Albuquerque, NM

Today's large RAM and EPROM chips (32k and 64k bytes and up) let you reduce the size, the complexity, and even the cost of EPROM-based microcontroller systems. Using a physical memory composed of two 32k-byte RAM chips and two 32k-byte EPROM chips (**Fig 1**), you can implement a 64k-byte memory in which the RAM and EPROM sections overlap almost completely.

This arrangement allows nearly full use of the addressable space because you can set the system's RAM/EPROM boundary where it belongs—near the application's highest EPROM location. A conventional system's boundary, on the other hand, must lie on an address location determined by the physical chip size (in bytes). For example, for a system based on three EPROM chips of 8k bytes each, the RAM must begin at the 24k-byte level. Therefore, if your application requires only 17k bytes of EPROM, you must forego 7k bytes of memory.

Fig 1's system also includes space for eight memory-mapped I/O devices, located at the top of the RAM for the convenience of microcontrollers such as the 8051, which lack an IO/$\overline{\text{M}}$ signal. The eight base addresses shown reserve 16 RAM locations for each device, leaving the top 128 RAM addresses inaccessible. You establish the RAM and EPROM boundary by using a DIP switch or jumpers to manually set the fence address B_{15}-B_8, shown in the memory's logical-organization diagram (**Fig 2**).

In **Fig 3**, the magnitude comparator IC_1 compares the high byte of the fence address with the high-byte address lines and issues a signal (0 for RAM, 1 for ROM). (Comparing only the high bytes simplifies the decoding circuit but leaves as much as 256 bytes of RAM unaddressable.) Next, the 2- to 4-line decoder IC_2 uses the decoder signal and the A_{15} address line to activate the appropriate memory chip. The 8-input NAND gate IC_3 and the 3- to 8-line decoder IC_4 generate chip-select signals for the eight I/O devices. For active I/O devices, another 8-input NAND gate (IC_5) generates an IO/$\overline{\text{M}}$ signal that disables the selection of RAM.

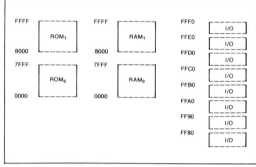

Fig 1—This 64k-byte memory system provides 64k bytes of physical RAM virtually overlapped by 64k bytes of physical EPROM.

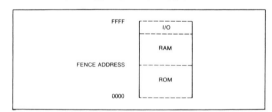

Fig 2—The logical organization of Fig 1's memory locates memory-mapped I/O space at the top of the RAM and lets you set the boundary between the RAM and EPROM by manually setting a fence address.

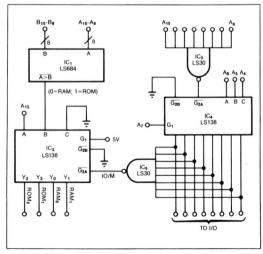

Fig 3—These ICs control Fig 1's memory. IC_1 and IC_2 select the RAM and EPROM chips according to the fence-address position, and IC_3 and IC_4 decode I/O addresses. IC_5 generates an IO/$\overline{\text{M}}$ signal.

58 Gain of two simplifies LP-filter design

> ## Simple active LP filters
>
> Here is another example of active filter design, by that guru of the subject, Arthur D. Delagrange.

Arthur Delagrange
US Navy, Dahlgren, VA

By setting the gain on a low-pass (LP) filter's stage equal to two, you can easily calculate the necessary component values for any desired filter response. Moreqver, you can use standard, equal-value capacitors, easing component-stocking problems.

The normalized low-pass-filter section shown in part (**a**) of the **figure** has a transfer function of

$$\frac{G/R_1 R_2 C_1 C_2}{S^2 + \left[\dfrac{1}{R_1 C_1} + \dfrac{1}{R_2 C_1} - \dfrac{1}{R_2 C_2}(G-1)\right]S + \dfrac{1}{R_1 R_2 C_1 C_2}}.$$

If you let $G=2$ and C_1 and C_2 equal one farad, this expression reduces to

$$\frac{2/R_1 R_2}{S^2 + \dfrac{1}{R_1}S + \dfrac{1}{R_1 R_2}}.$$

A conversion to component values now becomes easy. Filter handbooks (**reference**) give denominator-polynomial coefficients in the following form:

$$S^2 + aS + b.$$

Therefore, $R_1 = 1/a$ and $R_2 = a/b$. After obtaining the normalized resistor values for the desired response, you can scale the values according to the capacitors at hand.

As an example, consider the n-stage LP filter shown in (**b**). The **table** gives the normalized ($\omega = C_1 = C_2 = 1$) resistor values for Butterworth, Bessel, and 0.1-, 0.5- and 1-dB-ripple Chebyshev responses, for filters to the ninth order. Scale resistor values for your desired cutoff frequency and available capacitors, according to the relationship $\omega = 1/RC$. For convenience, the **table** also gives noise and 3-dB bandwidths (for the Chebyshev filters).

To tune each filter section, insert small trimmers in series with the circuit's resistors (slightly smaller than their calculated values), then use the filter's gain and phase characteristics to obtain the desired response. Gain and phase of a low-pass section are

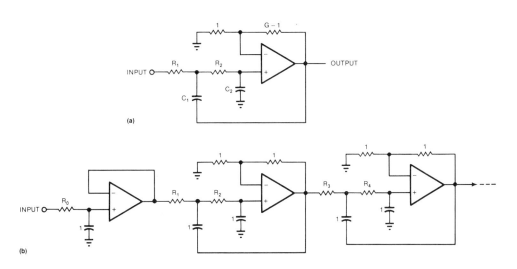

(a)

(b)

Setting G=2 in a classical low-pass-filter section (a) *simplifies circuit calculations. The **table** gives the normalized resistor values for an n-section filter **(b)**, for a variety of responses.*

LOW-PASS-FILTER CHARACTERISTICS

ORDER	R_0	R_1	R_2	R_3	R_4	R_5	R_6	R_7	R_8	3-dB BANDWIDTH	NOISE BANDWIDTH
1	1.0000										1.571
2		0.7071	1.4142								1.110
3	1.0000	1.0000	1.0000			BUTTERWORTH					1.047
4		0.5412	1.8478	1.3066	0.7654						1.026
5	1.0000	1.6180	0.6180	0.6180	1.6180						1.017
6		0.5176	1.9319	0.7071	1.4142	1.9319	0.5176				1.012
7	1.0000	2.2470	0.4450	0.8019	1.2470	0.5550	1.8019				1.008
8		2.5629	0.3902	0.9000	1.1111	0.6013	1.6629	0.5098	1.9616		1.006
9	1.0000	2.8794	0.3472	1.0000	1.0000	0.6527	1.5321	0.5321	1.8794		1.005
1	1.0000										1.571
2		0.4533	1.3599								1.152
3	0.7536	0.4758	0.9964			BESSEL					1.073
4		0.5062	0.7802	0.3678	1.3500						1.047
5	0.6636	0.5205	0.6197	0.3610	1.1367						1.038
6		0.5366	0.5124	0.3614	0.9674	0.3178	1.2202				1.039
7	0.5934	0.5492	0.4330	0.3624	0.8299	0.3100	1.0938				1.042
8		0.3045	0.9724	0.3628	0.7180	0.5583	0.3716	0.2837	1.1079		1.046
9	0.5384	0.5690	0.3256	0.3654	0.6317	0.3024	0.8706	0.2765	1.0238		1.049
1	0.1526									6.6039	10.292
2		0.4215	0.7159			CHEBYSHEV				1.9432	2.144
3	1.0316	1.0316	0.5737			0.1-dB				1.3890	1.442
4		0.7840	2.0475	1.8928	0.3972	RIPPLE				1.2131	1.233
5	1.8556	1.1468	1.3712	3.0024	0.2787					1.1347	1.142
6		1.1681	3.2506	1.5957	0.8999	4.3594	0.2031			1.0929	1.094
7	2.6541	1.4729	2.0560	2.1284	0.6238	5.9637	0.1535			1.0680	1.065
8		1.5545	4.4179	1.8336	1.3103	2.7442	0.4561	7.8149	0.1196	1.0519	1.047
9	3.4428	1.8319	2.7112	2.2471	0.8944	3.4428	0.3481	9.9131	0.0957	1.0410	1.034
1	0.3493									2.8629	4.498
2		0.7014	0.9403			CHEBYSHEV				1.3897	1.489
3	1.5963	1.5963	0.5483			0.5-dB				1.1675	1.167
4		1.1811	2.3756	2.8514	0.3298	RIPPLE				1.0931	1.066
5	2.7600	1.7058	1.2296	4.4658	0.2162					1.0593	1.021
6		1.7254	3.6917	2.3569	0.7191	6.4391	0.1518			1.0410	0.997
7	3.9037	2.1664	1.8182	3.1305	0.4719	8.7714	0.1122			1.0301	0.983
8		2.2801	4.9810	2.6895	1.0367	4.0251	0.3351	11.4626	0.0862	1.0230	0.974
9	5.0402	2.6818	2.3850	3.2897	0.6717	5.0402	0.2513	14.5126	0.0683	1.0182	0.967
1	0.5088									1.9654	3.088
2		0.9110	0.9957			CHEBYSHEV				1.2176	1.253
3	2.0236	2.0236	0.4971			1-dB				1.0949	1.041
4		1.4843	2.4114	3.5833	0.2829	RIPPLE				1.0530	0.973
5	3.4543	2.1349	1.0911	5.5892	0.1810					1.0338	0.943
6		2.1546	3.7217	2.9432	0.6092	8.0410	0.1255			1.0234	0.927
7	4.8682	2.7017	1.6062	3.9040	0.3920	10.9388	0.0921			1.0172	0.918
8		2.8409	5.0098	3.3511	0.8755	5.0153	0.2756	14.2824	0.0704	1.0132	0.911
9	6.2763	3.3395	2.1034	4.0965	0.5566	6.2763	0.2055	18.0718	0.0556	1.0104	0.907

given by

$$G = 2b/\sqrt{(b - \omega^2)^2 + (a\omega)^2}$$

$$\phi = \arctan\frac{a\omega}{b - \omega^2}.$$

Phase should be 90° at the frequency $\omega_{90}=\sqrt{b}$; gain at this point should be $G_{90}=2\sqrt{b/a}$. Inject a signal at the frequency ω_{90}, then adjust the trimmers for 90° phase shift and the calculated gain G_{90}.

Reference

Lam, H, *Analog and Digital Filters*, Prentice-Hall, Englewood Cliffs, NJ, 1979.

59 Thermal tester verifies transistors

Is your device well and truly heat-sunk?

An in-situ tester for the adequacy of heat sink arrangements. Ideal for the development lab and for sample testing of production units to ensure quality is maintained.

Carlo Venditti
C S Draper Lab, Cambridge, MA

The tester in **Fig 1** verifies the thermal interface between a power transistor and its heat sink. The tester measures the temperature-sensitive V_{BE} of the transistor under test.

The tester first calibrates the dissipation of the transistor under test with a fixed, low-level current. Then it switches on a high current for a certain time and finally returns to the original low level. You record the V_{BE} at the various stages in this test to calculate the thermal resistance of the transistor/heat-sink interface.

To find the T_J max, first find the decrease in V_{BE} between the reading at the end of the high-power stage and the steady-state value during the low-power stage. Then, $T_J°C$ = ambient temperature°C + decrease/2.2 mV/°C. Similarly, the effective total thermal resistance for the transistor/heat-sink assembly is (decrease/2.2 mV/°C) ÷ 10.

The tester uses an 11.4V input to yield 10W dissipation in the transistor under test. The tester comes up in the low-power mode; after warm-up, you can measure the low-level V_{BE}. When you press the test switch, the 555 timer turns on the DMOS switch, and the current in the transistor under test jumps to 1.1A. The timer times out in 2 minutes. You can use a variety of common lab instruments to record your data.

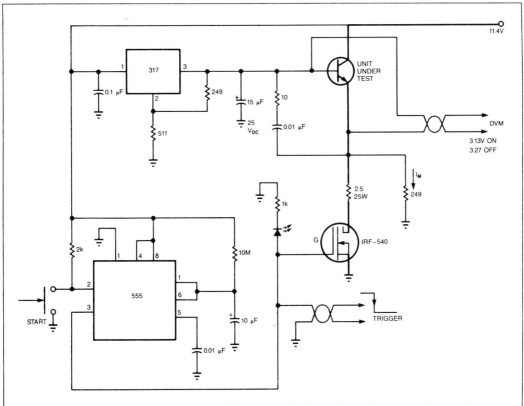

Fig 1—This 10W thermal tester *applies a known high current to the transistor under test for a period of 2 minutes. You can calculate the thermal resistance of your transistor/heat-sink assembly from the change in* V_{BE} *you observe at high and low power levels.*

60 Looking through the right window improves spectral analysis

Useful introduction to windowing

This 1984 article is now a little dated in detail: for example, the Kaiser window was then one of the best available whereas now something like a four-term Blackman Harris with its 74dB sidelobe level would usually be preferred. Nevertheless the article still forms a very useful basic introduction to the subject.

John O'Donnell, *Signix Corp*

When designing finite-impulse-response (FIR) or infinite-impulse-response (IIR) filters for digital-signal-processing (DSP) systems, you can evaluate your design's response by comparing the discrete Fourier transform (DFT) of filter input and output signals. To use the DFT for such purposes on a periodic or infinite waveform, though, you must limit your field of view. Windowing accomplishes this task by reducing the viewing range of an infinite waveform to a finite interval. You can choose from many window functions; however, it's important to select the right one for your application. The window detailed here, the Kaiser, is adjustable, and it offers minimal signal loss and distortion.

Windows can change the image

Windowing a periodic or infinite waveform is equivalent to multiplying it by a window function. This fact holds true only in the time domain, and to predict a digital filter's output response to an input waveform in the time domain, you would have to solve—via electronic means—the convolution integral. But even at electronic speeds, convolution is a time-consuming task.

Fortunately, you can avoid the convolution problem by transforming time-domain signals into frequency-domain signals. The easiest way to do that is to use a the fast Fourier transform (FFT) algorithm to perform the DFT. Today's DSP μCs perform the necessary multiplications at high speeds. For example, the TMS32010 requires roughly 200 nsec to perform a typical 16×16-bit multiply-and-accumulate operation. To perform the same operation, a conventional DSP chip might require 40 machine cycles at 200 nsec/cycle, or 8 μsec. Thus, a DSP μC combined with a method of generating window functions offers a powerful technique for evaluating the response and adjusting the parameters of digital filters.

Fig 1 shows how such a DSP μC transforms a time-domain signal into frequency-domain information. First, the digital signal processor digitizes the analog input; then, it multiplies each sample by the appropriate value of the selected windowing function, producing a windowed waveform. Next, the digital-signal processor applies the FFT algorithm to compute the DFT and uses the DFT components' magnitude-squared values to generate the input signal's spectrum.

The FFT algorithm processes a finite number of signal samples to produce a finite number of spectrum

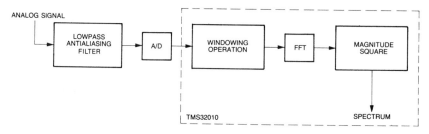

Fig 1—Windowing fits into spectrum computations *immediately after the stage at which an input signal is digitized. By using a DSP μC, you can apply the proper windowing function before executing the fast Fourier transform to obtain minimum spectral distortion.*

samples. Most FFT algorithms use a power of two or four to determine how many samples to analyze. If you choose 128 samples of a real-valued signal, then 64 complex spectrum samples result, providing magnitude and phase information for inputs in the frequency range between zero and one-half the sampling frequency. By selecting 128 samples from a periodic or infinite-duration signal, you effectively look at the signal through a finite-duration window. Such a window can pass input samples unmodified—this technique is called "rectangular windowing." In this case, no multiplications actually take place; the phrase "rectangular windowing" describes the process of merely selecting a finite block of samples from a periodic or long-duration signal.

Removing the window clouds the picture

Consider how processing signal samples with only an FFT (instead of using a window) can obscure spectral detail. A 2-tone test signal proves convenient for evaluating digital-filter response. **Fig 2a** shows the line spectrum of a 2-tone signal: 32 Hz at 0 dB and 36 Hz at −30 dB. This spectrum results when a 128-Hz, 128-point DFT is performed on the input, yielding a 1-sec window width. (Note that in **Fig 2** frequencies are

normalized to the sampling frequency; a 1-msec window and a 128-kHz sampling rate would produce **Fig 2's** spectrum for the 32-kHz and 36-kHz tones.) The spectral samples from the 128-point FFT appear at 1-Hz intervals from 0 to 63 Hz. When you sample a periodic signal, be sure that the highest tone is less than one-half the sampling frequency.

Fig 2b shows what happens when you shift the larger tone to 32.5 Hz: You lose the smaller tone (36 Hz) because of the leakage that occurs when a tone doesn't fall at one of the sample points in the DFT spectrum. Because the system samples at 128 Hz and uses a 128-point FFT, the sample points at 32 and 33 Hz bracket the 32.5-Hz tone so that the spectral lines in **Fig 2b** at those two frequencies have equal magnitude.

This result seems reasonable, but it doesn't explain the existence of the other lines in the spectrum. To see how the other lines arise, look at the 36-Hz line. **Fig 3a** shows how tones from 0 to 63 Hz affect the magnitude of the 36-Hz tone's DFT component. Putting 128 samples of a 36-Hz signal into the FFT produces a 0-dB response in the 36-Hz component; however, putting 128 samples of any other integral frequency between 0 and 63 Hz into the FFT produces no response in the 36-Hz component because these frequencies lie at the nulls of **Fig 3a's** response curve. The expanded plot (**Fig 3b**) shows that a 32-Hz tone falls at a null. However, a 32.5-Hz tone falls at the peak of the side lobe between 32 and 33 Hz. The response of the 36-Hz component to a 0-dB tone at 32.5 Hz is roughly −20 dB, obscuring the −30-dB, 36-Hz tone present in the sampled signal.

Because every DFT tone has a response curve similar to that in **Fig 3a**, but shifted so the main lobe is centered at the component frequency, the 32.5-Hz tone causes every DFT component to respond. Thus, using a tone that's not precisely equal in frequency to a DFT component produces energy leakage throughout the FFT-computed spectrum—and this leakage can obscure spectral detail.

Windows reduce leakage

You can reduce leakage and regain spectral detail by using a windowing function. Some popular windowing functions for estimating the spectral response of digital filters include the raised-cosine (Hann) window, the raised-cosine-on-a-pedestal (Hamming) window, and the Kaiser window (**table**).

Fig 4 shows what these windows look like in the time domain for 128 samples. (Note that a corresponding rectangular window would consist of 128 unity-valued samples.) These windows don't exhibit the sharp transitions of a rectangular window; therefore, they don't cause the high side lobes shown in **Fig 3a**.

To see how one of these, the Kaiser window, modifies a set of signal samples, examine **Fig 5**. First look at the unmodified (rectangular) block of input samples (**Fig 5a**). When you use a Kaiser window on these 128 samples, you get the values plotted in **Fig 5b**. Note that passing a signal through a filter reduces its strength; you can calculate that the reduction in energy from the samples in **Fig 4c** is 4.2 dB, which is the minimum

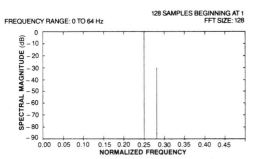

TONES AT 32 Hz (0 dB) AND 36 Hz (−30 dB)—RECTANGULAR WINDOW

(a)

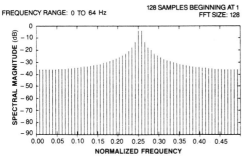

TONES AT 32.5 Hz (0 dB) AND 36 Hz (−30 dB)—RECTANGULAR WINDOWS

(b)

Fig 2—If you don't use a windowing function, *you'll find that changing the frequency of a strong tone so that it no longer lines up with one of the discrete Fourier transform components causes energy to spill into the rest of the spectrum. Shifting such a signal from 32 Hz* **(a)** *to 32.5 Hz* **(b)** *masks the 36-Hz tone and hides spectral details.*

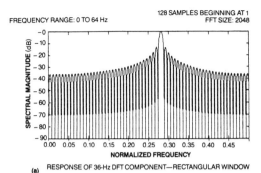

128 SAMPLES BEGINNING AT 1
FFT SIZE: 2048

(a) RESPONSE OF 36-Hz DFT COMPONENT—RECTANGULAR WINDOW

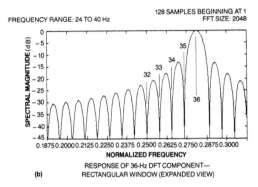

FREQUENCY RANGE: 24 TO 40 Hz

128 SAMPLES BEGINNING AT 1
FFT SIZE: 2048

(b) RESPONSE OF 36-Hz DFT COMPONENT—
RECTANGULAR WINDOW (EXPANDED VIEW)

Fig 3—Each discrete Fourier transform component *responds to signal energy in the entire spectrum from zero to one-half the sampling frequency. The 36-Hz DFT component's response, shown in* **a** *and magnified in* **b**, *has nulls at other DFT-component frequencies, but it exhibits large side-lobe responses to signal energy elsewhere.*

signal-energy loss you can expect. (The **box,** "Explore DFTs on your personal computer," contains a BASIC program that allows you to examine such aspects of the Kaiser window.)

How do windowing functions compare?

The above discussion shows how the Kaiser window handles inputs, but how does the Kaiser window compare to other popular window functions? To find out, consider the windows' side-lobe structures (**Fig 6**). (Note the inclusion of the rectangular window (**Fig 6a**) for comparison.) Each plot might, for example, show the effects that a 0-dB tone in the 0- to 63-Hz region would have on the 32-Hz component of a 128-point DFT. (This response curve is normalized relative to the response for a 32-Hz tone.) Similar response curves apply to all other DFT components.

WINDOW FUNCTIONS

HANN (RAISED COSINE)
$$w(k) = [1 - COS(k\ 2\ \pi/N)]/2$$
HAMMING (RAISED COSINE ON A PEDESTAL)
$$w(k) = 0.54 - 0.46\ COS\ (k\ 2\ \pi/N)$$
KAISER
$$w(k) = I_0 \left\{ B\ \sqrt{1 - [(k - N/2)/(N/2)]^2}\ \right\}/I_0(B)$$
BASIC SUBROUTINE FOR COMPUTING $I_0(X)$
1000 S = 1: DS = 1: D = 0   'S IS VALUE $I_{zero}(X)$
1010 D = D + 2: DS = DS *X   2/D : S = S + DS
1020 IF D3 > 1.0 E −6 * S THEN 1010 ELSE RETURN

SUMMARY OF WINDOW PROPERTIES

	KAISER			HANN	HAMMING
VALUE OF B	5.5	6.9	8.2		
MAIN-LOBE WIDTH RELATIVE TO RECTANGULAR WINDOW	2.02	2.4	2.8	2	2
MAXIMUM SIDE-LOBE LEVEL (dB)	−40.2	−50.4	−60.2	−31	−43

The rectangular (**Fig 6a**), Hann (**Fig 6c**), and Hamming windows (**Fig 6d**) have response nulls that correspond to the other DFT components. Their double-width main lobes, however, cause the 32-Hz component to respond to 31- and 33-Hz tones as well. This reduction in resolution is the tradeoff for the significant reduction in side-lobe levels. The Kaiser window (**Fig 6b**), too, has a double-width main lobe, and its response nulls don't correspond to the other DFT components, but its side lobes are low, and you can make them lower by changing parameter B.

Indeed, the Kaiser window's attractiveness lies in this adjustability. The **table** shows how you can use parameter B to control the Kaiser window's shape. Increasing B reduces the side lobes and increases the main lobe's width. Compared to the other windows, the Kaiser is among the best-performing windowing functions to offer adjustability. With the Kaiser window, you can approximate such functions as the Hann and Hamming windowing functions, but the main- and side-lobe parameters remain fully adjustable.

The **table** also shows the maximum levels (in dB) of the Kaiser side lobes relative to the rectangular window. As B increases, the side lobes become lower. Thus, the window's leakage rejection increases, letting you distinguish more easily between closely spaced frequency components of unequal magnitude. You pay for this reduced leakage, however, with a broader main lobe, which reduces frequency resolution.

Put the Kaiser window to work

To understand the difference between a signal that's

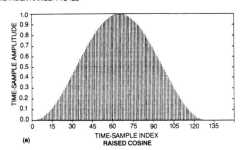

TIME-INDEX RANGE: 1 TO 128

128 SAMPLES BEGINNING AT 1

(a)
RAISED COSINE

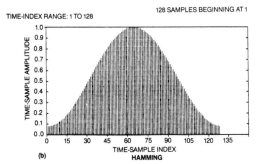

TIME-INDEX RANGE: 1 TO 128

128 SAMPLES BEGINNING AT 1

(b)
HAMMING

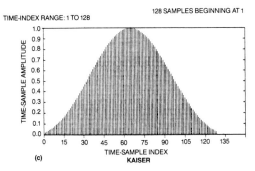

TIME-INDEX RANGE: 1 TO 128

128 SAMPLES BEGINNING AT 1

(c)
KAISER

Fig 4—**Windowing functions** *attain low side lobes in their frequency responses by avoiding abrupt transitions. Note the subtle differences in shape between the time-domain representations of the Hann (a), Hamming (b), and Kaiser (c) windows.*

analyzed through a rectangular window and one that's examined through a Kaiser window, compare the spectral plots in **Figs 2** and **7**. In both cases, sampling the signal at 128 Hz produces components from zero to 64 Hz, but you can adjust the sampling interval and frequency range as desired. Most software packages used for DSP design allow you to make adjustments easily. In the case of the Kaiser window, the software used operates with B=5.5.

Comparing **Fig 2b** to **Fig 7b** shows how dramatically the Kaiser window reduces leakage; the 36-Hz, −30-dB tone now becomes evident. However, a comparison of **Fig 7a** with **Fig 2a** shows that if the signal tones lie at DFT-component frequencies, the windowing destroys the perfect line spectrum.

Fig 8 illustrates both these aspects of the Kaiser

window's behavior; this analysis is similar to that done earlier for the rectangular window in **Fig 3**. In **Fig 3**, when the 0-dB tone changed from 32 to 32.5 Hz it produced a −20-dB response at the 36-Hz DFT component (**Fig 3b**). When you use a Kaiser window with B=5.5, the 36-Hz DFT component's response is less than −61 dB. Thus, the 36-Hz spectral line in **Fig 7b** represents the energy actually present in the signal.

Fig 8b, however, has a curious aspect: The response of the 36-Hz component to a 0-dB tone at 32 Hz equals −48 dB. This fact illustrates the earlier statement that Kaiser-window nulls don't fall at the DFT-component frequencies, and it explains why **Fig 7a's** spectrum differs in quality so much from the tone spectrum in **Fig 2a**.

When you apply the aforementioned spectral-analysis

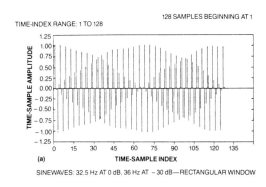

TIME-INDEX RANGE: 1 TO 128

128 SAMPLES BEGINNING AT 1

(a)

SINEWAVES: 32.5 Hz AT 0 dB, 36 Hz AT − 30 dB—RECTANGULAR WINDOW

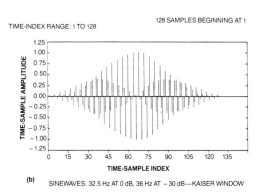

TIME-INDEX RANGE: 1 TO 128

128 SAMPLES BEGINNING AT 1

(b)

SINEWAVES: 32.5 Hz AT 0 dB, 36 Hz AT − 30 dB—KAISER WINDOW

Fig 5—**Applying a windowing function to a time function** *can reduce energy, yet produce more detail. For example, the time function in **a** produces the plot in **b** when passed through a Kaiser window.*

techniques to the testing of digital-filter responses, it's good to compare the results you get with and without the use of windowing functions. Remember, too, that the Kaiser window allows you to vary the B parameter to achieve a range of side-lobe levels. In most situations, you can't match your A/D-conversion rate precisely enough to the test signal's frequency so that all tones correspond to DFT-component frequencies. A good windowing function, though, reveals spectral de-

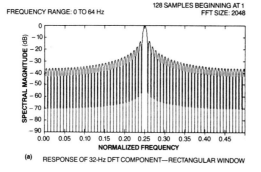

(a) RESPONSE OF 32-Hz DFT COMPONENT—RECTANGULAR WINDOW

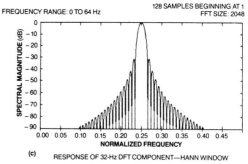

(c) RESPONSE OF 32-Hz DFT COMPONENT—HANN WINDOW

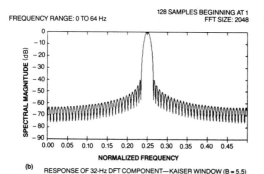

(b) RESPONSE OF 32-Hz DFT COMPONENT—KAISER WINDOW (B = 5.5)

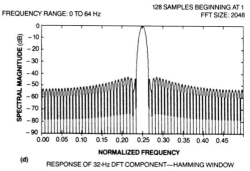

(d) RESPONSE OF 32-Hz DFT COMPONENT—HAMMING WINDOW

Fig 6—A comparison of DFTs for various windows *shows that the rectangular window* **(a)** *exhibits greater leakage than do the Kaiser* **(b)**, *Hann* **(c)**, *or Hamming* **(d)** *windows.*

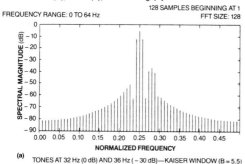

(a) TONES AT 32 Hz (0 dB) AND 36 Hz (−30 dB)—KAISER WINDOW (B = 5.5)

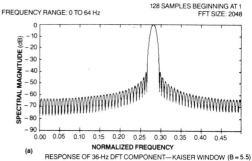

(a) RESPONSE OF 36-Hz DFT COMPONENT—KAISER WINDOW (B = 5.5)

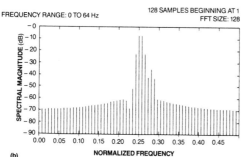

(b) TONES AT 32.5 Hz (0 dB) AND 36 Hz (−30 dB)—KAISER WINDOW (B = 5.5)

Fig 7—The Kaiser window's low side lobes *reduce spectral leakage. Not only won't a 32-Hz tone mask a 36-Hz tone* **(a)**, *but, unlike the signal in* **Fig 2b**, *a 32.5-Hz signal doesn't mask the 36-Hz tone* **(b)**. *Note in* **a**, *however, that windowing prevents* **Fig 2a's** *perfect line spectrum, which results when signal tones lie at DFT-component frequencies.*

(b) RESPONSE OF 36-Hz DFT COMPONENT— KAISER WINDOW, EXPANDED VIEW (B = 5.5)

Fig 8—When a Kaiser-windowing operation *precedes an FFT computation, each DFT component has a response similar to* **a**. *The expanded view* **(b)** *shows that with Kaiser windowing, the 36-Hz DFT component doesn't have a null response to signal tones at the other DFT-component frequencies.*

tail without masking the effects of leakage from strong signal components. Also, remember that using a windowing function can reduce signal energy by at least 4 to 4.5 dB, so you must interpret spectral line magnitudes appropriately.

Note that the use of specialized hardware and software can considerably simplify digital-filter design. One hardware example is Texas Instruments' TMS32010 digital-signal-processing microcomputer. Such software packages as Signix Corp's DISPRO v1.0—used to generate the plots of this article—facilitate illustration of the spectral effects of windowing (**reference**). You can incorporate this hardware/software package into a Texas Instruments or IBM personal computer, for example.

Reference

Cushman, Robert H, "Novel CAD software generates DSP coefficients—painlessly," *EDN*, August 18, 1983, pgs 137-158.

Explore DFTs on your personal computer

To explore the properties of the DFT and windowing functions on your personal computer, you can use this BASIC program. It's written for the IBM PC, but you can easily change it to any dialect of Microsoft BASIC. Included for program checkout is a simple test function; you can replace it with your own to see the effects of leakage on signals of interest to you.

Note that you obtain Fourier series coefficients, which are valid only for periodic signals, from the DFT components by scaling and a sign change (line 330). Furthermore, you can make leakage reduction more visible by using the Kaiser window. The program also provides plotting capability that allows you to see the magnitude spectrum on a dB scale of 0 to −100 dB; the scale is normalized to the spectrum's maximum peak. For a detailed plot, try 256 samples with T=1.1632 and BE=10. Under PC- or MS-DOS version 2,

you can get a hard copy of the graphics screen by using the GRAPHICS command before running the program.

Compiling the program speeds up execution by a factor of 10 (approximately). If you compile this program, though, be sure to move the DIM statement from line 200 to line 170, dimensioning each array to meet your requirements (for instance, N=512).

```
10 '    This is a test program for the real-valued-input FFT routine.  To
20 '    obtain the test results use NSAMP=32, a time window of T0=1 and a
30 '    frequency BE=1.  The FFT output will be 16 complex-valued frequency
40 '    samples.  The result will be a line spectrum with lines at FFT com-
50 '    ponents 1,3,5,7, and 9 (double these numbers to get indices to
60 '    the array X).  The frequency samples will have the (real,imaginary)-
70 '    values: (-12,-36),(36,4),(-12,12),(0,-12), and (4,0).
80 '    To see a "continuous" spectrum use a time window of T0=1.1632 and a
90 '    frequency BE=1; peaks of spectrum will be at the odd multiples of
100 '   1.1632 (which will not coincide with FFT sample values, but will be
110 '   close).
120 '        The FFT routine operates on N complex-valued numbers.  The test
130 '   function generated has 2*N real values; these are packed as if they
140 '   were N real-imaginary pairs.  The FFT output is processed to give N
150 '   complex-valued positive frequency spectral values.
160 '                              [Copyright (C) Signix Corporation]
170 DEFINT N,M,L,K,I,J,E,O: CLS
180 INPUT") Number of real-valued samples to FFT ";NSAMP: M=LOG(NSAMP)/LOG(2): I
F NSAMP-2^M <> 0 THEN PRINT"--- Must be a power of 2": PRINT: GOTO 180
190 N=NSAMP/2: M=M-1  'N is size of complex-input FFT
200 DIM X(2*N-1),S(N-1): PI=3.1415926535#: TP=PI/N : PRINT
210 INPUT") Length of time window (T0) ";T0: PRINT: INPUT") Frequency of sine wa
ve (BE) ";BE  'NSAMP/T0 is the sampling frequency.  This must be greater than
                 18*BE in order to avoid aliasing.
220 FOR L=0 TO NSAMP-1 : TH=BE*TP*L*T0: X(L)=(SIN(TH)+COS(3*TH))^3: NEXT      'Ti
me function is cube of the sum of a sine and cosine wave of frequencies BE and 3
*BE. This gives tones at BE,3*BE,5*BE,7*BE, and 9*BE
230 PRINT: INPUT") Print time samples (Y/N) ";A$: IF A$="Y" OR A$="y" THEN FOR K
=0 TO N-1: PRINT 2*K;2*K+1,X(2*K),X(2*K+1): NEXT
240 PRINT: INPUT") Kaiser window time samples (Y/N) ";A$: IF A$="N" OR A$="n" TH
EN 290
250 PRINT: INPUT") Value for B ";B      ' Sidelobe levels: B=5.5 => -40 dB,
                 B=6.9 => -50 dB, B=8.2 => -60 dB
```

Explore the properties of DFTs and windowing functions *on your personal computer with this program, which is written in Microsoft BASIC. You can modify the test function to see leakage effects on the computation of your signal's spectrum.*

```
260 WM=B: GOSUB 430: IZB=S   'Get Izero(B)
270 FOR L=0 TO NSAMP-1: WM=B*SQR(1-((L-N)/N)^2): GOSUB 430: WEIGHT=S/IZB:
280 X(L) = WEIGHT*X(L): NEXT   'Window time function samples
290 PRINT: PRINT TIME$: PRINT "...computing FFT...": GOSUB 1000: PRINT TIME$: BEE
P: PRINT
300 INPUT") Display spectral values on screen (S), printer (P),or no display (N)
 ";A$: IF A$="N" OR A$="n" THEN 340 ELSE IF A$="P" OR A$="p" THEN OPEN"LPT1:" FO
R OUTPUT AS #1 ELSE OPEN "SCRN:" FOR OUTPUT AS #1
310 PRINT#1,:PRINT#1,TAB(14)"DFT Component"TAB(40)"Fourier Series Coefficients"
320 PRINT#1, TAB(3)"K"TAB(11)"(Real , Imaginary)"TAB(37)"(Real , Imaginary)"TAB(
61)"Magn.(dB)": PRINT#1,
330 FOR K=0 TO N-1: PRINT#1, USING"####   (##.##^^^^ , ##.##^^^^)    (####.####,
 ####.####)    #####.##";K,X(2*K),X(2*K+1),X(2*K)/N,-X(2*K+1)/N,10*LOG((X(2*K)/N
)^2 + (X(2*K+1)/N)^2)/LOG(10): NEXT
340 PRINT: INPUT") Plot spectrum (Y/N) ";A$: IF A$="N" OR A$= "n" THEN 410
350 SCREEN 2,0,0: TLOG=LOG(10)
360 FOR L=0 TO N-1: X(L)=10*LOG(X(2*L)^2 + X(2*L+1)^2)/TLOG: NEXT
370 XMAX=X(0): FOR L=0 TO N-1: IF X(L) > XMAX THEN XMAX=X(L)
380 NEXT: XSCALE=640/N
390 FOR L=0 TO N-1: YP=2*(XMAX-X(L)): XP=L*XSCALE: LINE (XP,199)-(XP,YP): NEXT
400 IF INKEY$="" THEN 400 ELSE SCREEN 0,0,0
410 END
420 '
430 S=1: DS=1: D=0  ' S = Izero(WM)
440 D=D+2: DS=DS*WM^2/D^2: S=S+DS: IF DS > .000001*S THEN 440 ELSE RETURN

1000 '
1010 '   ##### Subroutine for real-valued-input FFT #####
1020 '        INPUT: 2*N real-valued time samples
1030 '        OUTPUT: N complex-valued frequency samples
1040 '                ordered as ...real,imaginary...
1050 '
1060 '   Note: Because this is an "in-place" algorithm the time samples in
1070 '        array X are overwritten by the frequency samples.
1080 '
1090 PI=3.1415926535#
1100 '
1110 '        BEGIN COMPLEX-INPUT FFT
1120 '
1130 K2=1: FOR K=1 TO M: K2=2*K2: K1=K2/2: TH=(2*PI/N)*K1: NK=N/K2: N1=N/K1
1140 FOR I=1 TO NK: A6=(I-1)*TH: WR=COS(A6): WI=-SIN(A6)
1150 FOR J= N1 TO N STEP N1: J1=J-N1+(I-1): J2=J1+NK: E1=2*J1:E2=2*J2
1160 O1=E1+1: O2=E2+1: DR=X(E1)-X(E2): DI=X(O1)-X(O2)
1170 X(E1)=X(E1)+X(E2): X(O1)=X(O1)+X(O2): X(E2)=WR*DR-WI*DI
1180 X(O2)=WI*DR+WR*DI: NEXT  J,I,K
1190 '
1200 '        END OF COMPLEX-INPUT FFT
1210 '   ------------------------------------------
1220 '
1230 '        BEGIN BIT-REVERSAL UNSCRAMBLING
1240 '
1250 J=0: FOR I=0 TO N-2: IF I<J THEN EI=2*I: EJ=2*J: T=X(EI):  X(EI)=X(EJ):
    X(EJ)=T: T=X(EI+1): X(EI+1)=X(EJ+1): X(EJ+1)=T
1260 K=N/2
1270 IF K>J THEN J=J+K ELSE J=J-K: K=K/2: GOTO 1270
1280 NEXT
1290 '        END OF BIT-REVERSAL
1300 '   ------------------------------------------
1310 '
1320 '        UNPACK TO GET POSITIVE-FREQUENCY SPECTRUM
1330 '        (Note that X(1) is Nyquist frequency component.)
1340 '
1350 T=X(0)+X(1): X(1)=X(0)-X(1): X(0)=T: X(N+1)=-X(N+1): N2=2*N
1360 FOR K=1 TO N/2-1: K2=2*K: NK=N2-K2: AR=X(K2)+X(NK): AI=X(K2+1)-X(NK+1)
1370 BR=X(NK)-X(K2): BI=-X(NK+1)-X(K2+1): S=SIN(K*PI/N): C=COS(K*PI/N)
1380 CR=BR*S-BI*C: CI=BR*C+BI*S: X(K2)=(AR+CR)/2: X(K2+1)=(AI+CI)/2
1390 X(NK)=(AR-CR)/2: X(NK+1)=(CI-AI)/2: NEXT: RETURN
1400 '
1410 ' Variables X(2k) and X(2k+1) are the real and imaginary parts
1420 '  of the k-th spectral component.  X(0) is d-c, X(1) is at FS/2
```

61 Divider displays uncanny accuracy

Exact voltage divider

Here is a solution just waiting for a problem to solve. If you need to derive a half reference-voltage point and just happen to have a clock waveform handy, but cannot afford precision resistors, here is your answer. Perspicacious readers will spot a misprint in Figure 2 and will also realize that Rp and Rn do not, in fact, cancel out. But provided they are not badly unbalanced and are also very small compared with 100 K, then the circuit does indeed do the job. You could alternatively use the flip-flop to control CMOS switches likewise, to produce a midpoint voltage between any two voltages VREF1 and VREF2.

Michael A Wyatt
SSAvD Honeywell Inc, Clearwater, FL

The voltage divider in **Fig 1** divides V_{REF} in half with uncanny accuracy yet uses no precision components. Note that unlike dividers based on precision resistors, which can divide a voltage in virtually any proportion, this circuit will only divide V_{REF} in half.

The circuit uses a CMOS flip-flop to toggle the divider resistors, R_1 and R_2, between V_{REF} and ground. R_1 and R_2 need not be precision resistors because the toggling action, along with C_1, averages any error toward zero.

To better understand the operation of this circuit, consider **Fig 2**. In **Fig 2a**, the flip-flop's Q output is high and R_1 and R_2 (along with the flip-flop's output

transistors' on-resistances, R_P and R_N) form a simple voltage divider. When the flip-flop changes state, R_1 and R_2, in effect, exchange their positions on the voltage-divider totem pole.

Because the effects of the flip-flop's output transistors' on-resistances and any mismatch between R_1 and R_2 tends to average out, the major source of inaccuracy in this circuit is asymmetry in the flip-flop's time division. You could further improve the accuracy of this circuit by buffering the Q and $\overline{Q}$ outputs with an HC-type line driver with paralleled outputs. This device would further reduce the effects of the flip-flop's output transistors' on-resistances.

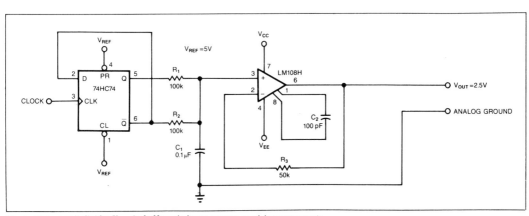

Fig 1—*This circuit divides V_{REF} in half precisely yet uses no precision components.*

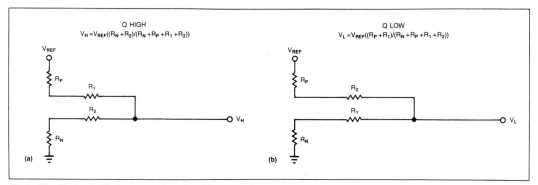

Fig 2—The flip-flop in Fig 1 reverses the order of R_1 and R_2 between V_{REF} and ground developing, alternately V_H **(a)** and V_L **(b)**. The capacitor C_1 averages V_H and V_L, which yields a voltage precisely half that of V_{REF}.

62 Test whether a noise source is Gaussian

Test whether a noise source is Gaussian

The frequency distribution of a noise source's output may (or may not) be white, up to a given frequency. This can easily be checked by a spectrum analyser. Likewise, its output amplitude distribution may not have the normal distribution of true random noise. Founded upon basic theory, this article describes how to assess whether a noise source's amplitude distribution is, in practical terms, Gaussian, that is to say following the normal distribution.

Stuart R Michaels
ILC Data Device Corp, Bohemia, NY

A spectrum analyzer permits you to measure the bandwidth of a noise source, but you need different equipment to determine whether or not the noise amplitudes have a Gaussian probability distribution. One approach is to use a simple circuit (**Fig 1**) and a dc voltmeter to measure the circuit's output.

First, it's useful to review the basics. A Gaussian noise voltage (or current) with rms value S and instantaneous value V has a probability-density p(V) distribution defined by the equation

$$p(V) = \frac{e^{-V^2/2S^2}}{S\sqrt{2\pi}}.$$

For given values of S, the equation produces curves such as those in **Fig 2**. The probability that the instantaneous value of V will occur between any particular two levels is the area under the curve between those levels. And the area under each curve from $-$infinity to $+$infinity is unity because the chance that V will occur between those limits is 100%.

You can calculate the probability that V will occur between the arbitrary levels V_1 and V_2 by integrating p(V) between those levels. Or you can calculate the cumulative probability that V will occur between a level V_1 and $+$infinity. To do this, integrate p(V) from V_1 to $+$infinity for V_1 values between 0V and 10 times the rms value S (**Fig 3**). Because the cumulative probability falls off sharply as V_1 increases, you need only consider V_1 values to 10× the rms level; the probability that noise will exceed 10S is less than 1 ppm. Note also that the noise voltage near 0V has a near-equal chance of being positive or negative. Consequently, the cumulative probability for Gaussian noise near 0V is 0.5, regardless of the rms level.

You can use the cumulative-probability circuit of **Fig 1** to generate the curves of **Fig 3**. First, connect the noise source and dc voltmeter as shown and then adjust

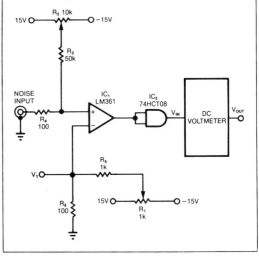

Fig 1—This circuit measures the cumulative probability (V_O/5V) of the input noise-voltage excursions exceeding the V_1 threshold.

R_1 for the desired V_1 value at the comparator's inverting input. The AND-gate output V_{IN} will be high when the input noise is above V_1 and low otherwise, producing a duty cycle corresponding to the cumulative probability that V will exceed V_1.

The dc voltmeter's output divided by 5V equals the cumulative probability if the voltmeter input swings between 0 and 5V. The CMOS gate IC_2 provides such an output swing when lightly loaded, provided you adjust the power supply to obtain an accurate 5V output level.

Then, with the noise source connected and V_1=0V, you can remove the effect of comparator-offset voltage by adjusting R_2 for a voltmeter reading of 2.5V. Under these conditions, V_{IN} will spend 50% of the time at 0V and 50% at 5V, yielding a cumulative probability of 2.5V/5V=0.5. A nonzero, positive V_1 will cause V_{IN} to spend less time at 5V, resulting in a lower value of cumulative probability.

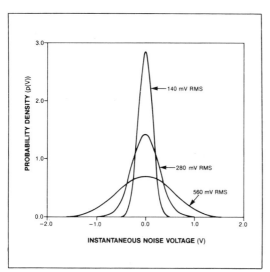

Fig 2—The classical Gaussian distributions for noise change shape with the rms level, but the area under all such curves is unity.

For accurate measurements, the comparator's bandwidth should exceed that of the input noise by a minimum factor of 10. Otherwise, it will cause error in the comparison of measured and theoretical cumulative probabilities—that is, by reducing the measured rms voltage. To avoid this problem, you should take into account certain factors. For $V_1 = S$, the theoretical cumulative probability for Gaussian noise is 0.1589. If you adjust V_1 until $V_0 = 794.3$ mV (which corresponds to a cumulative probability of 0.1589), V_1 will equal the rms noise voltage S. Further, the noise source is Gaussian if you get this same value of V_0 for various multiples and

submultiples of V_1.

Fig 4 illustrates the result obtained when using **Fig 1**'s circuit to test a Gaussian source that's part of a commercial noise tester. The congruence of the curves for measured and theoretical data indicates the source is "very" Gaussian.

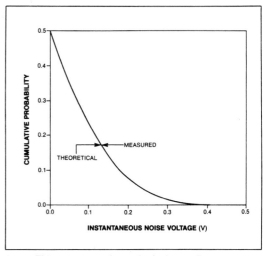

Fig 4—This curve shows the result of using the Fig 1 test circuit and illustrates near-ideal Gaussian characteristics for the noise source in a commercial noise tester.

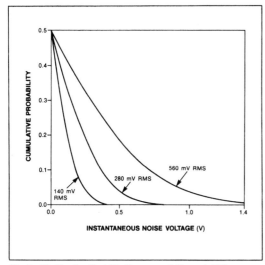

Fig 3—Fig 1's circuit yields these cumulative-probability curves, which correspond to the Gaussian distributions in *Fig 2*.

63 Routine gives nonrepeat random numbers

Simple random number algorithm

Here is a simple algorithm to produce from an initial number (which should be irrational, hence the incorporation of PI in the seed) an endless sequence of random numbers, all in the range nought to one. It certainly works, as a few moments with your pocket calculator will show. But surely the resultant distribution cannot be truly flat across the range 0 to 1, since then the quoted mean would be nearer 0.5?

Paul Conant
Gulton Industries, Plano, TX

Microcomputers typically generate pseudorandom numbers using the linear congruential method (see **reference**), which takes the following form: $X_n^{+1} = a * X_n + b \pmod{T}$. Coefficients a, b and T include ratioed relative primes that must be large (a limitation in μCs) in order for the sequence's repetition period to be large. Successive values of X serve as "seeds" for subsequent random numbers. The routine presented here represents a new class of pseudorandom-number generator. It's nonrepeating, requires no coefficient other than the initial seed, and is very fast.

The method entails successively taking the mantissa of a reciprocated "seed," X_i, in the following form:

$$X_{n+1} = 1/(X_n - INT(X_n)) - INT(1/(X_n - INT(X_n))).$$

The initial seed is the nonzero product of π and any real number. As before, successive seeds ensure the randomness of subsequent numbers—but without sequence repetitions.

Statistical analysis of more than 33,000 random numbers, ranging from 0 to 1.0, yielded the following parameters:

- Mean = 0.4423576339
- Standard deviation = 0.2871775770
- Variance = 0.0824684750.

Reference

Abramowitz and Stegun, *Handbook of Mathematical Functions*, General Publishing Co Ltd, Don Mills, Ontario, Canada.

64 Current-feedback amplifiers benefit high-speed designs

Current-feedback op-amps

This article introduces current-feedback op-amps and the benefits they offer. The punch line in this type of device is the realization that an op-amp does not need a high input impedance at the inverting terminal, only at the non-inverting (NI) terminal. For in the inverting connection, the I input is a virtual earth, whereas in the non-inverting connection this terminal is internal to the circuit and not seen by the input. Taking advantage of this fact enables the op-amp designer effectively to remove a pole in the response, providing vastly improved performance at high frequencies, especially in high gain applications.

Sergio Franco, *San Francisco State University*

Amplifiers based on the current-feedback topology are now more widely available than ever. They offer designers of high-speed systems some key advantages over conventional op amps (**Ref 1**). First, you can independently vary their gain and bandwidth; second, they have a virtually unlimited slew rate. The absence of slew-rate limiting not only allows for faster settling times, but also eliminates slew-rate-related nonlinearities such as intermodulation distortion. Thus, current-feedback amps are attractive for use in high-quality audio-amplifier applications.

These two advantages are the result of the amps' current-mode operation, which has long been recognized as inherently faster than voltage-mode operation. The effects of stray inductance in a circuit are usually less severe than those of stray capacitance (or the Miller effect), and bipolar transistors can switch currents much more rapidly than voltages. Current amplifiers must still have a voltage output, however, and op-amp designers sidestep some of the problems associated with voltage-mode operation by using gain configurations such as common-collector and cascode configurations, which provide immunity to the Miller effect. Further, thanks to manufacturing processes that ensure symmetrical npn- and pnp-transistor switching characteristics, manufacturers can now create monolithic op amps that achieve high speeds that were previously available only from hybrid devices.

In many ways, current-feedback amps are very similar to their conventional op-amp counterparts (**Ref 2**). For a standard circuit configuration, you derive the transfer functions for current-feedback amplifiers in the same way that you do for conventional op amps. However, if you're going to use a current-feedback amp in your design, you'll have some other considera-

tions to make. For example, you'll have to decide how to use reactive feedback elements, which cause oscillation when connected directly from output to input. Thus, before designing with current-feedback amps, you need a thorough understanding of the current-feedback architecture.

The easiest way to understand the advantages of the current-feedback topology is to compare it with the architecture of a conventional op amp (**Ref 3**). The conventional op amp consists of a high-input-impedance differential stage followed by additional gain stages, the last of which is a low-output-impedance stage. The op amp's transfer characteristic is:

$$V_{OUT} = a(jf)V_D, \qquad (1)$$

where V_{OUT} is the output voltage; $V_D = V_P - V_N$ is the differential input voltage; and a(jf), a complex function of frequency (f), is the open-loop gain (**Fig 1a**). Connecting an external resistor network as shown in **Fig 1b** creates a feedback path; the voltage signal derived from the output is applied to the noninverting input. You can solve for V_D to obtain

$$V_D = V_{IN} - \frac{R_1}{R_1 + R_2} V_{OUT}. \qquad (2)$$

By substituting **Eq 2** for V_D in **Eq 1** and solving for the ratio V_{OUT}/V_{IN}, you obtain the familiar closed-loop transfer characteristic for a noninverting amplifier:

$$A(jf) = \frac{V_{OUT}}{V_{IN}} = \left(1 + \frac{R_2}{R_1}\right)\frac{1}{1 + 1/T(jf)}, \qquad (3)$$

where $1 + R_2/R_1$ is the ideal gain value, and

$$T(jf) = \frac{a(jf)}{1 + R_2/R_1} \qquad (4)$$

represents the loop gain. The denominator of the loop-gain expression is called the noise gain. In this case, it's equal to $1 + R_2/R_1$. Note that in this example, the noise gain just happens to be equal to the ideal closed-loop gain. It's important not to confuse the two.

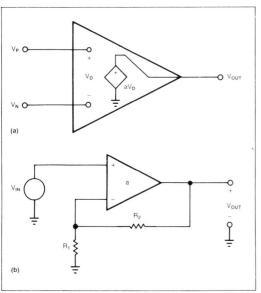

Fig 1—The circuit model of a conventional op amp includes a differential input stage and a gain stage **(a)**; resistive feedback configures the op amp as a noninverting amplifier **(b)**.

Loop gain determines stability

Eq 4 represents the loop gain, because if you break the loop as shown in **Fig 2a** and inject a test signal (V_X) with V_{IN} suppressed, the circuit will first attenuate V_X to produce $V_N = V_X/(1 + R_2/R_1)$, and then amplify V_N to produce $V_{OUT} = -aV_N$. Hence, the gain that a signal experiences when it goes around the loop is $V_{OUT}/V_X = -a/(1 + R_2/R_1)$. The negative of this ratio represents the loop gain, T.

The loop gain provides a measure of how close A is to the ideal value of $1 + R_2/R_1$. The larger the value of T, the better. To help the user achieve high loop gains over a wide range of closed-loop gains, op-amp manufacturers strive to make the open-loop gain (a) as large as possible. Consequently, V_D will assume extremely small values, because $V_D = V_{OUT}/a$ (see **Eq 1**). As the value of the open-loop gain approaches infinity, V_D approaches zero; that is, the value of V_N approaches that of V_P. This fact is the basis of the familiar op-amp rule: When it's operated with negative feedback, an op amp will ideally provide whatever output voltage and current are needed to force V_N to equal V_P.

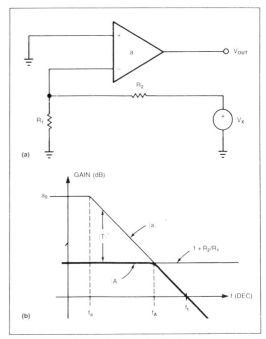

Fig 2—You can find the loop gain by injecting a signal V_X with V_{IN} grounded and solving for V_{OUT}/V_X **(a)**; the loop gain is, graphically, the difference between the open-loop curve and the noise-gain curve.

Op amps require a familiar tradeoff

In practice, op amps can physically realize large open-loop gains only over a limited frequency range. Beyond this range, the gain rolls off with respect to frequency because of the op amps' internal frequency compensation. Most op amps are designed for a constant rolloff of -20 dB/decade, so the open-loop response can be expressed as

$$a(jf) = \frac{a_0}{1 + j(f/f_a)}, \qquad (5)$$

where a_0 represents the dc gain and f_a is the -3-dB frequency of the open-loop response.

By substituting **Eq 5** for a(jf) in **Eq 4** and then substituting **Eq 4** for T(jf) in **Eq 3**, and recognizing the fact that $(1 + R_2/R_1)/a_0 < 1$, you can obtain

$$A(jf) = \frac{1 + R_2/R_1}{1 + j(f/f_A)}, \qquad (6)$$

where

$$f_A = \frac{f_t}{1 + R_2/R_1} \qquad (7)$$

represents the closed-loop bandwidth and $f_t = a_0 f_a$ represents the open-loop unity-gain frequency—that is, the frequency at which |a| is equal to 1. For instance, the 741 op amp has an f_t equal to 1 MHz.

205

Eq 7 reveals the familiar gain-bandwidth tradeoff. As you raise the R_2/R_1 ratio to increase the closed-loop gain, you decrease its bandwidth. Moreover, the loop gain also decreases, leading to a greater closed-loop-gain error.

You can see this tradeoff by plotting the frequency response on a graph. From **Eq 4**, $|T|_{dB} = |a|_{dB} - (1 + R_2/R_1)_{dB}$. Thus, you can think of the loop gain as the difference between the open-loop gain and the noise gain **(Fig 2b)**. The intersection of the two curves is the crossover frequency or -3-dB point, at which T has a magnitude of 1 and a phase shift of $-90°$.

As you increase the closed-loop gain, the noise-gain curve shifts upward, thus reducing the loop gain. Also, the intersection point will move up the $|a|$ curve, thus decreasing the closed-loop bandwidth. Clearly, the circuit with the widest bandwidth and the highest loop gain is also the one with the lowest closed-loop gain. This circuit is the voltage follower, for which $R_2/R_1 = 0$, so $A = 1$ and $f_A = f_t$.

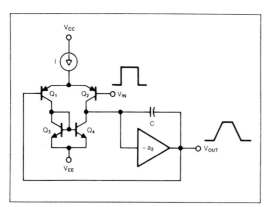

Fig 3—As shown in this simplified slew-rate model, *there is limited current to charge and discharge C when the transconductance stage saturates.*

Slew-rate limiting is also a factor

To fully characterize the dynamic behavior of an op amp, you also need to know its transient response. In many applications, the dynamic parameter of greatest concern is the settling time, a characteristic in which slew-rate limiting plays an important role. If you apply a small voltage step to an op amp connected as a unity-gain voltage-follower, the amp's dynamic behavior will be similar to that of an RC network. The input step, ΔV_{IN}, will cause the output to undergo an exponential transition with a magnitude of $\Delta V_O = \Delta V_{IN}$ and a time constant of $\tau = 1/(2\pi f_t)$. For the 741 op amp, $\tau = 1/(2\pi \times 10^6) \approx 170$ nsec.

The rate at which the output changes with time is highest at the beginning of the exponential transition, when its value is $\Delta V_{OUT}/\tau$. Increasing the step magnitude increases this initial rate of change, until the latter saturates at a value called the slew rate (SR). This fact is due to the limited ability of the internal circuitry to charge and discharge the compensation capacitor

as well as capacitive loads.

The input stage of a typical op amp is a transconductance block consisting of differential pair Q_1-Q_2 and current mirror Q_3-Q_4 **(Fig 3)**. The remaining stages, considered together, comprise an integrator block consisting of an inverting amplifier and the compensation capacitor, C. Slew-rate limiting occurs when the transconductance stage saturates, so all the current available to charge and/or discharge C is the bias current (I) of this stage.

For example, for the 741 op amp, $I = 20$ μA and $C = 30$ pF, so $SR = I/C = 0.67$ V/μsec. The step magnitude corresponding to the onset of slew-rate limiting is such that $\Delta V_{IN}/\tau = SR$; that is, $\Delta V_{IN} = SR \times \tau = (0.67$ V/μsec$) \times (170$ nsec$) = 116$ mV. As long as the step is less than 116 mV, a 741 op amp configured as a voltage follower will respond with an exponential transition governed by $\tau \approx 170$ nsec, whereas for a greater input step the output will slew at a constant rate of 0.67 V/μsec.

Current-feedback-amp architecture

The architecture of the current-feedback amp differs from the conventional op amp in two respects **(Fig 4)**. First, the current-feedback amp's input stage is a unity-gain voltage buffer connected across the inputs of the op amp. Its function is to force V_N to follow

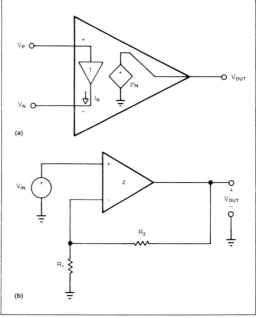

Fig 4—The circuit model of a current-feedback amp *includes a unity-voltage-gain input buffer and a transimpedance block (a). Connected as a noninverting amplifier (b), the current-feedback amp looks identical to its conventional-op-amp counterpart.*

V_P, very much as negative feedback forces V_N to follow V_P in a conventional op amp. However, because of the low output impedance of this buffer, current can easily flow in or out of the inverting input. During normal operation, this current is extremely small.

Second, a current-feedback amp has a transimpedance amplifier, which senses the current delivered by the buffer to the external feedback network and produces an output voltage V_{OUT} such that

$$V_{OUT} = z(jf)I_N, \qquad (8)$$

where $z(jf)$ represents the transimpedance gain of the amplifier and I_N represents the output current of the inverting input.

To fully appreciate the inner workings of the current-feedback amp, you need to examine the simplified cir-

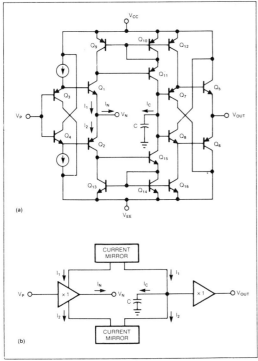

(a)

(b)

Fig 5—When you look into the actual circuit inside a current-feedback amp, you'll find both push-pull and Darlington transistor configurations at the input (a) (diagram courtesy Comlinear Corp). The block diagram of the circuit (b) shows the current-feedback amp's basic features.

cuit diagram of **Fig 5a**. The input buffer consists of transistors Q_1 through Q_4. Q_1 and Q_2 form a low output-impedance push-pull stage. Q_3 and Q_4 provide V_{BE} compensation for the push-pull pair and have a Darlington function, which raises the input impedance.

Summing the currents at the inverting node yields $I_1 - I_2 = I_N$, where I_1 and I_2 are the push-pull transistor currents. Two Wilson current mirrors, consisting of transistors Q_9 through Q_{11} and Q_{13} through Q_{15}, reflect these currents and recombine them at a common node, whose equivalent capacitance to ground is designated "C" in **Fig 5**.

A closer look at the internal circuit

By mirror action, the current through this capacitance is $I_C = I_1 - I_2$; that is, $I_C = I_N$. The voltage devel-

oped by C in response to this current is then conveyed to the output by a second buffer, which consists of Q_5 through Q_8. **Fig 5b**'s block diagram summarizes the salient features of the current-feedback amp.

When the amplifier loop is closed, as in **Fig 4b**, and an external signal attempts to imbalance the two inputs, the input buffer will begin sourcing (or sinking) an imbalance current, I_N, to the external feedback network. The Wilson mirrors convey this imbalance to C, causing V_{OUT} to swing in the positive (or negative) direction until the imbalance is neutralized via the negative feedback loop. Thus, I_N plays the role of error signal in the system.

To obtain the closed-loop transfer characteristic, refer again to **Fig 4b**. By summing the currents at the inverting node, you obtain

$$I_N = \frac{V_N}{R_1} - \frac{V_{OUT} - V_N}{R_2}. \qquad (9)$$

Because the buffer ensures that $V_N = V_P = V_{IN}$, you can rewrite **Eq 9** as:

$$I_N = \frac{V_{IN}}{R_1 \| R_2} - \frac{V_{OUT}}{R_2}, \qquad (10)$$

which confirms that the feedback signal, V_{OUT}/R_2, is now in the form of a current. By substituting **Eq 10** for I_N in **Eq 8**, and solving for the ratio V_{OUT}/V_{IN}, you obtain

$$A(jf) = \frac{V_{OUT}}{V_{IN}} = \left(1 + \frac{R_2}{R_1}\right)\frac{1}{1 + 1/T(jf)}, \qquad (11)$$

where $A(jf)$ represents the closed-loop gain of the circuit, and

$$T(jf) = \frac{z(jf)}{R_2} \qquad (12)$$

represents the loop gain. As for a conventional op amp, this terminology is derived from the fact that if you break the loop as shown in **Fig 6a**, and inject a test voltage (V_X) with V_{IN} suppressed, the circuit will first convert V_X to $I_N = -V_X/R_2$ and then convert I_N to $V_{OUT} = zI_N$, so $T = z/R_2$, as expected.

To ensure that the circuit will have substantial loop gain, and, therefore, minimal closed-loop gain error, manufacturers strive to make z as large as possible in relation to the expected values of R_2. Consequently, because $I_N = V_{OUT}/z$, the inverting-input current will be very small, even though this input is a low-impedance node because of the buffer. As a current-feedback amp's open-loop gain (z) approaches infinity, its I_N approaches 0, so the amplifier will provide whatever output voltage and current are needed to drive I_N to zero. Thus, the conventional op-amp conditions, $V_N = V_P$ and $I_N = I_P = 0$, hold for current-feedback amps as well.

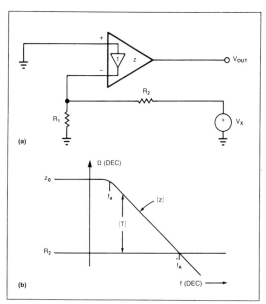

(a)

(b)

Fig 6—As with conventional op amps, you can use this test circuit (a) to determine the loop gain. The loop gain is represented graphically as the difference between the open loop gain, |z|, and the noise-gain curve, R_2 (b).

No gain-bandwidth tradeoff

The transimpedance gain of a practical current-feedback amp rolls off with frequency according to

$$z(jf) = \frac{z_0}{1 + j(f/f_a)}, \qquad (13)$$

where z_0 is the dc value of the transimpedance gain and f_a is the frequency at which rolloff begins. For instance, the data sheets of Comlinear's CLC401 current-feedback amp state that $z_0 \approx 710$ kΩ and $f_a \approx 350$ kHz.

By substituting **Eq 13** for z(jf) in **Eq 12**, and then substituting **Eq 12** for T(jf) in **Eq 11**, and recognizing the fact that $R_2/z_0 < 1$, you obtain

$$A(jf) = \frac{1 + R_2/R_1}{1 + j(f/f_A)}, \qquad (14)$$

where

$$f_A = \frac{z_0 f_a}{R_2} \qquad (15)$$

represents the closed-loop bandwidth. When R_2 is in the kilohm range, f_A is typically in the 100-MHz range. The noise-gain curve is now simply R_2, and f_A can be represented graphically as the frequency at which the R_2 curve meets the |z| curve (**Fig 6b**).

These closed-loop-gain expressions are formally identical to those for the conventional op amp **Eqs 6** and 7. However, the bandwidth now depends only on R_2 rather than on the closed-loop gain $1 + R_2/R_1$. Conse-

quently, you can use R_2 to select the bandwidth and R_1 to select the gain. **Fig 7** highlights these frequency-response differences between current-feedback amps and conventional op amps.

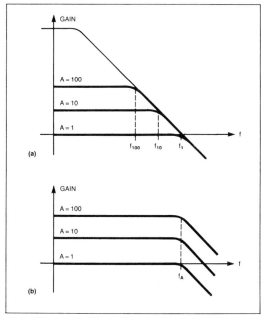

(a)

(b)

*Fig 7—The most significant advantage that current-feedback amps have over conventional op amps can be seen in this simple frequency-response plot. Note the gain-bandwidth tradeoff for conventional op amps in **a** and the absence of such a compromise in **b**.*

The other major advantage of current-feedback amps is their inherent absence of slew-rate limiting. This feature is due to the fact that the current available to charge the internal capacitance at the onset of a step is now proportional to the step, regardless of its size. Indeed, applying the step ΔV_{IN} induces, according to **Eq 10**, an initial current imbalance $I_N = \Delta V_{IN}/(R_1 \tau R_2)$, which the Wilson mirrors then convey to the capacitor. The initial rate of charge is, therefore,

$$\begin{aligned} I_C/C &= I_N/C \\ &= \Delta V_{IN}/((R_1 \tau R_2)C) \\ &= (\Delta V_{IN}(1 + R_2/R_1))/(R_2 C) \\ &= \Delta V_{OUT}/(R_2 C), \end{aligned}$$

which indicates an exponential output transition in which the time constant, τ, is equal to $R_2 C$. Like the frequency response, then, the transient response is governed by R_2 alone, regardless of the closed-loop gain. When R_2 is in the kilohm range and C is in the picofarad range, τ will be in the nanosecond range.

The rise time is defined as the amount of time, t_r, that it takes for the output to swing from 10% to 90% of the step size. For an exponential transition, $t_r = \tau \times \ln(0.9/0.1) = 2.2\tau$. For example, the CLC401 has a t_r equal to 2.5 nsec for a 2V output step, indicating an effective τ of 1.14 nsec. The time it takes for the output to settle to within 0.1% of the final value is $t_s = \tau \times \ln 1000$, which is approximately 7τ. For the CLC401, therefore, t_s is approximately 8 nsec, which is in reasonable agreement with the data-sheet value of 10 nsec.

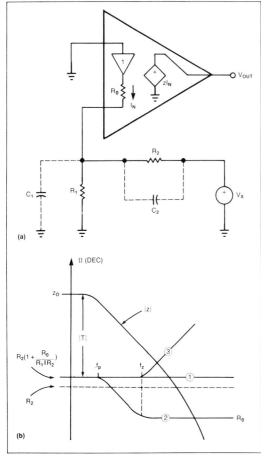

Fig 8—By using the more real-world circuit model in **a**, you can determine the effects, shown in **b**, of R_O (curve 1), feedback capacitance (curve 2), and input capacitance (curve 3).

So far, this analysis indicates that once R_2 has been set, the dynamics of the amplifier are unaffected by the closed-loop-gain setting. In practice, you'll find that a current-feedback amp's bandwidth and rise time do vary somewhat with gain, though not as drastically as do those of conventional op amps. The main cause of this nonideal behavior is the input buffer's nonzero output impedance (R_O), which alters the loop gain and, hence, the closed-loop dynamics.

As **Fig 8a** shows, the circuit first converts V_X to a current, $I_{R2} = V_X/(R_2 + R_1 \tau R_O)$, and then divides I_{R2} to produce $I_N = -I_{R2}R_1/(R_1 + R_O)$. Finally, it converts I_N to the voltage $V_{OUT} = V_N$. Eliminating I_{R2} and I_N and letting T equal $-V_{OUT}/V_X$ yields $T = z/Z_2$, where

$$Z_2 = R_2\left(1 + \frac{R_0}{R_1\|R_2}\right). \qquad (16)$$

Thus, the effect of R_O is to increase the noise gain from R_2 to $R_2(1 + R_O/(R_1\tau R_2))$ (**Fig 8b**, curve 1.) Consequently, both the bandwidth and the rise time will be reduced by a proportional amount.

You can replace R_2 in **Eq 15** with Z_2 from **Eq 16**, and, after simple manipulation, obtain

$$f_A = \frac{f_t}{1 + \dfrac{R_0}{R_2}\left(1 + \dfrac{R_2}{R_1}\right)}, \qquad (17)$$

where $f_t = z_0 f_a/R_2$ represents the extrapolated value of f_A in the limit $R_O \to 0$. **Eq 17** indicates that the bandwidth reduction caused by R_O will be more pronounced at high closed-loop gains. For example, suppose a current-feedback amp has $R_O = 50\Omega$, $R_2 = 1.5$ kΩ, and $f_t = 100$ MHz, so $f_A = 10^8/(1 + (50/1500)A_O) = 10^8/(1 + A_O/30)$, where $A_O = 1 + R_2/R_1$. Then, the bandwidths corresponding to $A_O = 1$, $A_O = 10$, and $A_O = 100$ are, respectively, 96.8 MHz, 75.0 MHz, and 23.1 MHz. Note that these values still compare favorably with those of a conventional op amp, whose bandwidth would be reduced, respectively, by 1, 10, and 100.

If you wish, you can predistort the external resistance values to compensate for the bandwidth reduction at high gains. By solving for R_2 in **Eq 17**, you can obtain the required value of R_2 for a given bandwidth (f_A) and gain (A_O), which is

$$R_2 = \frac{z_0 f_a}{f_A} - R_0 A_0, \qquad (18)$$

while the required value of R_1 for gain A_O is

$$R_1 = \frac{R_2}{A_0 - 1}. \qquad (19)$$

For example, suppose you want the above amplifier to retain its 100-MHz bandwidth at a closed-loop gain of 10. When $R_2 = 1.5$ kΩ, this device has a $z_0 f_a/R_2$ equal to 100 MHz, so it follows that $z_0 f_a = 10^8 \times 1500 = 1.5 \times 10^{11}\Omega \times$ Hz. Then, **Eqs 18** and **19** yield $R_2 = (1.5 \times 10^{11}/10^8) - (50 \times 10) = 1$ kΩ, and $R_1 = 1000/(10 - 1) = 111\Omega$, respectively.

Current-feedback amps have higher-order poles

In addition to the dominant pole at f_a, the open-loop response of a practical current-feedback amp also has poles above the crossover frequency. As **Fig 8b** shows, the effect of these poles is to cause a steeper gain rolloff at higher frequencies, further reducing the closed-loop bandwidth. Moreover, the additional phase shift caused by these poles decreases the phase margin somewhat, thus causing a small amount of peaking in the frequency response and creating some ringing in the transient response.

Like the real current-feedback-amp bandwidth characteristics, the transient response also strays from the ideal. The rise time of a practical current-feedback amp increases somewhat with the step size, primarily because of the transistor's current-gain degradation at high current levels. For instance, the rise time of the CLC401 changes from 2.5 to 5 nsec as the step size changes from 2 to 5V. Despite their second-order limitations, current-feedback amps provide dynamics superior to those of conventional op amps.

Consider other feedback configurations

This discussion has focused so far on the noninverting configuration, but you can use current-feedback amps in most other resistive feedback configurations, such as the inverting amplifier, the summing and difference amplifier, current-to-voltage and voltage-to-current converters, and KRC active filters (**Ref 3**).

You should take special care, however, with circuits in which the feedback network includes reactive elements, whether they're intentional or parasitic. Consider first the effect of feedback capacitance (C_2) in parallel with R_2 in the basic circuit of **Fig 8a**. By replacing R_2 in **Eq 16** with $Z = R_2\tau(1/sC_2)$, you obtain a noise gain of $Z_2 = Z(1 + R_0/(R_1\tau Z))$. After expanding the equation (and performing some algebraic manipulation), you'll find that the noise-gain curve now has a pole at $f_p = 1/(2\pi R_2 C_2)$, and a zero at $f_z = 1/(2\pi(R_0\tau R_1\tau R_2)C_2)$, as curve 2 of **Fig 8b** shows.

This new pole and zero move the crossover frequency or intersection point into the region where the loop gain, T, will have increased negative phase shift (remember that there are higher-order poles in the open-loop transfer function). It is the phase shift of the loop-gain curve at the crossover frequency that determines amplifier stability. If the overall shift reaches $-180°$ at that frequency, then $T = -1$, and the circuit will oscillate. Even if the phase shift fails to reach $-180°$, the closed-loop response may still exhibit intolerable peaking and ringing. Hence, when you use current-feedback amps, you must avoid applying direct capacitive feedback between the output and the input. To minimize the effect of stray feedback capacitances, manufacturers often provide R_2 internally.

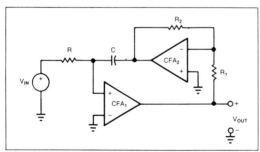

Fig 9—To implement an integrator, you must use circuit configurations that involve indirect feedback, such as this actively compensated current-feedback integrator.

Use unique integrator topologies

To synthesize the integrator function in current-feedback form, you must use configurations that don't have direct capacitance between the output and the inverting input. (The integrator function provides the basis for dual-integrator-loop filters and oscillators as

well as for other popular circuits.) One possibility is to use the Deboo integrator (**Ref 3**), which belongs to the class of KRC filters. It has a drawback, however: If you desire lossless integration, you must make sure the circuit resistances are tightly matched.

The alternative circuit shown in **Fig 9** provides indirect feedback and also features active compensation, a highly desirable feature for coping with Q-enhancement problems in dual-integrator-loop filters (**Ref 3**). By using standard op-amp-analysis techniques, you can see that the unity-gain frequency of this integrator is $f_0 = (R_2/R_1)/(2\pi RC)$. The availability of current-feedback amps in dual monolithic packages, such as the OP-260 from Precision Monolithics, makes this circuit cost-effective.

Compensate for stray input capacitance

Next, consider the effect of input capacitance (C_1) in parallel with R_1 in the basic circuit of **Fig 8a**. By replacing R_1 in **Eq 17** with Z, and letting $Z = R_1\tau(1/sC_1)$, you obtain a noise gain of $Z_2 = R_2(1 + R0/(Z\tau R_2))$. After expanding the equation and performing more algebraic manipulation, you find that, as curve 3 of **Fig 8b** shows, the noise-gain curve now has a zero at

$$f_z = 1/(2\pi(R_0\tau R_1\tau R_2)C_1).$$

Again, recall that T is equal to ⊠ in decibels *minus* the noise gain in decibels. Likewise, the phase of T is equal to the phase of Z minus the phase of the noise-gain curve. So, the positive phase shift contributed by the new zero in the noise-gain curve looks like negative phase shift to T. If C_1 is sufficiently large, the phase of T at the crossover frequency will again approach $-180°$, placing the circuit on the verge of instability. This fact is of particular concern in current-mode-DAC output buffering, where C_1 is the output capacitance of the DAC, typically in the range of a few tens to a few hundreds of picofarads, depending on the DAC type.

As with a conventional op amp, you can stabilize the current-feedback amp by using feedback capacitance (C_2) to introduce sufficient negative phase shift in the noise-gain curve (positive phase shift to T), thus compensating for the effect of the input capacitance (C_1). For a phase margin of 45°, choose the value of C_2 so that the noise-gain pole, $f_p = 1/(2R_2C_2)$, coincides with the crossover frequency, f_A (**Fig 10a**). Using linearized Bode-plot reasoning (**Ref 3**), also known as straight-line approximation, you find that:

$$f_A = (z_0f_af_z/(R_0 + R_1))^1,$$

where $f_z = 1/(2\pi(R_0\tau R_2)C_1)$. Setting $f_p = f_A$ yields

$$C_2 = \left[\frac{R_0}{2\pi R_2 z_0 f_a}C_1\right]^{1/2}. \qquad (20)$$

To cope with impractically low values of C_2, it's convenient to drive C_2 with a voltage divider as in **Fig 10b**; this action will scale the value of C_2 to a more practical value:

$$C_c = \left(1 + \frac{R_B}{R_A}\right)C_2. \qquad (21)$$

(Note that this circuit configuration will provide an additional zero in the noise-gain curve that lies to the right of the compensation pole, f_A, in (**Fig 10a**).

For this technique to be effective, R_B must be much less than R_2. For example, suppose that a DAC in which C_1 equals 100 pF feeds the current-feedback amp considered earlier. **Eq 20** yields:

$$C_2 = (50 \times 100 \times 10^{-12} \div (2\pi \times 1.5 \times 10^3 \times 1.5 \times 10^{11}))^{\frac{1}{2}}$$
$$= 1.88 \text{ pF}.$$

To scale C_2 to a more practical value, you can use $R_A = 50\Omega$ and $R_B = 500\Omega$ (**Ref 4**). **Eq 20** then yields $C_c = (1 + 500/50) \times 1.88$ pF = 21 pF. You may need to fine-tune this estimate to optimize the transient response.

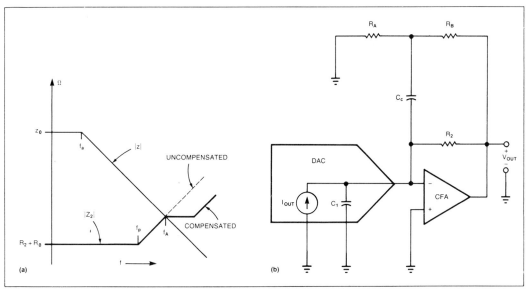

Fig 10—To compensate for input capacitance, *you should add a pole at f_A (**a**) that will add positive phase shift to the loop gain, thereby stabilizing the circuit. Use the circuit in **b** to achieve practical compensation-capacitor values.*

References

1. Harold, Peter, "Current-feedback op amps ease high-speed circuit design," *EDN*, July 7, 1988, pg 84.

2. *A new approach to op amp design*, Application Note 300-1, Comlinear Corp, March 1985.

3. Franco, Sergio, *Design with operational amplifiers and analog ICs*, McGraw-Hill, New York, NY, 1988.

4. *Current-feedback op amp applications circuit guide*, Application Note OA-07, Comlinear Corp, 1988.

65 Step-up converter produces 5 V from 1.5 V

> ## Power your kit from a low voltage battery
>
> It is attractive to power equipment from a low voltage in certain circumstances, for example where the battery is to be kept topped up by a solar cell, and this circuit enables you to do just that. Since the circuit requires at least 1.5 V to start, a single primary zinc/carbon Leclanche cell is not on, but a couple of NICAD cells would do nicely.

Gerald Grady
Maxim Integrated Products, Sunnyvale, CA

You can produce a regulated 5V output from a 1.5V battery cell by using the step-up dc/dc-converter circuit shown in **Fig 1**. The circuit can operate with V_S as low as 1V, but it requires at least 1.5V to start. The output can deliver 100 mA when V_S is 1.5V or 1.7A at 70% minimum efficiency when V_S is 3V.

Supply voltage for the switching regulator IC_1 appears first at pin 4 (start-up mode) and then at its own V_{OUT} terminal, pin 5. The chip includes an oscillator, bandgap reference, three voltage comparators, a catch diode, and associated control circuitry. An internal MOSFET lets you implement low-power applications; higher power calls for an external device: Q_1 in **Fig 1**. The on-chip oscillator provides a 55-kHz square-wave drive to both the internal and external MOSFET.

When Q_1 turns off, current through inductor L_2 drives the drain-node voltage higher. Similarly, current through L_1 drives the voltage at pin 5 higher when the internal MOSFET turns off. This action generates two independent voltages, each higher than V_S. Q_1 and L_2 generate sufficient overhead voltage to enable the regulator chip to produce a regulated 5V output, and the internally generated voltage ensures adequate gate drive to Q_1. The internal voltage, clamped by the 10V zener diode D_3, ranges from 10V (turn-on) to 15V (normal operation). Q_1's resulting $R_{DS(ON)}$ is only 0.085Ω.

Resistors R_1 and R_2 determine the regulated output level. For V_{REG} outputs other than 5V, set

$$R_1 = R_2\left(\frac{V_{OUT}}{1.31} - 1\right).$$

You choose an R_2 value in the range from 10 kΩ to 10 MΩ.

For low values of V_S, losses in the internal and external diodes and the Q_1 inductor sharply limit the maximum output current. The following design equations let you determine component values while calculating this current. First, Q_1 must be able to handle the peak current I_{PK} of inductor L_2:

$$I_{PK} = V_S t_{ON}/L_2,$$

where $t_{ON} = 0.55/f_{OSC}$. For this circuit, then, $I_{PK} = 1.07A$. The circuit loss V_{LOSS} is

$$V_{LOSS} = I_{PK}(R_{DS(ON)} + 2R_{L_2}) + V_{D_2},$$

where R_{L2} is the dc resistance of L_2 and V_{D2} is the forward voltage drop of D_2. For this circuit, $V_{LOSS} = 0.56V$. The output current is

$$I_{OUT} = \frac{0.5 L_2 I_{PK}^2 f_{OSC}}{V_{REG} - (V_S - V_{LOSS}) - I_{L_1}}.$$

Therefore, $I_{OUT} = 103$ mA for the circuit shown. **Table 1** shows the output currents you can obtain for various values of V_S and L_2. The corresponding conversion efficiencies range from 70 to 85%.

TABLE 1—OBTAINABLE VALUES OF I_{OUT} MAX

V_S	L_2 14 µH	27 µH	50 µH
1.5V	105 mA	48 mA	30 mA
2.0V	220 mA	95 mA	60 mA
2.5V	390 mA	160 mA	100 mA
3.0V	1.75A	1.5A	1.25A

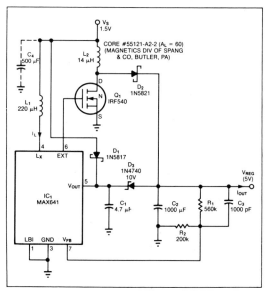

Fig 1—This switching-regulator circuit converts a dc input (as low as 1.5V) to a higher regulated value—to 5V, for example.

66 Simple logarithms speed microprocessor math operations

Simple log algorithm

Just as logs enabled the slide-rule to calculate rapidly, they can do the same for a microprocessor system, given a suitable means of taking logs and antilogs easily. This article explains how.

Peter Guagliano, *Comtech Government Systems*

To perform complicated arithmetic in assembly language on 8-bit µPs, consider using logarithms to simplify your calculations. Such an approach eliminates the need for an expensive math coprocessor, which can occupy a lot of pc-board real estate. The logarithm-based approach can also eliminate the need for slow high-level-language library routines, which often enforce strict format requirements on parameters.

Using logarithms, you can readily program a µP to multiply and divide (despite the lack of hardware multiply and divide instructions on most 8-bit µPs) or to extract roots and raise numbers to powers. A review of logarithm properties illustrates how to perform these operations:

- $log(ab) = log a + log b$.
- $log(a/b) = log a - log b$.
- $log\sqrt{a} = \frac{1}{2} log a$.
- $log a^2 = 2 log a$.
- $log a$, for $a \le 0$, is undefined.

To make use of these properties in µP applications, you need an algorithm that converts a binary number to a binary logarithm. Because the logarithms of negative numbers and zero are undefined, assume that the binary numbers are positive. To simplify the algorithm, require the binary numbers to be greater than or equal to one. If you have to multiply or divide by a positive number less than one, use the inverse operation. For example, for $2 \div 0.1$, use 2×10.

Base-2 logarithms easily approximated

Fig 1 shows a curve for base-2 logs; **Fig 2** shows an enlarged area of **Fig 1**'s curve. The function is nearly linear in this region, a fact that simplifies approximations used in the conversion algorithm.

Now, consider the details of the algorithm. Let X be any binary number. Let N be the power of 2 given by the position of the most significant binary one in the number, remembering that the ones and zeros in a binary number are the coefficients a_K in the series

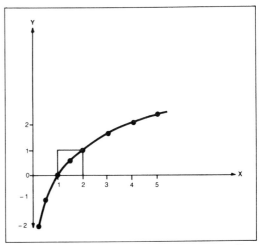

Fig 1—The function $Y = \log_2 X$ is nearly linear for $1 \le X \le 2$. Fig 2 expands that region.

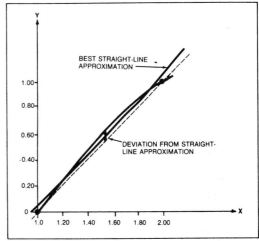

Fig 2—You can use straight-line approximations for $Y = \log_2 X$ for $1 < X < 2$. The solid line represents the best approximation.

213

$$a_0 2^0 + a_1 2^1 + \ldots + a_K 2^K.$$

Thus, a_N is the coefficient of 2^N. Therefore, for 00010110, N=4; for 01011001, N=6; and for 11010011, N=7.

Using the algorithm, you can represent the binary logarithm of an arbitrary number as N (the characteristic) plus an easily determined fraction (the mantissa). The following proof shows how you can determine both N and the fraction.

Let X be any positive binary integer, which can be expressed as

$$X = 2^N + (X - 2^N).$$

This can be rewritten as

$$X = 2^N + 2^N \left[\frac{X - 2^N}{2^N} \right].$$

Factoring yields

$$X = 2^N \left[1 + \frac{X - 2^N}{2^N} \right].$$

Taking logs and applying the identity $log(ab) = log a + log b$ yields

$$log\ X = log\ 2^N + log \left[1 + \frac{X - 2^N}{2^N} \right].$$

Then,

$$log\ X = N + log \left[1 + \frac{X - 2^N}{2^N} \right].$$

Note that the fraction $(X - 2^N)/2^N$, which is the remainder after the most significant binary one has been shifted out, varies from zero to one.

The dashed line in **Fig 2** suggests for **Eq 1** the following linear approximation for values of X between 1 and 2:

$$log\ X = N + \frac{X - 2^N}{2^N}.$$

This approximation, however, yields errors that can be as large as 9%. Moreover, the errors are one-sided (ie, the approximation is always too low). This yields average errors of 4%—the total error increases as the number of operations increases.

As a first approach to minimizing the errors, use the best straight-line approximation (shown in **Fig 2**) of the logarithmic curve. To obtain this approximation, you need only add a constant to the dashed-line approximation. This constant's value should be about 5%, or 13 parts in 256. Adding the constant reduces the worst-case error to about 4%, but, better yet, it reduces the

average error to zero. Thus, errors tend to cancel, provided that you have an even distribution of data (ie, some of the logarithm errors are high and some are low). Note, though, that you can still accumulate large errors if the data happens to fall where the errors are

```
COMPUTELOG:  LD    B,15D         ; MAXIMUM LOOP COUNT.
LOGLOOP:     ADD   HL, HL        ; SHIFT HL LEFT.
             JR    C, GOTN       ; FOUND N ON CARRY.
             DJNZ  LOGLOOP       ; LOOP.
             LD    H, B          ; RETURN ZERO IN HL.
             RET                 ; RETURN.
GOTN:        LD    L, H          ; L GETS 8 BIT REMAINDER FRACTION.
             LD    H, LOGTABLE   ; H GETS PAGE OF LOG LOOK-UP TABLE.
             LD    A, (HL)       ; PERFORM TABLE LOOK-UP.
             LD    L, A          ; RETURN MANTISSA.
             LD    H, B          ; RETURN CHARACTERISTIC.
             RET                 ; RETURN.
LOGTABLE:    EQU   88H           ; PAGE OF LOG LOOK-UP TABLE.
```

Fig 3—By using this Z80 assembly-language program, you can compute the binary logarithms of 16-bit integers.

largest—in the center of the curve or at the endpoints.

A better approach is to use the fraction $(X - 2^N)/2^N$ to address a 256-byte look-up table and fetch the true binary logarithm. This method holds worst-case errors well below 1%, and the errors tend to cancel. This extra operation takes only 3μsec (on a Z80), but it does require two 256-byte tables, one to convert to logarithms, and another to convert back.

Applications prove usefulness

In the applications that follow, the routines accept the integers to be processed in a 16-bit register. The routines also express the logarithm in 16 bits. An 8-bit register holds the characteristic (N); another 8-bit register holds the mantissa (the remaining fraction). The results of the computations are also expressed in 16 bits. This gives a range of possible input and output numbers of

$$1 \leq X \leq 2^{16} - 1.$$

When using logarithms to solve equations, the intermediate results of the computations, expressed as a 16-bit logarithm, range from 1 to 2^{255}. This follows from the fact that the characteristic is expressed in eight bits, which allows a maximum characteristic of 255 before overflow occurs. The precision is basically limited to eight bits, but you can employ several techniques to improve this.

Fig 3 lists a Z80 assembly-language program that computes the binary logarithm of a 16-bit integer, which is assumed to be positive and greater than one. The 8-bit characteristic N is returned in register H, and the 8-bit mantissa is returned in register L. The algorithm shifts the register-pair HL left until a carry occurs. Subtracting the required number of shifts from 16 yields N, and register H contains the remainder. The remainder gives the address in the 256-byte log table that contains the precise logarithm. This subroutine's execution time depends on the data to be converted, but a conservative average execution time is around 100 μsec at a 4-MHz clock rate.

Fig 4 contains a subroutine that reverses the algorithm that the **Fig 3** code implements: The **Fig 4** subroutine converts the logarithm back to the binary number. This subroutine requires an additional 256-byte inverse-log look-up table. Again, the subroutine's execution time depends on the data to be converted, but a conservative average execution time is around 120 μsec at a 4-MHz clock rate. The **Fig 5** Pascal program generates the logarithm and inverse logarithm look-up tables.

```
ANTILOG:   LD    A, H              ; GET CHARACTERISTIC.
           CP    16D               ; OVERFLOW?
           JP    OVERFLOW          ; JUMP ON OVERFLOW.
           LD    B, H              ; MOV CHARACTERISTIC INTO LOOP COUNT.
           INR   B                 ; INCREMENT LOOP COUNT BY 1.
           LD    H, INVLOGT        ; H GETS PAGE OF INVERSE LOG TABLE.
           LD    A, (HL)           ; PERFORM INVERSE LOOK-UP.
           LD    HL, 0000          ; ZERO HL.
           STC                     ; SET CARRY.
INVLOOP:   RL    L                 ; CY <—— L <—— CY.
           RL    H                 ; CY <—— H <——CY.
           SLA   A                 ; CY <—— A <—— 0.
           DJNZ  INVLOOP           ; LOOP.
           RET                     ; RETURN.
OVERFLOW:  LD    HL, 0FFFFH        ; MAXINT.
           RET                     ; RETURN.
INVLOGT:   EQU   89H               ; PAGE OF INVERSE LOG TABLE.
```

Fig 4—Once you have an intermediate logarithmic result, this Z80 assembly-language program takes its antilogarithm.

Run times hold constant with number size

Note that it takes more time to calculate the antilogarithm of a large number than it does to calculate its logarithm. Conversely, it takes more time to calculate the logarithm of a small number than it does to calculate its antilogarithm. Thus, the time it takes to calculate a number's logarithm and then immediately calculate its antilogarithm tends to remain constant over the entire range of numbers.

Illustrating an application for the conversion algorithm, **Fig 6**'s routine uses the **Fig 3** and **4** subroutines and computes $Y = X^{2.5}$. Register-pair HL passes the

```
PROGRAM LOG_TABLES (INPUT,OUTPUT ) ;
VAR
     I : INTEGER ;
BEGIN
     WRITELN ('  LOG TRANSFORMATION TABLE....') ;
     WRITELN ('  = = = = = = = = = = = = = = = =') ;
     FOR I := 0 TO 255 DO
          WRITELN (I:5 , ROUND(256•LN(1 + I/256) / LN(2)):9) ;
     FOR I := 0 TO 10 DO WRITELN ;
     WRITELN ('  ANTI-LOG TRANSFORMATION TABLE....') ;
     WRITELN ('  = = = = = = = = = = = = = = = = = =') ;
     FOR I := 0 TO 255 DO
          WRITELN (I:5 , ROUND (256•(EXP(I/256•LN(2))-1)):9) ;
END.
```

Fig 5—Use this Pascal program to generate the logarithm and inverse logarithm look-up tables used by the subroutines in Figs 3 and 4.

```
EXP2FIVE:  CALL  COMPUTELOG   ; COMPUTE BINARY LOGARITHM.
           PUSH  HL           ; SAVE LOGARITHM.
           SRL   H            ; 0 —> H —> CY. COMPUTE SQR ROOT.
           RR    L            ; CY —— > L —— > CY.
           PUSH  HL           ; PUSH SQUARE ROOT.
           POP   DE           ; DE GETS SQUARE ROOT.
           POP   HL           ; GET LOGARITHM.
           ADD   HL, HL       ; COMPUTE SQUARE.
           ADD   HL, DE       ; ADD IN SQUARE ROOT.
           CALL  ANTILOG      ; CONVERT BACK TO BINARY.
           RET                ; RETURN.
```

TEST DATA

INPUT	IDEAL RESULT	ACTUAL RESULT	ERROR
14	733	734	.08%
27	3788	3776	.3%
50	17678	17664	.07%
63	31503	31488	.05%
81	59049	59008	.07%

Fig 6—You can use logarithms in routines such as this one to raise numbers to powers, even when the exponents are fractions.

input X to the routine; it also accepts the value Y returned by the routine. Note how the routine computes a square root by merely executing a right shift (ie, binary division of the log by two). Left shifts (binary multiplication of the log by two) raise numbers to powers of 2.

Save the cost of a coprocessor

Estimated average execution time is 250 μsec for the **Fig 6** routine running on a 4-MHz Z80. In contrast, an Intel 8231A, a likely math-coprocessor choice for a Z80 system, takes 2.5 msec to raise a number to a power. (In other respects, using the $190 8231A could be overkill for many applications. This chip, which communicates with the Z80 over an 8-bit bus, performs 16- and 32-bit floating-point operations and also handles transcendental functions, inverse transcendental functions, natural logarithms, and common logarithms.)

Further demonstrating the usefulness of the **Fig 3** and **4** routines, **Fig 7**'s routine uses them to compute the following square root of a sum of squares:

$$X = \sqrt{\frac{A^2}{313} + \frac{B^2}{462}}.$$

In **Fig 7**, arguments A (16 bits) and B (also 16 bits) are passed to the routine in registers HL and DE, respectively. The routine returns its results in register HL. Both arguments are assumed to be ≥1. Note that the intermediate results of the squared terms are expressed as a 16-bit logarithm and are therefore not in danger of overflow, even with large input numbers.

No effort was spent in maximizing this code's efficiency, yet it runs at an average time of 700 μsec at a 4-MHz clock rate. Using the 8231A, solving the same equation would probably take about 500 μsec.

You can extend this general algorithm embodied in the **Fig 3** and **4** code in many ways. For example, you can adapt it to yield greater precision for some applications. Or you can adapt it to applications requiring fractional results.

You can employ one of two methods to extend precision. First, you can continue using 16 bits to represent the logarithm, but you specify the characteristic in 4 bits and the mantissa in 12. However, this procedure limits the range of intermediate results because of the 4-bit characteristic. Second, if your application can't tolerate this limitation, you can increase the precision by expressing the characteristic in 8 bits and the mantissa in 16 bits, using an additional register to provide the required 24 bits that the 8-bit characteristic and 16-bit mantissa will occupy.

With either of these precision-extending methods, you must modify the way you use the look-up table to find logarithms. For example, the modified algorithm that implements the second method computes the 16-bit mantissa as follows. First, it expresses the remainder left by the shifting operation as a 16-bit binary number. It then uses the most significant 8 bits to address a table of 16-bit logarithms. Once the algorithm has

determined the 16-bit log, it adds to this number the eight least significant bits, using the straight-line approximation for the log (**Fig 2**), Adding the eight least significant bits helps to offset the interpolation errors associated with a 256-entry look-up table.

If your application requires fractional results, you could modify the algorithm to treat its 16-bit inputs as an 8-bit integer (most significant byte) and an 8-bit fraction (least significant byte). Basically, you would have to change the algorithm's initial loop count; the loop count determines the characteristic. When you make this change, a number which has its most significant binary one in the least significant byte returns a negative characteristic.

Sometimes, an equation that doesn't appear amenable to logarithm-based solutions can in fact be solved using logarithms if you express the equation in suitable form. Consider an example that uses the cosine function. Assume you need a routine that takes a 16-bit integer and multiplies it by the cosine of an angle (also a variable). The angle is restricted to the range

$$-90° < \theta \le +90°.$$

The equation is

$$Y = X \cos\theta,$$

which can't be solved directly using logarithms because $log(cos 90°)$ is undefined. However, rewriting the equation in the form

$$Y = X(1 + cos\theta) - X$$

makes this equation suitable for a logarithmic approach. You can easily code a routine to solve this equation. However, you need a third look-up table containing values of $log(1 + cos\theta)$ to go with this new code.

```
RMS:    CALL    COMPUTELOG   ; COMPUTE LOG OF A.
        ADD     HL, HL       ; PERFORM SQUARE.
        LD      BC, LOG313   ; BC GETS LOG OF 313. COULD
                             ;   EASILY BE ANOTHER PARAMENTER.
        OR      A            ; RESET CARRY.
        SBC     HL, BC       ; PERFORM DIVISION.
        CALL    ANTILOG      ; CONVERT BACK TO BINARY.
        PUSH    HL           ; SAVE FIRST TERM.
        PUSH    DE           ; PUSH TERM B.
        POP     HL           ; HL GETS TERM B.
        CALL    COMPUTELOG   ; COMPUTE LOG OF TERM B.
        ADD     HL, HL       ; PERFORM SQUARE.
        LD      BC, LOG462   ; BC GETS LOG OF 462.
        OR      A            ; RESET CARRY.
        SBC     HL, BC       ; DO DIVISION BY 462.
        CALL    ANTILOG      ; CONVERT BACK TO BINARY.
        POP     DE           ; GET FIRST TERM.
        ADD     HL, DE       ; PERFORM ADDITION.
        CALL    COMPUTELOG   ; COMPUTE LOG OF THE SUM.
        SRL     H            ; 0 ——> H ——> CY. PERFORM SQR ROOT.
        RR      L            ; CY ——> L ——> CY.
        CALL    ANTILOG      ; CONVERT BACK TO BINARY.
        RET                  ; RETURN.
LOG313: EQU     084AH        ; LOG OF 313.
LOG462: EQU     08DAH        ; LOG OF 462.


                        TEST DATA
        A   |   B   | IDEAL RESULT | ACTUAL RESULT
       1000 | 2000  |    108.9     |     108
        782 |  418  |     48       |      48
        219 |   87  |     13       |      13
```

Fig 7—Demonstrating the power of logarithms, this routine can compute the square root of a sum of squares.

Index

Articles are listed under the categories that describe them. For brevity, each article is referred to by the serial number under which it appears in the *Contents list* at the front of the book. The following abbreviations are used for the different categories.

AN Analog
CP Components
CR Circuits
DI Digital
PR Power/PSUs
RF Radio frequency
SF Software and algorithms
ST Standards
SY Systems
TM Test and measurement

Article	*Other applicable categories*	*Page*
Circuits		
Analog		
1	DI	1
2		2
5	DI	14
6	RF, TM	16
7	DI	21
9		29
10		30
11	CP, SY	32
14		47
15		49
17		57
18		58
20		65
22	TM	71
24	DI	79
25	TM	80
26	CP, SY	81
27		87
31	DI, ST, SY	101
32		109
38		130
39		134
40	RF	135
41		139
43		142
49	DI	163
50		164
52		168

Article	Other applicable categories	Page
53		170
54	SY	176
55	SY	179
56	CP	180
58		189
61		199
62	TM	201
64	CP	204
Digital		
1	AN	1
5	AN	14
7	AN	21
24	AN	79
25		80
31	AN, ST, SY	101
34		119
36	RF	126
42	RF	140
49	AN	163
57		188
Power		
4		12
12		39
30		99
37	SY	128
44		146
46		155
47	SY	156
51		167
65		212
RF		
6	AN, TM	16
36	DI	126
40	AN	135
42	DI	140
Components		
8	DI, ST, SY	22
11	AN, CR, SY	32
16	AN	51
19	AN	59
23	PR	72
26	AN, SY	81
28	ST, SY, TM	88
35	ST, SY	120

Article	Other applicable categories	Page
56	AN, CR	180
59	PR	191
64	AN	204

Software and algorithms

13		40
21		67
45	DI	147
63		203
66		213

Standards

3	DI, SY	3
8	CP, DI, SY	22
28	CP, SY, TM	88
31	AN, CR, DI, SY	101
33		110
35	CP, SY	120

Systems

3	DI, ST	3
8	CP, DI, ST	22
11	AN, CP, CR	32
26	AN, CP	81
31	AN, CR, DI, ST	101
35	CP, ST	120
37	CR, PR	128
47	CR, PR	156
54	AN, CR	176
55	AN, CR	179

Test and measurement

6	AN, CR, RF	16
22	AN, CR	71
25	AN, CR	80
28	CP, ST, SY	88
62	AN	201